CASE MANAGEMENT
for Rehabilitation Health Professionals

S E C O N D E D I T I O N

Volume 1
FOUNDATIONAL ASPECTS

Edited by

FONG CHAN
University of Wisconsin-Madison

MICHAEL J. LEAHY
Michigan State University

JODI L. SAUNDERS
University of Iowa

Aspen Professional Services

W9-BVQ-472

PUBLISHED BY
Aspen Professional Services
750 Malibu Road
Osage Beach, MO 65065

Copyright © 2005 by Aspen Professional Services
Jandrew@socket.net

Includes bibliographical references and subject index
ISBN 0-9721642-1-9

Cover design by: Lake Printing Company, Osage Beach, MO
Production Editor: Jason D. Andrew, Ph.D., CRC/R, NCC

To secure additional copies, contact:

Aspen Professional Services
750 Malibu Road, 201U
Osage Beach, MO 65065
jandrew@socket.net
573.302.7972
573.286.0418 (Cellular)

Table of Contents

VOLUME 1
FOUNDATIONAL ASPECTS

Table of Contents

VOLUME 2
ADVANCED PRACTICE: Applications with special populations

Preface

Case Management for Rehabilitation Health Professionals was designed as a second edition of the text, *Healthcare and Disability Case Management*, published in 1999, by Chan and Leahy. In the process of designing this second edition, it became evident that significant changes and additions to the content were warranted. For example, 16 of the chapters retained from the original version have been revised, and 11 new chapters have been added. We also changed publishers to Aspen Professional Services, and added a co-editor, Jodi Saunders, who joined the senior editors Fong Chan and Michael Leahy in the development of this expanded, second edition. We also decided to produce two volumes of the text for this edition to better accommodate 27 chapters. Volume One, *Foundational Aspects*, is organized into four sections: (1) historical and conceptual framework of case management; (2) foundational knowledge related to case management; (3) case management practice setting; and (4) accountability. Volume Two, *Advanced Practice: Applications with special populations*, is organized into two sections: (1) biopsychosocial aspects of disability; and (2) special populations and applications.

This two-volume text was written to respond to the pre-service and continuing education needs of rehabilitation counselors and case managers who practice in today's health care and rehabilitation service delivery systems. It is intended to serve as a textbook for students in pre-service training programs and a collateral reading resource for those who wish to gain a deeper knowledge about case management for professional development purposes. While there have been a few texts that have addressed case management from a "process" or "how to standpoint", it was our goal to produce a comprehensive text that would bring together the knowledge underpinning case management practices in sufficient breadth and depth to prepare students and case managers for the demands of actual practice. To accomplish this, we used recent empirical research to identify the essential knowledge dimensions in case management, as practiced by various disciplines across a variety of work settings, to provide explicit guidance in terms of the selection of the content for this text (Chan, Leahy, Downey, Lamb, Chapin & Peterson, 2000; Leahy, 1994).

In addition to the enormous growth of case management services in health care and disability-related service delivery systems over the past decade, there are a number of trends and emerging needs that we have paid particular attention to in designing this text. First, we believe that more case managers will be employed to manage the care of clients who experience chronic illness and disabilities throughout their recovery process (i.e., from medical treatment to return to work). As a result, case managers will have to be knowledgeable with respect to both medical and vocational case management to be effective in managing the care of individual clients throughout the full spectrum of the medical and rehabilitation process. Secondly, there appears to be a growing need to provide cross-training among those disciplines involved in case management (e.g., nurses, rehabilitation counselors and specialists, social workers) in order to increase their knowledge of the entire process as well as the potential contributions of various types of professional providers. Finally, it appears increasingly clear that there must be a more informed understanding of the specific expertise of the various professionals involved in case management, so that their talents and specific competencies can be used effectively at specific points, or to address particular client issues, with regard to the health care and rehabilitation process.

We would like to thank our friends and colleagues for taking the time to write such high-quality chapters for this text. As the editors of this book, we have tried to create a text that represents the essential knowledge dimensions required in case management practice across various disciplines and work settings. We hope that by reading and studying this text, either as part of a pre-service training curriculum or as part of your ongoing professional development efforts, you will be able to expand the depth and breadth of your knowledge of case management and that these efforts will benefit the clients you serve in the future.

Fong Chan
Michael J. Leahy
Jodi L. Saunders

≈

The Editors

Fong Chan, Ph.D., CRC
Dr. Chan is a Professor in the Department of Rehabilitation Psychology and Special Education, University of Wisconsin-Madison. From 1995 to 1999, he also served as Director of Research for the Foundation for Rehabilitation Education and Research, which provides research support for the Commission on Rehabilitation Counselor Certification, the Certification of Disability Management Specialists Commission, and the Commission for Case Manager Certification. Dr. Chan is a licensed psychologist and a Certified Rehabilitation Counselor. He is also a Fellow in the American Psychological Association and a National Institute on Disability and Rehabilitation Research Distinguished Research Fellow. Dr. Chan has more than 20 years of experience conducting applied rehabilitation health research in the topical areas of psychosocial aspects of disability, multi-cultural counseling, professional competency studies, computer-based case management simulations, and rehabilitation assessment.

He has published more than 140 refereed journal articles and book chapters. He is also the editor of a textbook entitled "Counseling theories and techniques for rehabilitation health professionals." Repeatedly recognized for his achievements, his awards include four Research Awards (American Rehabilitation Counseling Association), Research Award (American Counseling Association), James R. Garrett New Career Research Achievement Award (American Psychological Association, Division of Rehabilitation Psychology), James R. Garrett Distinguished Career in Rehabilitation Research Award (American Rehabilitation Counseling Association), and Educator of the Year Award (National Council on Rehabilitation Education). He has also received a distinguished alumni award from the Rehabilitation Psychology Program at the University of Wisconsin-Madison and recently a James Huff Stout Distinguished Alumni Award from University of Wisconsin-Stout.

Michael J. Leahy, Ph.D., CRC
Dr. Leahy is a Professor and the Director of the Office of Rehabilitation and Disability Studies at Michigan State University. He has a doctorate in Rehabilitation Counseling Psychology from the University of Wisconsin-Madison, and over 28 years of experience in rehabilitation as a counselor, administrator, researcher, and educator. Dr. Leahy is a Licensed Professional Counselor (LPC), and a Certified Rehabilitation Counselor (CRC). His continuing research interests include issues related to professional competency development and education, professionalization of practice,

vii

vocational assessment, case management, evidenced-based practice research, and vocational outcomes.

Dr. Leahy is a Past-President of the National Council on Rehabilitation Education, a Past Chair of the Alliance for Rehabilitation Counseling, and a Past-President of the American Rehabilitation Counseling Association (ARCA). He has published more than 90 journal articles, books, book chapters, and research monographs, and presented his research to a variety of rehabilitation and business audiences, including international presentations.

He is a recipient of the 1989 Outstanding New Career Award in Rehabilitation Education, a two-time recipient of the American Rehabilitation Counseling Association Research Award (1990,1993), recipient of the 1995 American Counseling Association (ACA) Research Award, the 1994 Rehabilitation Educator-Researcher Award from NCRE, the 1993 Award for Outstanding Leadership by ARCA and NRCA, 1997 ARCA Professional Service Award, recipient of the Lifetime Rehabilitation Achievement Award from the Commission on Rehabilitation Counselor Certification (CRCC) in 1997, Switzer Scholar Award in 1998, Exemplary Professional Service Award from the Alliance for Rehabilitation Counseling in 1999, the George N. Wright Varsity Award from the University of Wisconsin-Madison, and the Distinguished Career Award from the Alliance for Rehabilitation Counseling in 2001, and the 2002 Award of Excellence from the Michigan Rehabilitation Association. Most recently, in 2004, Dr. Leahy was a recipient of the Michigan State University Distinguished Faculty Award, and the James F. Garret Distinguished Career in Rehabilitation Research Award from the American Rehabilitation Counseling Association.

Jodi L. Saunders, Ph.D., CRC

Dr. Saunders is an Assistant Professor in Rehabilitation Counseling and the Associate Director of the Institute on Ethics in Disability Policy and Rehabilitation Practice at the University of Iowa. She is also a Senior Research Analyst at the Center for Law, Health Policy and Disability Studies at the University of Iowa. She has over 12 years of experience as a rehabilitation counselor primarily in the State/Federal rehabilitation program. She has several publications including two books in press, and has presented nationally in the area of ethics. She holds several national positions in rehabilitation including an executive board position on the American Rehabilitation Counseling Association board, and Chair of Examination and Research, & member of the Ethics Committee of the Commission on Rehabilitation Counseling Certification. She is also the recipient of a 2003-2004 NIDRR/Mary Switzer Research Fellowship and the 2004 National Council on Rehabilitation Education's New Career in Rehabilitation Education award.

The Contributors

It is with deep gratitude that we acknowledge the following authors who gave generously of their time and expertise in contributing chapters to Volume 1 of *Case Management for Rehabilitation Health Professionals.*

Peter Blanck is the Charles M. and Marion Kierscht Professor of Law, and Professor of Public Health (by courtesy) and Psychology at the University of Iowa, and Director of the Law, Health Policy, and Disability Center.

Elizabeth da Silva Cardoso is an assistant professor, Rehabilitation Counseling Program, Department of Educational Foundations and Counseling Programs, Hunter College, City University of New York.

Martha H. Chapin is an assistant professor and director, Undergraduate Rehabilitation Services Program, Department of Rehabilitation Studies, East Carolina University.

Julie A. Chronister is an assistant professor, Rehabilitation Counseling Program, Department of Educational Foundations and Counseling Programs, Hunter College, City University of New York.

Charles Degeneffe is an assistant professor, Rehabilitation Counseling Program, California State University-Fresno.

Paul M. Deutsch is President of Paul M. Deutsch and Associates, P.A., Orlando, Florida.

Norman Hursh is an associate professor and director, Vocational Evaluation Program, Department of Rehabilitation Counseling, Boston University.

Julie A. Kitchen is a Certified Disability Management Specialist, Case Manager and Life Care Planner in Central Florida, working with Paul M. Deutsch & Associates; she is also an instructor with MediPro/University of Florida, in their Life Care Planning educational program.

Lynn C. Koch is an associate professor and coordinator, Rehabilitation Counseling Program, Department of Educational Foundation and Special Services, Kent State University.

ix

Gloria K. Lee is an assistant professor, Rehabilitation Counseling Program, Department of Counseling, School and Educational Psychology, University at Buffalo-State University of New York.

John Lui is director of the Stout Vocational Rehabilitation Institute, University of Wisconsin-Stout.

Kathe Matrone is the director of RRCEP Region X, Western Washington University.

Charles Merbitz is an associate professor, the Chicago School of Professional Psychology.

Nancy Hansen Merbitz is a psychologist, MHRC, Inc. and AimStar Precision Learning Services.

Susan Dominy Michaelson is a doctoral candidate in the Rehabilitation Counselor Education Program in the Department of Counseling, Rehabilitation and Student Development at The University of Iowa.

David B. Peterson is an associate professor, Rehabilitation Psychology Program, Institute of Psychology, Illinois Institute of Technology.

Steven R. Pruett is an assistant professor, Department of Rehabilitation Counseling, University of Florida.

Christine Reid is associate professor and chair, Department of Rehabilitation Counseling, Virginia Commonwealth University.

David A. Rosenthal is an assistant professor, Department of Rehabilitation Psychology and Special Education, University of Wisconsin-Madison.

Phillip D. Rumrill is a professor, Rehabilitation Counseling Program, Department of Educational Foundation and Special Services, Kent State University.

Helen Schartz is Director of Research at the Law, Health Policy & Disability Center.

James Schmeling is Associate Director of the Law, Health Policy & Disability Center.

Marcia J. Scherer, Institute for Matching Person & Technology, and University of Rochester Medical Center, and International Center for Hearing and Speech Research, National Technical Institute for the Deaf/Rochester Institute of Technology.

Linda R. Shaw is an associate professor and graduate coordinator, Department of Rehabilitation Counseling, University of Florida.

Vilia M. Tarvydas is a Professor and Program Coordinator of The Graduate Programs in Rehabilitation in the Department of Counseling, Rehabilitation and Student Development at The University of Iowa. She is also Director of the Institute on Ethics in Disability Policy and Rehabilitation Practice.

Wolfgang Zimmermann is executive director, National Institute of Disability Management and Research, Victoria, Canada.

This page intentionally left blank.

Section 1

Historical and Conceptual Foundations of Case Management

1

In This Section

Section 1, *Historical and Conceptual Foundations of Case Management*, contains two chapters. In Chapter 1, Shaw, Leahy, and Chan provide an understanding of the underpinnings of case management by offering a brief history of its evolution as a practice area, and identifying current trends in case management. The chapter also identifies the major disciplines involved in case management, discusses the various credentials available to practitioners, and provides some clarification regarding role differentiation in the delivery of case management services.

To complete this historical development section, Chapter 2 by Leahy, Matrone, and Chan reviews the various contemporary models of case management, as they are depicted in today's rehabilitation and health care delivery systems. The principles and competencies associated with case management are also reviewed, with a particular emphasis on those principles that guide, and provide a useful framework for the delivery of case management services. Finally, diversity issues and cultural competence are explored within the context of providing effective case management services.

≈

1

Case Management: Historical Foundations and Current Trends

Linda R. Shaw
Michael J. Leahy
Fong Chan

Chapter Highlights

- Evolution of case management

- Contemporary case management

- Emerging needs

- Case management research

- Credentials and role differentiation

- Current issues and trends

- Conclusion

Case management is typically viewed as a process that involves the timely coordination of an array of services to meet an individual's needs in a cost effective manner. Today, many different professionals practice case management in a variety of settings. While the specific nature of the health-related or rehabilitation problems addressed may differ, as well as the delivery system, services provided, outcomes, and professional grounding of the individual delivering services, the process involved appears quite similar.

The American health care system and the insurance industry have been undergoing significant reform in recent years in order to rein in the high cost of delivering health care services. Managed care has clearly emerged as the cornerstone of the new health reform age (Strickland, 1995). Case management, with its focus on cost containment, managed competition, and quality care, has played an increasingly important role in the managed care environment (Mullahy, 1995). Accordingly, the number of case managers has risen from an estimated 5,000 to 10,000 in 1985 to a total of 50,000 to 100,000 (Mullahy, 1995). These practitioners come from diverse training backgrounds, disciplines, and practice settings that include rehabilitation counseling, nursing, and social work. Presently, there are an estimated 23,000 Certified Case Managers (CCMs).

The role of the case manager is to facilitate the delivery of cost-efficient, individualized, and coordinated care to clients and patients with disabilities and chronic illnesses in today's technologically advanced medical and health care environment. Case management is a disciplined application of skills, tools, and techniques that facilitates positive movement toward a desired outcome. Case management has been defined as a "collaborative process which assesses, plans, implements, coordinates, monitors, and evaluates options and services to meet an individual's health needs through communications and available resources to promote quality, cost-effective outcomes" (*The Case Manager*, 1994, p.59).

The purpose of this introductory chapter is to provide the reader with an understanding of the historical foundations of case management by providing a brief history from which the evolution of the practice can be viewed. The status of the research that has been initiated to identify the knowledge and skills required to provide effective case management services will also be provided. This descriptive information has direct application within both the credentialing process and the design and development of pre-service and continuing education programs to prepare practitioners for case management responsibilities in a variety of settings within the rehabilitation and health care arenas. In addition, this chapter will identify the major disciplines involved in case management, discuss the various credentials available to practitioners, and provide some clarification regarding role differentiation in the delivery of case management services. Finally, current issues and trends affecting case management practice and the practitioners who provide these services will be discussed.

THE EVOLUTION OF CASE MANAGEMENT

Despite the recent flurry of professional activity centering on case managers, the concept of case management is not new. Many rehabilitation, social services, and health care professions have a history of using various case management concepts and techniques within their service delivery systems. Service coordination has always been a focus of public health nursing (Bower, 1992). For many years, social workers have coordinated the provision of services to people with mental health problems (Sledge, Astrachan, Thompson, Rakfeldt, & Leaf, 1995), and rehabilitation counselors have historically applied case management and coordination functions in carrying out their multifaceted role (Wright, 1980). However, modern case management practice has only recently become visible as an integral part of our rehabilitation and health care service delivery system. Upon closer examination, the evolution of case management appears to be closely tied to a series of events and advances in rehabilitation practice that had their beginnings at the turn of the 20th century.

THE EMERGENCE OF REHABILITATION

In many respects, the history of case management is inextricably woven into the history of rehabilitation itself. The term "case management" has been variously defined, but in every case, involves the process of linking, managing, and/or organizing services to meet client needs (Huber, 1996). Prior to the turn of the century, however, there were few rehabilitation and health care services to link, manage, or organize.

During the first decade of the 20th century, initial signs of a change in attitude toward people with disabilities became apparent as schools for crippled children began to appear. During this period, the increased mechanization of the workplace produced ever-growing numbers of individuals who were unemployed due to work-related injuries. The number of individuals with disabilities expanded further when the United States entered World War I. Along with a dramatic increase in the number of individuals with disabilities came a new sense of responsibility to address not only the physical rehabilitation needs, but also the educational and vocational needs of individuals with disabilities.

5

There were economic, humanistic, and patriotic motivations for society's and the government's newfound concern. First, the wartime economy had created a demand for workers. With many able-bodied males committed to the war effort, productivity at home was lagging. Providing services that could return disabled veterans to work would benefit both the veterans and the economy. Additionally, the country felt that it owed something to these men who had suffered physical harm in its defense.

During this time, multiple groups emerged to claim jurisdiction over the rehabilitation effort, including several physician's groups, physical therapists, occupational therapists, and others (McCourt, 1993). The issue of control was partially determined by the passage of the Smith-Fess Act in 1920, which extended eligibility for services that were being provided to veterans (Soldiers Rehabilitation Act, 1918) to citizens with physical disabilities who qualified for services. This legislation provided for federal control of public vocational rehabilitation efforts, separate from the jurisdiction of the Surgeon General or other medical organizations (McCourt, 1993). However, while control over available funds became centralized, the number of disciplines providing rehabilitation services expanded, as the knowledge base increased. Treatment of individuals with disabilities became more sophisticated. Increasingly, rehabilitation and health care providers became "specialists" in treating different types of disabilities, and in treating different kinds of functional deficits that might result from any one type of disability.

The trends toward specializing in a particular disability, and bringing together all of the disciplines needed to treat a particular disability were given added emphasis when the disease poliomyelitis swept through the country. Founded upon the pioneering work of Sister Elizabeth Kenny, centers for the treatment of polio were established in the United States (McCourt, 1993). These centers, which brought together the best-trained specialists in a variety of disciplines, necessitated a system of coordinated care. Most often, care was centered on the treating physician, with the roles of the other disciplines being rigorously defined. Research dollars aimed at ameliorating the physical and psychological effects of polio resulted in many advances in rehabilitation, including new techniques and equipment to facilitate respiration; hand splints and prototypes for other orthoses; and mobility devices (Raymond, 1986). With such advances, came a further broadening of the number of specialists required to treat any given disability, accompanied by an increased challenge in how best to coordinate care.

Over the next several decades, the Public Rehabilitation Program, created by the Smith-Fess Act of 1920, experienced significant growth, in the amount of federal dollars committed to the program, the scope of services provided, the

6

kinds of disabilities considered appropriate for the receipt of public rehabilitation services, and the sheer number of individuals served. Technological advancements in medicine, including the discovery and use of antibiotics, had a dramatic effect on the numbers of individuals who survived devastating illnesses and injuries, but who survived with some degree of functional loss. The Social Security Act of 1935 and subsequent federal legislation further supported the provision of rehabilitation services to individuals receiving support due to their disabilities.

Initially, the Public Rehabilitation Program was staffed with individuals from a variety of disciplines. As the scope and complexity of the services expanded, it became apparent that a new professional discipline was needed — one which would consist of professionals trained in disability, counseling, assessment and placement, and a unique set of skills termed "case management" — the skills needed to plan, implement, monitor, and coordinate services provided by multiple service providers (Shaw, 1995). The 1954 Vocational Rehabilitation Act Amendments established funds for training these professionals, termed "rehabilitation counselors." Subsequently, when the Council on Rehabilitation Education (CORE) established accreditation standards in 1973 for these new programs, case management services were among the content areas which the curriculum of accredited rehabilitation counselor programs were required to include.

In the decades following World War II, both medical and vocational rehabilitation continued to develop and expand. The many disciplines that had developed began to coalesce into distinct professions, each with its own identity, professional association, and credentialing body. Medicine developed separate rehabilitation-related specializations and the physiatrist and rehabilitation nurse became prominently represented on rehabilitation centers' multidisciplinary teams. The rehabilitation nurse often provided not only direct patient care, but frequently took a leadership role in coordinating the many specialists involved in the patient's medical care by assuming medical case management responsibilities. Nurses also assumed case management functions within the community and public health venues, while social workers were often called upon to perform case management functions within mental health settings.

The rise of rehabilitation in this country established a need for case management services and several disciplines stepped in to fill the void. Rehabilitation counselors took the lead in providing case management in those arenas where the emphasis was on employment outcomes, while nurses, many of whom were rehabilitation nurses, stepped in to coordinate medical treatment for those whose primary focus was on medical rehabilitation.

7

WORKERS' COMPENSATION AND PRIVATIZATION

Although public rehabilitation programs and services provided the initial incentive for the development of case management services, the development of case management as a primary professional function occurred largely within the context of private, for-profit rehabilitation and workers' compensation programs. In the late 1970s and early 1980s, rehabilitation facilities experienced another growth spurt, this time due to both the continually expanding population of individuals with disabilities and the availability of government funding for rehabilitation services. Rehabilitation units and centers were exempt from the prospective payment system that had overtaken health care institutions. Consequently, many tertiary care medical centers established rehabilitation units and many freestanding rehabilitation centers were created to address emerging populations of individuals with disabilities, such as those with spinal cord and traumatic brain injuries. Many of these programs began to focus on issues related to community integration, including vocational re-entry, in addition to medical rehabilitation (McCourt, 1993).

Concurrently, workers' compensation programs in several states had taken the plunge into the provision of rehabilitation services. Since the early part of the 20th century, various states evolved their own workers' compensation programs providing medical and wage replacement benefits to employees who acquired work-related injuries that prevented them from returning to their jobs. Because these programs developed independently, each program covered different kinds of services, resulting in wide variations from state to state regarding the degree to which, or in many cases, whether the state provided *any* rehabilitation services.

Consequently, in 1970, the National Commission for State Workers' Compensation Laws was created by the Occupational Safety and Health Act (OSHA) to study the effectiveness of each state's workers' compensation system. The commission's report generated considerable interest in what other states were doing to control costs. The costs for workers' compensation programs had been escalating rapidly, in terms of both medical and rehabilitation treatment, and wage loss payments. States that had not previously provided vocational rehabilitation services became aware of the rationale for such services through the commission's report, i.e. a rapid return to work would result in substantial cost savings (Lynch, Lynch & Beck, 1992; Matkin, 1995).

By 1976, 27 states had developed some type of vocational rehabilitation program and, during the late 1970s and early 1980s, many more enacted mandatory provision of vocational rehabilitation within their workers' compensation laws. Fewer and fewer programs relied solely on the public rehabilitation program to return their claimants to work. As costs continued to

8

rise, the insurance companies covering workers' compensation insurance looked elsewhere for help in containing costs and affecting a more rapid return to work. As Weed and Field (1990) note:

> With rising costs of medical expenses and payment of lost wages for industrially injured, a number of companies began to look at possible ways to contain costs as well as to have more control over vocational rehabilitation of injured workers. Many insurance companies found that public rehabilitation counselors were placing injured workers into two or more years of training, thereby obligating insurance carriers to continue compensation payments until clients had completed training programs. (p. 4)

The passage of the Rehabilitation Act of 1973 further affected the degree to which workers' compensation carriers became disenchanted with their reliance on the public vocational rehabilitation system (Habeck, Leahy, Hunt, Chan & Welch, 1991). The 1973 Act established priority within the service delivery system for individuals with severe disabilities. Consequently, less severely industrially injured persons and their agents simply were not receiving timely services.

George Welch has been credited with the birth of private rehabilitation in 1970. At that time, he was employed with the Insurance Company of North America (INA), which later merged with Connecticut General to become CIGNA. Mr. Welch formed International Rehabilitation Associates (later Intracorp) in what may have been the first for-profit rehabilitation business (Holt, 1993). Rehabilitation nurses and rehabilitation counselors were hired to provide both medical and vocational case management services to workers' compensation claimants. Other insurance carriers began to hire and to contract with rehabilitation "specialists" to contain the astronomical costs associated with medical treatment and return to work services necessary for those with catastrophic disabilities (Matkin, 1982; Shaw, 1993; Shrey, 1979). By 1982, more than 1,000 companies had been created to furnish these specialists, resulting in a private, for-profit rehabilitation industry with revenues of nearly $25 million dollars (Lauterbach, 1982, Shaw, 1993).

A primary role of both rehabilitation nurses and counselors employed within the workers' compensation industry is providing the set of services generically known as case management, such as planning and coordinating client services, etc. (Matkin, 1983; Matkin, 1985; McMahon & Matkin, 1983). Such specialists came to be called "insurance specialists" or, not surprisingly, "insurance case managers." Most recently, the 1990 Americans with Disabilities Act has provided a further catalyst for private-sector rehabilitation

9

growth as employers seek assistance with compliance (Gilbride, Stensrud & Connolly, 1992).

CONTEMPORARY CASE MANAGEMENT

As practiced today, the case management process generally includes (1) assessment of individual needs; (2) development of individualized case management plans; (3) facilitation, implementation, and coordination of services; (4) monitoring and evaluating of services and outcomes; and (5) documentation of activity (Case Management Association Coalition, 1994). Given the general definitions of process and practice, it is important to recognize that case management is not a new concept. As indicated earlier, many rehabilitation, social services, and health care professions have a long history of using case management models as a central or primary function in the delivery of services. For example, in many psychiatric rehabilitation work settings, social workers are frequently hired as case managers to coordinate the provision of community-based services to people with mental health problems. Case management is also an extremely important function of rehabilitation counselors in all their work settings, as well as rehabilitation specialists in the private sector (c.f., Leahy et al., 1997; Leahy, Szymanski, & Linkowski, 1993; Leahy, Chan & Saunders, 2003; Matkin, 1995). Similarly, nursing case management is increasingly being viewed as the embodiment of professional nursing practice in today's health care environments and those that will emerge in the future (Lamb, 1993). Clearly, the concept of case management as applied in insurance rehabilitation workers' compensation can be readily adapted to the management of health insurance claims.

Strickland (1995) has predicted that rehabilitation and case management companies in the private sector will increasingly be procured by new major players in the disability and health care marketplace such as managed care organizations, health and workers' compensation insurance carriers, hospital management companies, and home health care organizations. Case managers will be employed to manage the care of patients who will experience chronic illnesses and disabilities throughout the recovery process from medical treatment to return to work. Potentially, case managers will need to be knowledgeable with respect to both medical and vocational case management to be effective in managing the care of individual patients or clients within the full spectrum of the medical and rehabilitation process.

EMERGING NEEDS

Given these developments, a number of significant needs emerged that health care and rehabilitation professionals desired to address. First, there was a clear need to identify the essential knowledge and skills applicable to all those disciplines involved in case management activities, so that professionals would be able to describe and understand the commonality that existed between practitioners from various disciplines and training backgrounds who worked in a variety of settings. Related to this concern, there appeared to be a growing need to provide cross-training among those disciplines involved in case management (e.g., nurses, rehabilitation counselors and specialists, social workers) in order to increase their knowledge of the entire process and the potential contributions of various types of professional providers. Finally, it appeared increasingly clear that there must be a more informed understanding of the specific expertise of the various professionals involved in case management, so that their talents and specific competencies are effectively used at specific points or to address particular client/patient issues effectively in the rehabilitation and health care process.

To address some of the concerns noted above, 29 organizations involved in the field of case management gathered in Dallas, Texas, at a consensus meeting convened in February 1991 by the Individual Case Management Association. The objective was to explore the possibility of developing a certification program that would provide an industry standard and definition for the case management process, as well as national standards of practice for those individuals providing case management.

As a result of this meeting, a National Task Force on Case Management was created to coordinate efforts to develop a transdisciplinary case management credential. By July of 1991, the task force had completed its initial research to identify case management philosophy, definitions, and existing standards of practice. On the basis of these findings, a steering committee of the original task force began soliciting certification proposals from various credentialing organizations. The selection criteria included in the request for proposals stipulated that the credentialing organization must demonstrate its ability to provide both administrative and technical expertise as well as the in-place systems needed to develop a certification process for individuals practicing case management.

In February of 1992, the steering committee of the National Task Force on Case Management accepted a proposal from the Certification of Insurance Rehabilitation Specialists Commission (CIRSC, now known as the Certification of Disability Management Specialists Commission or CDMSC) to develop the voluntary credential. Using its own resources, previous experience, and the

11

initial research completed by the task force, CIRSC, with technical and administrative support from the Foundation for Rehabilitation Education and Research, worked with a panel of case management experts to identify appropriate certification eligibility criteria (educational background and acceptable work experience) and content areas for the initial certification examination.

While the existing definitions of case management (e.g., Case Management Association Coalition, 1994; Case Management Society of America, 1994) are quite helpful in providing a general sense of the commonalties present within the process of case management, they do not adequately address the core knowledge requirements shared by the many different professionals working in various service environments who deliver case management services.

CASE MANAGEMENT RESEARCH

Job analyses, role-and-function, professional competency, and knowledge validation research are all terms that describe a process whereby practitioners in a particular area of practice are systematically studied to identify and describe important functions and tasks, or knowledge and skills associated with their practice (e.g., Chan et al., 2000; Chan et al., 2001; Leahy, Shapson, & Wright, 1987; Leahy, Szymanski & Linkowski, 1993; Leahy, Chan, & Saunders, 2003; Muthard & Salamone, 1969; Rubin, Matkin, Ashley, Beardsley, May, Onstott, & Pucket, 1984).

While role-and-function approaches generally provide an empirically derived description of the functions and tasks associated with the role, the knowledge required to perform these functions is more indirectly assessed, and inferred on the basis of the described functions and tasks. Conversely, knowledge validation and professional competency approaches provide an empirically derived description of the knowledge and skills associated with a particular role, but the actual functions and tasks performed are more indirectly assessed and inferred on the basis of the knowledge and skills needed to practice. In selecting a research approach that would provide a direct assessment of the knowledge required for case management practice that would serve as the empirical foundation for the examination content and certification process, a knowledge validation approach was initially selected.

According to Leahy (1994), the overall purpose of this first nationwide study was to survey practitioners providing case management services in a variety of work settings in order to examine the perceived importance of various knowledge areas to the practice of case management. The results of this initial study were then used to (1) provide evidence regarding the content validity of individual knowledge areas; (2) provide an empirically derived description of the knowledge areas important to the practice of case management; (3) serve as the basis for the content design and test specifications for future versions of the Certified Case Manager (CCM) examination; and (4) identify content areas that required further item development for the examination.

Specifically, Leahy (1994) surveyed 14,078 Certified Case Managers (CCMs) to validate empirically the common knowledge dimensions required for case management practice. He developed a 132-item knowledge importance instrument based on a comprehensive review of the literature, an inspection of 500 job descriptions of case managers, and the recommendations of 30 content experts. Leahy found five knowledge domains to be important to case management practice: (a) coordination and service delivery; (b) physical and psychosocial aspects; (c) benefit systems/cost benefit analysis; (d) case management concepts; and (e) community re-entry. Although CCMs practice in a variety of settings and within many different professions, this research suggested that CCMs do share a common core of knowledge areas required for effective case management practice. The CCM credential has proven to be much in demand and the certification of CCMs has increased at a rapid pace, not only among nurses, but also among other specializations that consider case management to be a critical part of their job responsibilities.

With the changing nature of health care, the Commission on Case Manager Certification (CCMC) initiated further research in the late 1990's to re-examine the professional functions and required knowledge competencies of CCM's. There were two phases to this project. Chan, Leahy, McMahon, Mirch, and DeVinney (1999) described the results of Phase One of this project where a panel of health care and disability management experts were participants in a study to help identify job functions and knowledge areas essential for case management practice. Using a modified Delphi technique, the panel developed and reviewed a list of 40 job task/function areas and 62 knowledge statements to assess their importance for case management practice. Seventeen job function/task items were considered "very important" to "extremely important" for case management practice. The primary focus of these job tasks was on medical case management, advocacy, outreach, discharge planning, and professional development. Twenty-six knowledge statements were considered very important to extremely important for case management practice. Medical care and case management, health care and benefit systems, assessment, interpersonal relationships, psychosocial and legal issues, and family dynamics were the focus of these items. The top ranked job and knowledge areas focused

13

on medical case management more so than disability case management, although disability case management was still seen as important.

The second phase of the CCMC research project required that these job tasks and knowledge requirements for case management practice, as delineated by the expert panel in the first study, be validated through a national study of case management practitioners (Chan et al., 2000). The primary purpose of this investigation was to determine the underlying work-role dimensions and knowledge domains of case management. In 1998, using a 20% random sample (N=3,771) from the CCM certificate listing, which served as the sampling frame for the study, the CCMC Certified Case Manager's Job Task and Knowledge Inventory was mailed to study participants. Based on the completed questionnaires from 1,128 participants (33% response rate), and empirical analysis of these data, the authors concluded that there were four major job functions associated with case management practice. These included Disability Case Management, Health Care Management, Program Management and Evaluation, and Monitoring Care and Follow-up. In addition to these functions and the specific tasks associated with them, the authors also concluded that there were six major knowledge domains that informed the application of these functions. They included knowledge of Service Delivery, Disability Case Management, Process and Relationships, Health Care Management, Psychosocial Intervention, and Community Resources and Support. The essential knowledge required for case management practice reported by certified case managers (Chan et al., 2000) is quite consistent with the experts' opinion in the Delphi study (Chan et al., 1999), and the knowledge domains identified by Leahy (1994) in the original knowledge validation study, which formed the basis for developing the test specifications for the CCM examination.

CREDENTIALS AND ROLE DIFFERENTIATION IN CASE MANAGEMENT

As indicated previously, many different professionals within the rehabilitation and health care service delivery systems practice case management in a variety of settings. As case management practices have expanded, it has become increasingly clear that there must be a more informed understanding of the specific expertise of the various professionals involved in case management so that these talents and specific competencies can be effectively used.

In addition to the expansion of case management practices, there have been, over the past 30 years, increased efforts to develop professional

14

credentials, particularly certification, to identify those professionals who have met the educational, work experience, and knowledge standards of their respective profession or disciplines (e.g., CRC, CDMS, CCM). While these certification efforts have developed primarily in response to the need to protect the public and identify qualified service providers, they have also created a great deal of confusion among practitioners, other related professional groups, consumers, payers, legislators, and other stakeholders in the health care and rehabilitation process.

FORMS OF CREDENTIALS

Credentialing is the process of granting an individual practitioner a credential that designates that professional as having attained a specified level of competence in a subject or area (Fabrey, 1996). The three generally accepted forms of credentials include licensure, certification, and registration. Among the three credentials, licensure is clearly the most restrictive and refers to a mandatory government (usually state-level) requirement necessary to practice in a particular profession or occupation. Licensure includes both practice and title protections. This means that only licensed practitioners are permitted to practice and use a particular title (Fabrey, 1996). The most frequently licensed professions involved in the delivery of case management services include rehabilitation counselors who have become Licensed Professional Counselors (LPCs) in states requiring licensure, and nurses (LPN).

The second form of credentialing is the granting of certification. This process is usually voluntary, and instituted by a non-governmental agency, with individuals certified as possessing specific (advanced) knowledge and skill in a particular area. Similar to licensure, the certification process normally requires an assessment of knowledge and an evaluation of education and/or work experience. In some cases, individuals seeking certification already hold specific licenses (e.g., LPN, LPC). Certification implies a title protection (e.g., CRC, CCM, CDMS), but unlike licensure, it does not protect the practice unless employers, payers, and government agencies use it as a mandatory requirement to deliver services. The ultimate intent of licensure is to protect the public from incompetent practitioners who do not possess the appropriate level of education, work experience, and knowledge. While the general intent of certification is to inform the public that individuals who hold the certification have demonstrated a specific level of knowledge and skill. The only method of direct public protection that credentialing can offer is through the enforcement of its ethical code (Fabrey, 1996).

Finally, registration is the third recognized form of credentialing. This is used where protection of the public is not as critical. The granting of registration may imply the recognition of certain types of training and education related to a specific knowledge and skill set.

CERTIFICATION IN CASE MANAGEMENT

There is no question that, among the three credentials described above, certification, particularly as is relates to case management, is the most widely accepted, yet potentially confusing credential in the rehabilitation and health care arenas. There are currently at least three separate credentialing organizations that offer certifications related to the provision of case management services.

The first of these organizations, which emerged some 30 years ago, is the Commission for Rehabilitation Counselor Certification (CRCC). Its credentialing process is the oldest and most established certification mechanism in the counseling and rehabilitation professions. Since the inception of the Certified Rehabilitation Counselor (CRC) credential in 1973, more than 30,000 qualified professionals have participated in the certification process. Today, there are more than 15,500 CRCs practicing in the United States and in several foreign countries (Susan Gilpin, March 29, personal communication). This certification process was based exclusively on the rehabilitation counseling profession and has, as its primary purpose, the provision of assurances that professionals engaged in rehabilitation counseling who hold this certification will have met acceptable national standards of education, experience, and knowledge (MacAlees & Schumacher, 1975) and practice in accordance with the Code of Professional Ethics for Rehabilitation Counselors.

In 1983, a new certification organization called the Certified Insurance Rehabilitation Specialist Commission (CIRSC) was developed for professionals delivering direct rehabilitation services to individuals receiving benefits from various disability compensation systems. This certification process was established primarily around the provision of case management and vocational rehabilitation services in a particular setting. Unlike the CRC credential, the Certified Insurance Rehabilitation Specialist (CIRS) credential certified numerous professionals (with different professional backgrounds) who held in common the provision of their services to clients receiving benefits from disability compensation systems. In the late 1990's, this organization changed its name to the Certification of Disability Management Specialists Commission (CDMSC). At present, approximately 3,700 individuals hold the Certified Disability Management Specialist (CDMS) credential (Susan Gilpin, March 29, personal communication).

The CIRSC (now the CDMSC) also began the process of developing a voluntary case management certification process in 1992. Operating for the first few years as an interim commission within CIRSC, it was renamed and separately incorporated in 1995 as the Commission for Case Manager Certification (CCMC). Its certification process was established primarily around the process of case management as practiced by many different professionals in a variety of rehabilitation and health care settings. This credentialing process represents the newest effort in relation to certification and presently has 22,000 individuals who hold the Certified Case Manager (CCM) credential (Susan Gilpin, March 29, personal communication).

One of the most basic distinctions among the three credentials relates to whom the credential was intended and what formed the primary basis of the credential. For example, the CRC credential is intended for appropriately trained rehabilitation counselors and the credential is exclusively organized around the role of the rehabilitation counselor and the required levels of knowledge and skill to practice in a variety of rehabilitation and health care settings. The CDMS credential is intended for a variety of qualified professionals and is organized around the role and knowledge/skills required to provide case management and rehabilitation services to those clients served by disability compensation systems. Finally, the CCM credential is intended for a variety of licensed or certified professionals who meet the work experience requirements of case management. The credential is organized around the "process of case management" and the essential knowledge and skills that are common to the practice of case management in a variety of settings.

With these distinctions in mind, it is also important to recognize the centrality of case management as an important function for professionals who obtain any of these three credentials. For many years, rehabilitation counseling research has consistently identified case management as a primary function of the rehabilitation counselor. In addition, research has consistently identified case management as a central professional function of those rehabilitation professionals who specialize in disability management. Finally, the case management credential itself has been organized exclusively around the process of case management.

Clearly, knowledge associated with the case management function is evident in all three of the credentials, together with medical, functional, and psychosocial aspects of illness and disability. Specific emphasis on vocational knowledge domains, including vocational assessment, is present only in the CRC and CDMS credentials, while individual and group counseling knowledge is associated only with the CRC credential. Further, in relation to role differentiation within case management, it appears evident that the knowledge domains associated with the credentials and the professional background of the practitioner provides a logical basis to identify the type of practitioner specialization needed to address the specific case management concerns of

17

individual cases. For example, nurses who are Certified Case Managers would appear to be ideally prepared to address medical case management issues, while Certified Rehabilitation Counselors are uniquely qualified to address the counseling and vocational issues associated with particular cases.

The philosophy of case management, as reported in the CCM Certification Guide, provides additional guidance in terms of understanding how to view case management within today's complex health care and rehabilitation delivery system. It reads as follows:

> Case management is not a profession in itself, but an area of practice within one's profession. Its underlying premise is that when an individual reaches the optimum level of wellness and functional capacity, everyone benefits; the individuals being served; their support systems; the health care delivery systems; and the various reimbursement sources. Case management serves as a means for achieving client wellness and autonomy through advocacy, communication, education, identification of service resources, and service facilitation. The case manager helps identify appropriate providers and facilities throughout the continuum of services, while ensuring that available resources are being used in a timely and cost-effective manner in order to obtain optimum value for both the client and the reimbursement source. Case management services are best offered in a climate that allows direct communication between the case manager, the client, and appropriate service personnel, in order to optimize the outcomes for all concerned... (p. i)

CURRENT ISSUES AND TRENDS IN CASE MANAGEMENT

MANAGED CARE

The escalation of costs in health care has been described as a "crisis" with good reason. The effort to contain health care costs has resulted in a variety of strategies, each designed to lower costs and maximize the value of services received and the resources used (Huber, 1996). One of the first strategies to be used on a widespread basis by the many managed care organizations that have evolved in recent years is case management. Case management was first used as a managed care strategy within hospital and acute care settings to coordinate the care of complicated and potentially costly high-risk and/or catastrophically injured patients across treatment settings and among numerous specialty services (Simpson, 1993).

As the structure of health care evolved into integrated delivery systems that require careful monitoring and coordination between the various levels of care and numerous medical services, the need for internal case management systems has increased (Beckley, 1995; Kreider, 1996). Such changes have created new opportunities for case managers within managed care organizations and the provider-based systems with which managed care organizations contract. Typically, such case managers are likely to have heavy responsibilities in the area of information management, patient care coordination, utilization management, and cost containment. The personal face-to-face contact attractive to many nurses and counselors is minimized in these settings. Indeed, the term "telephonic case management" is used with ever-increasingly regularity.

The effects of managed care have also penetrated to more traditional workers' compensation case management roles (Daiker, 1995). Increasingly, workers' compensation services are provided within managed care arrangements, with many states mandating such arrangements. As managed care has penetrated more deeply, workers' compensation case managers have found themselves needing to learn to work with internal case managers and gatekeepers, restrict themselves to providers chosen from a panel, accustom themselves to care paths and other treatment protocols as well as the myriad of managed care strategies increasingly employed by such systems.

It is difficult to predict with any certainty the direction in which case management will evolve in the future, given the rapid changes taking place in the health care profession. Some trends are beginning to emerge, however, and others can be surmised based upon changes occurring in our population base, advances in science and medicine, and general trends in health care in this country. Predictions about the future of case management have become a popular topic in the case management literature. Based upon a review of the literature and the authors' observations, case management is likely to affect and be affected by the following trends.

BLENDING OF TRADITIONAL ROLES
Disciplinary boundaries and responsibilities have become blurred, a trend that is likely to continue. Increasingly, nurse case managers are working with employers on return-to-work issues and vocational and social work case managers perform ever-increasing amounts of medical case management. Due to the rapid changes in the manner in which health care services are provided, case managers have had to expand their roles beyond traditional disciplinary lines. Such "blurring" is seen as a positive step by leaders in the profession who note that, although nurses, rehabilitation counselors, and others have unique skills and backgrounds, they must all begin to identify as "case managers" in order to lobby together for a secure foothold in the changing field of health

care. As Barbara Sheffel notes "It's not an issue of what career training an individual has, or the concept of specialization. It's an issue of improving our image...It's a matter of pulling together to establish ourselves as competent, knowledgeable professionals who are fully prepared to be key players in the health care world of tomorrow" (Romaine, 1995, p.28). Gambosh (1997) adds that, in the coming years, cross training will become essential for anyone seeking a career in case management in order to acquire the requisite skills. The need for cross training was observed in a study by Shaw, McMahon, Chan, Taylor, and Wood (1997), as rehabilitation counselor respondents revealed that they did not feel sufficiently prepared in regard to medical management issues.

PROFESSIONALIZATION
The trend toward the forging of a stronger professional identify that has evolved over the past several years will likely continue and gain strength. Leaders in case management tend to agree that the CCM credential will likely continue to be increasingly recognized as the standard for practitioners of case management activities (Romaine, 1995). Scheffel notes, however, that "now we need to move on to a process that keeps up with the changes in our field. We need to identify and support specialties" (cited in Romaine, 1995, p.28). The development of specialty certifications may help to assure that case managers practicing in various settings and working with various populations are acquiring the skills and knowledge necessary to provide quality services within a particular work arena. As the responsibilities of case managers increase and as they broaden their work settings, it may become necessary to look to the creation of specialty certifications, as Scheffel suggests. Such specialization is already seen in the development of such professional groups as The National Association of Professional Geriatric Care Managers (http://www.caremanager. org/index.htm).

The trend toward consolidation of the currently splintered professional associations representing case managers may also be expected to continue. The merger of the Case Management Society of America (CMSA) and the Individual Case Management Association (ICMA) was a first step in the process of bringing together case managers from diverse backgrounds and practice settings. The need to develop cooperation and collaboration between organizations representing case managers is seen as essential to survival in a time of intense change. Given the certainty of change in health care, further consolidation and cooperation among different groups with similar goals is to be expected (Romaine, 1995).

20

CHANGING REIMBURSEMENT PATTERNS

The trend away from fee-for-service reimbursement systems and toward risk-sharing arrangements, outcome-based payment, and other nontraditional payment mechanisms will continue to affect the way in which case management is practiced. As Scheffel notes, "Where once strong clinical skills were a key asset in the case manager's role as patient advocate, today's case manager must also be well-versed in insurance coverage and resource availability" (Romaine, 1995, p. 26). As reimbursement systems increasingly shift toward capitation, and as concerns increase about the quality of health care services, case managers are likely to spend a larger proportion of their time on quality control, outcomes monitoring, and watching for underutilization rather than over utilization (Severson, 1996). Case managers will become pivotal in provider monitoring and accountability as payers increasingly use performance-based incentives, including cost-effectiveness and quality measurements, as mechanisms for determining provider reimbursement (Masso, 1995).

Shifts in reimbursement mechanisms will directly affect the way in which case managers are paid, thereby affecting the manner in which case management activities are performed. Scheffel notes that, whereas case managers in the past have had fairly wide latitude to bill by the hour, case managers are increasingly controlled by payers, and are pressured to be reimbursed according to diagnosis and/or to participate in performance-based payment structures. In order to thrive under such arrangements, and to ensure that case management services are perceived as essential in a time of cutting any non-essential costs, case managers are increasingly required to demonstrate the cost-effectiveness of their own services (Romaine, 1995). Consequently, case managers themselves must devote specific attention to the documentation of outcomes and accountability issues, and must market their services as essential elements of the managed care arsenal of cost-effective strategies.

TECHNOLOGY

Case management is increasingly becoming a technology-driven activity. With the need for more cost-effective and efficient service comes the need to use more rapid means for information management and transmittal. Masso (1995) notes that paperless transmittal via electronic data interchange will be the norm for all facets of business. Reliance on information systems to provide rapid access to patient information or current practice and to manage outcome databases will be essential. Instantaneous reporting via computer modem, instant billing, and electronic funds transfer has sped up the reimbursement process and facilitated the rapid movement of patients through the health care system. Consequently, it will be even more essential than it is today for case managers to become computer literate. Gambosh notes that, even now, case managers use the Internet to locate providers, examine protocols, and conduct research to obtain current information on what treatments are appropriate for patients (Gambosh, 1997).

In addition to information systems, case managers are likely to find themselves in the role of evaluating and recommending new equipment and procedures related to advances in medical science and biotechnology. Gambosh (1997) notes that case managers are likely to become the "gatekeepers for biotechnology usage" (p. 22), observing that, while it is one thing to create a piece of equipment, a body part, or a technical device in a laboratory, it is quite another to "match that product to the right person, at the right time and at the right price" (p.22). Similarly, advances in genetic therapies and research in such areas as central nervous system regeneration and other areas of bioscience will surely lead to revolutionary forms of treatment that will be in demand by patients and providers (DeBack & Cohen, 1996). It will be critical for case managers to stay up to date and be able to comment on the appropriateness of such procedures to payers and patients alike.

Case managers have also become increasingly reliant on telephone communications with patients, providers, insurers, and others. Gambosh (1997) notes that, in the late 1980s, telephonic consulting constituted only about 15% of case managers' activity. By the early 1990s, she estimated that about 85% of all case management was done telephonically. Increasingly, computer-based communication systems are replacing some phone time as more people become accustomed to communicating through e-mail.

POPULATION SHIFTS

Changes occurring in our population patterns will undoubtedly affect the kinds of patients and conditions served by case managers in the future. The aging of America is expected to transform the very fabric of society, particularly as increasing numbers of the baby-boom generation enter retirement. Geriatric case management is increasingly becoming prominent (Davidhizar & Bowen, 1996). Currently, there are over 1,500 registered Geriatric Care Managers in the United States (http://www.caremanager.org/index.htm). The number of people with chronic disabilities is expected to grow dramatically, due to the combined effects of the growing population of the elderly and the success of medicine and science in saving lives. The recent resurgence in infectious diseases and resistance to antibiotics and other drugs may create yet another population needing case management services (DeBack & Cohen, 1996). Gambosh notes that, in the future, case management is likely to address itself to a broader range of patients and health service needs with a greater emphasis on chronic disease management (Romaine, 1995). Prevention efforts are likely to shift to a different set of risk factors, including diet, exercise, lifestyle modifications, and other factors amenable to a "wellness" approach (DeBack & Cohen, 1996).

ETHICAL ISSUES

Today's case managers are no strangers to the ethical dilemmas presented by competing obligations to advocate for their clients while containing costs for the payer. Ethical dilemmas tied to dual obligation issues may be expected to continue to challenge case managers for some time. Increasingly, case managers are likely to find themselves squarely in the center of ethical concerns regarding the just distribution of scarce resources (Severson, 1996). Ethical issues related to advances in medicine and biotechnologies are also looming on the horizon. As Gambosh notes, case managers are often intimately involved in the consequences of doctors saving one-pound babies and the need to secure organs for transplants (Gambosh, 1997). Right-to-die issues loom large for case managers actively involved in working with chronically ill patients. Additionally, as new techniques and discoveries emerge, case managers are challenged to stay current. Continuing education is a must and case managers who relax for a moment will quickly find themselves out of date and lacking the skills necessary to practice competently and ethically.

NONTRADITIONAL SETTINGS AND DIVERSIFICATION

In a time of rapid change, nothing is certain. Once plentiful funding streams are likely to "dry up" overnight, and whole populations vanish or emerge due to population shifts and advances in medicine and technology. Case management may be perceived by any given payer to be essential one day, and "gravy" the next. Case managers with their pulse on the rapid fluctuations and trends in today's health care market know only one thing for sure. Change is inevitable and cannot be perfectly predicted. Consequently, successful case managers are carefully observing the trends and "hedging their bets" by developing multiple product lines, positioning themselves to benefit from market changes (Severson, 1996; Shaw & Betters, 2004). In addition to seeking out new product lines, case managers may also seek out alternative settings where their skills are valued and where a market may be created for their services (e.g., managed care firms, accounting firms, benefits review firms, wellness and prevention firms, third-party administrators, large employers, PPOs and HMOs, medical groups, and law firms).

CONCLUSION

Case management services have evolved throughout this century to become a critical element in today's rehabilitation and health care system. Along with changes in medicine, demographics, technology, health care financing, and health care systems, case management has been and is currently undergoing rapid change. Gains made in establishing standards and credentials must be accompanied by close attention to gathering outcome data as well as educating policymakers and funding sources about the effectiveness of case management services. Case management is currently used in nontraditional settings and with new populations so that the skills and knowledge areas required by case managers is expanding as well. Negotiating the changes ahead will require case managers to be alert to such changes, to be flexible, and to be creative.

REFERENCES

Beckley, N. J. (1995). Case management and integrated delivery. *Case Review, 1*, 25-30.

Bower, K. A. (1992). *Case management by nurses.* Washington, DC: American Nurses Association.

Case Management Society of America (1994). CMSA proposes standards of practice. *The Case Manager*, 59-70.

Chan, F., Leahy, M. J., McMahon, B. T., Mirch, M., & DeVinney, D. (1999). Foundational knowledge and major practice domains of case management. *The Journal of Care Management,* 5(1), 10, 13-14, 17-18, 26-28, 30.

Chan, F., Leahy, M. J., Downey, W., Lamb, G., Chapin, M., & Peterson, D. (2000). A work behavior analysis of Certified Case Managers. *The Journal of Care Management, 6*(4), 50-62.

Chan, F., Taylor, D., Currier, K., C. H. Chan, Wood, C., & Lui, J. (2001). Disability management practitioners: A work behavior analysis. *Journal of Vocational Rehabilitation, 5 (1)*, 47-56.

Commission for Case Manager Certification (2003). *CCM certification guide.* Rolling Meadows, IL: Author.

Daiker, B. (1995). Managed care in workers' compensation. *AAOHN Journal, 43*, 422-427.

Davidhizar, R. & Bowen, M. (1996). Adjusting to frustrating changes in health care: Strategies for case managers. *The Journal of Care Management, 2*, 80-86.

DeBack, V. & Cohen, E. The new practice environment. In E. Cohen (Ed.), *Nurse case management in the 21st century* (pp 3-9). St. Louis, MO: Mosby-Year Book, Inc.

Fabrey, L. (1996). Basic psychometric principles. In A. H. Browning, A. C. Bugbee, & M. M. Mullins (Eds.), *Certification: A NOCA Handbook* (pp. 1-40). Washington, DC: National Organization for Competency Assurance.

Gambosh, M. (1997). Case management: Meeting the challenges of change. *Continuing Care, 16*, 18-23.

Habeck, R. V., Leahy, M. J., Hunt, H. A., Chan, F., & Welch, E. M. (1991). Employer factors related to workers' compensation claims and disability management. *Rehabilitation Counseling Bulletin, 34*(3), 210-225.

Haw, M. A. (1996). Case management education in universities: A National survey. *The Journal of Care Management, 2*(6), 10-22.

Holt, L. (1993). The history of private sector rehabilitation. In L. E. Perlman & C. E. Hansen (Eds.), *Private sector rehabilitation: Insurance, trends, and issues for the 21st centry* (pp. 63-65). Alexandria, VA: National Rehabilitation Association.

Huber, D. (1996). *Leadership and nursing care management.* Philadelphia: W. B. Saunders.

Kreider, J. (1996). All lines case management coverage. *The Case Manager, 7*, 47-52.

Lamb. G. S. (1995). Case management. In G. S. Lamb (Ed.), *Annual review of nursing research* (pp. 117-136). New York: Springer.

Lauterbach, J. R. (1982). Coaching the disabled back to work. *Industry Week,* April 5, 52-55.

Leahy, M. J. (1994). *Validation of essential knowledge dimensions in case management.* Rolling Meadows, IL: Foundation for Rehabilitation Education and Research.

Leahy, M. J., Shapson, P. R., & Wright, G. N. (1987). Rehabilitation practitioner competencies by role and setting. *Rehabilitation Counseling Bulletin, 31*, 119-131.

Leahy, M. J., Szymanski, E. M., & Linkowski, D. C. (1993). Knowledge importance in rehabilitation counseling. *Rehabilitation Counseling Bulletin, 37*, 130-145.

Leahy, M. J. & Holt, E. (1993). Certification in rehabilitation counseling: History and process. *Journal of Applied Rehabilitation Counseling, 24*(4), 5-9.

Leahy, M. Chan, F., Shaw, L. R. & Lui, J. (1997). Preparation of rehabilitation counselors for case management functions in health care settings. *Journal of Rehabilitation, 63*(2), 53-59.

Leahy, M. J., Chan, F., Taylor, D., Woods, C., & Downey, W. (1998). Evolving knowledge and skill factors for practice in private sector rehabilitation. *The NARPPS Journal, 6*(1), 34-43.

Leahy, M. J., Chan, F., & Saunders, J. (2003). Job functions and knowledge requirements of certified rehabilitation counselors in the 21st century. *Rehabilitation Counseling Bulletin, 46*(2), 66-81.

Lynch, R. K., Lynch, R. T., & Beck, R. (1992). Rehabilitation counseling in the private sector. In R. M. Parker & E. M. Szymanski (Eds.), *Rehabilitation counseling. Basics and beyond* (pp. 73-102). Austin, TX: Pro-Ed.

Masso, A. R. (1995). Managed care and alternative-site health care delivery. *The Journal of Care Management, 1*, 45-51.

Matkin, R. E. (1983). The roles and functions of rehabilitation specialists in the private sector. *Journal of Applied Rehabilitation Counseling, 14*, 14-27.

Matkin, R. E. (1985) The state of private-sector rehabilitation. In L. J. Taylor, M. Golter, G. Golter, & T. E. Backer (Eds.), *Handbook of private sector rehabilitation* (pp 1-14). New York: Springer Publishing Co.

Matkin, R. E. (1986). *Insurance Rehabilitation*. Austin, TX: Pro-Ed.

Matkin, R. E. (1995). Private rehabilitation. In S. E. Rubin, & R. T. Roessler (Eds.), *Foundations of the vocational rehabilitation process* (4th ed.) (pp. 375-398). Austin, TX: Pro-Ed.

McCourt, A. E. (1993). *The specialty practice of rehabilitation nursing: A core curriculum* (3rd ed.). Skokie, IL: Rehabilitation Nursing Foundation.

McMahon, B. T. & Matkin, R. (1983). Pre-service graduate education for private sector rehabilitation counselors. *Rehabilitation Counseling Bulletin, 27*, 54-60.

Muthard, J. E., & Salamone, P. (1969). The roles and functions of the rehabilitation counselor. *Rehabilitation Counseling Bulletin, 13*, 81-168.

National Association of Professional Geriatric Care Managers (2003). Retrieved October 4, 2003, from http://www.caremanager.org/index.htm.

Raymond, C. (1986). Polio survivors spurred rehabilitation advances. *Journal of the American Medical Association, 255*, 1403-1404.

Romaine, D. S. (1995). Case management challenges, present and future. *Continuing Care, 14*, 25-31.

Rubin, S. E., Matkin, R. E., Ashley, J., Beardsley, M. M., May, V. R., Onstott, K., & Puckett, F. D. (1984). Roles and functions of certified rehabilitation counselors. *Rehabilitation Counseling Bulletin, 27*, 199-224.

Severson, M. (1996). Survival strategies for independents. *Continuing Care, 15*, 17-20, 34.

Shaw, L. (1995). Forensic rehabilitation: Historical and future perspective. In W. H. Burke (Ed.), *The handbook of forensic rehabilitation* (pp. 1-16). Houston: HDI Publishers.

Shaw, L. R. & Betters, C. (2004). Private sector practice. In Riggar, T. & Maki, D. (Eds.). *The handbook of rehabilitation counseling* (pp. 236-251). New York: Springer Publishing Company.

Shaw, L. R., McMahon, B. T., Chan, F., Taylor, D. & Wood, C. (1997). Survey of CORE accredited programs in rehabilitation counseling regarding private sector case management. *Journal of Rehabilitation, 63*(2), 46-51.

Shrey, D. (1979). The rehabilitation counselor in industry: A new frontier. *Journal of Applied Rehabilitation Counseling, 9*, 168-172.

Simpson, R. (1993). Case-managed care in tomorrow's information network. *Nursing Management, 24*, 14-16.

Sledge, W. H., Astrachan, B., Thompson, K, Rakfeldt, J. & Leaf, P. (1995). Case management in psychiatry: An analysis of tasks. *American Journal of Psychiatry, 152*, 1259-1265.

Strickland, T. (1995, Fall). Moving toward 2000: Trends and tribulations in case management. *CCM Update* pp. 4-6.

2

Contemporary Models, Principles, and Competencies of Case Management

Michael J. Leahy
Kathe Matrone
Fong Chan

Chapter Highlights

- Contemporary models

- Similarities and differences in models

- Principles

- Competencies

- Cultural competence

- Multicultural perspective

- Conclusion

The term "case management" has many different meanings in today's rehabilitation and health care delivery systems. In some instances, case management is considered a professional role, where all the associated functions and tasks serve the purpose of providing effective case management services to individuals with disabilities, within some specific service delivery setting. In other situations, case management may represent one specific function and associated tasks within the overall role of the professional, as in the case of the Rehabilitation Counselor and other disciplines (e.g., Mental Health Counselor, Social Worker). Over the years, a variety of case management models have emerged and evolved that provide a framework for the case management process. While these models may differ in relation to the specific nature of the health-related or rehabilitation problems addressed, the delivery system, services provided, outcomes, and professional grounding of the individual delivering services, the process involved appears quite similar. As indicated by Shaw, Leahy, and Chan (2005), the human service environment in which case management takes place, regardless of the model used to provide services, has undergone rapid change and evolution over the past decade or so. In today's environment of increased accountability and scarce resources, the case manager needs refined skills in teamwork and resource development, networking, referral, and coordination, in order to identify, provide, or arrange services that address the needs of the consumer in an ever increasingly complex, evolving, and diverse process (Woodside & McClam, 2003).

The purpose of this chapter is to review the various contemporary models of case management as they are depicted in today's rehabilitation and health care delivery systems. In addition to describing the models employed in delivering case management services, the principles and competencies associated with case management will be reviewed. Particular emphasis will be placed on those principles that guide and provide a useful framework for the delivery of case management services in the rehabilitation service delivery system by Rehabilitation Counselors, and related personnel. Finally, diversity issues and cultural competence will be explored within the context of providing effective case management services.

CONTEMPORARY MODELS
OF CASE MANAGEMENT

The complexity encountered in understanding the various contemporary models in case management creates a daunting task. There are many definitions and a diversity of models employed in practice. Despite this lack of standardization, the terms case management and case management models are commonly used in the literature without any specific description of their meaning. This lack of specificity has resulted in a general inability to accurately compare models, outcomes, and effectiveness of case management services (Huber, 2002). In this section of the chapter, we will describe some of these various models and their application within the service delivery process.

BASIC MODELS
A review of the literature suggests that one of the most basic and useful sets of models has been described by Woodside and McClam (2003), who identified three fundamental case management models grounded in roles, organizations, and responsibilities. In their conceptualization, the three models include (a) role-based case management; (b) organization-based case management; and (c) responsibility-based case management. Each of these models is briefly described below.

Role-based Case Management. This model focuses on the overall role the case manager performs. For example, a case manager may act exclusively as one who arranges or coordinates services, while a more discipline-based case manager may provide case management services in addition to an array of other services and functions, which, taken together, form their overall role. A good example of this latter model would be Rehabilitation Counselors or Mental Health Counselors, who in addition to case management, provide counseling or therapeutic services directly to the client as part of their professional role, and within the working alliance established with the consumer of services.

Organization-based Case Management. This model is focused on providing a comprehensive set of services available within a particular organization or agency, e.g., a comprehensive rehabilitation center or a non-profit community-based rehabilitation organization. Each client served within the organization is assigned a case manager who arranges, coordinates, and monitors services provided to the individual consumer and progress toward specific rehabilitation related goals and objectives.

Responsibility-based Case Management. This type of case management model provides for functions to be performed by family members, supportive personnel, volunteers, or the consumer. The focus in this type of model is on the transition of care from human service professional to non-professionals, including the consumer (Woodside & McClam, 2003).

MENTAL HEALTH MODELS
In a related effort within the mental health arena, Mueser, Bond, Drake, and Resnick (1998), identified three core models of case management, each containing two models deemed similar. These models included (a) the standard case management (brokerage and clinical case management models); (b) rehabilitation-oriented case management (strengths and rehabilitation models);

30

and (c) intensive case management (including both intensive and assertive models) models. Each of these core models is very briefly described below.

Standard Case Management Models. In brokerage models, the case manager acts solely as an advocate for the consumer or service user, and as a purchaser and arranger of services for the consumer. In the clinical case management model, the case manager has the professional training, credentials, and knowledge and skill, to develop a therapeutic relationship or working alliance with the consumer and provides an array of clinical and counseling services, in addition to case management services, to the consumer.

Rehabilitation-oriented Models. According to Simpson, Miller, and Bowers (2003), the strengths and rehabilitation-orientated models should really be viewed as one, with an emphasis on the strengths model. These models were first developed in the area of social work as a response to some of the concerns that existing approaches to psychiatric treatment and management over-emphasized limitations and disability effects, and de-emphasized the consumer's assets and strengths, which may be helpful in achieving individual goals. The focus of the work in this model is on the strengths of the individual rather than on the pathology, and the working alliance between the case manager and consumer is central to the model and collaborative in nature.

Intensive Case Management Models. In the Assertive Community Treatment (ACT) model, case management emphasizes the work of a team to address multiple consumer needs, and provide interventions in the consumer's home or work site. As a result of the intensity of this model, it requires rather low caseloads and the use of assertive outreach. This model places an emphasis on medication compliance and offers 24-hour coverage, as well as an array of daily living supports. Intensive Case Management is either viewed as a more intensive version of clinical case management, with smaller caseloads, or similar to ACT, employing smaller caseloads and more assertive approaches to consumers with significant and multiple needs (Simpson et al., 2003).

SIMILARITIES AND DIFFERENCES IN MODELS

One conceptualization that has promise in helping the field identify the similarities and differences among existing models of case management has been the work done by Ridgely and Willenbring (1992) to define the continuous dimensions of case management. These dimensions, or variables, can be applied to any case management model, and are not only helpful in specific comparisons among models, but serve further as a general description of how and in what way models may vary from one another (Hall, Carswell, Walsh, Huber & Jampoler, 2002). The 11 dimensions identified are as follows: (1) duration; (2) intensity and frequency of contact; (3) caseload-staff ratio; (4) type of service; (5) availability; (6) site of case management; (7) consumer (client) direction; (8) advocacy/gatekeeper; (9) case manager training; (10) case management authority; and (11) case management structure (Ridgely & Willenbring, 1992).

Although it may be helpful to understand the distinctions between different models of case management described in the literature, the commonality across models is equally important. Case management, for example, has been described as a process or method for ensuring that clients are provided with the services they need in a coordinated, effective, and efficient manner. The specific meaning of case management, however, depends on the system that is designed to provide it, and the particular characteristics of that system are shaped by the context to which it is expected to operate (Intagliata, 1982). These systems are also defined by their objectives, functions, and structural elements (Simpson et al., 2003). Although the critical or core concepts of all models focus on the coordination of care and services, case management may be best understood by looking at its goals and objectives (Hall, et al., 2002). For example, Intagliata (1982) described the following five goals for case management that appear to be relevant regardless of the particular model employed. They are:

1. enhancing the continuity of care,
2. providing access to cross-sectional service delivery that is comprehensive, coordinated, and ongoing,
3. enhancing accessibility by overcoming administrative barriers,
4. enhancing accountability by designation of a case manager as the single point of responsibility for assuring the overall effectiveness of the system, and
5. enhancing efficiency by increasing the likelihood of consumers receiving timely delivery of appropriate services.

While each of the case management models described above are an active part of the human services delivery system, the remaining part of this chapter will focus primarily on the role-based or clinical case management models (e.g., Rehabilitation Counselor, Mental Health Counselor, Social Worker, Rehabilitation Nurse) and the organization-based case management model (agency-based case manager in non-profit and for-profit sectors) in relation to philosophical principles, competencies and cultural competence.

PRINCIPLES

The guiding principles of case management, described by Woodside & McClam (2003), have direct application in the operationalization of each of the models described above and have particular importance in establishing a philosophical framework for the delivery of services and the relationship between the individual receiving services and the case manager. These general principles include the following: (1) integration of services; (2) continuity of care; (3) equal access to services; (4) quality care; (5) advocacy; (6) working with the whole person; (7) consumer empowerment; and (8) evaluation.

BASIC PRINCIPLES OF REHABILITATION PHILOSOPHY

In the rehabilitation counseling literature, there are a number of additional guidelines that directly affect the delivery of case management services. First, over the years there has been an effort to identify the basic principles of rehabilitation philosophy that serve to guide practice, as well as providing a useful framework for the development of ethical standards of practice. These principles and guidelines, known as the basic principles of rehabilitation philosophy, were first introduced by DiMichael (1969), expanded upon by Wright (1983), and modified by Parker & Szymanski (2000). The 20 principles are as follows:

- Every human being has an inalienable value and is worthy of respect for his/her own sake.
- Every person has membership in society, and rehabilitation should cultivate his/her full acceptance.
- The assets of people with disabilities should be emphasized, supported, and developed.
- Reality factors should be stressed in helping the person to cope with his/her environment.
- Comprehensive treatment involves the "whole person," because life areas are interdependent.
- Treatment should vary and be flexible to deal with the special characteristics of each person.
- Every person should assume as much initiative and participation as possible for the rehabilitation plan and its execution.
- Society should be responsible, through all possible public and private agencies, for the providing of services and opportunities to people with disabilities.
- Rehabilitation programs must be conducted with interdisciplinary and interagency integration.
- Rehabilitation is a continuous process that applies as long as help is needed.
- Psychological and personal reactions of the individual are ever present and often crucial.

- The rehabilitation process is complex and must be subject to constant reexamination – for each individual and for the program as a whole.
- The severity of handicap can be increased or decreased by environmental conditions.
- The significance of disability is affected by the person's feelings about the self and his/her situation.
- The client is seen not as an isolated individual but as part of a larger group that includes other people, often the family.
- Predictor variables, based on group outcomes in rehabilitation, should be applied with caution to the individual case.
- Self-help organizations are important allies in the rehabilitation effort.
- Provision must be made for the effective dissemination of information concerning legislation and community offerings of potential benefit to persons with disabilities.
- Basic research can profitably be guided by the question of usefulness in ameliorating problems, a vital consideration in rehabilitation fields, including psychology.
- Persons with disabilities should be called upon to serve as co-planners, co-evaluators, and consultants to others, including professional persons.

The importance of these principles as foundational guidelines for the practice of case management in rehabilitation settings cannot be overstated. It should be noted, however, that for Rehabilitation Counseling and other professional disciplines (e.g., Mental Health Counseling, Social Work) that provide case management services as part of their larger role, there are specific ethical codes of conduct and practice guidelines that regulate professional practice in case management, in addition to the general guidance provided by these long-standing philosophical principles.

CASE MANAGEMENT COMPETENCIES

In case management, regardless of the specific model employed, there appears to be three main domains of competence that interact with the consumer and the environment in the delivery of services provided by the case manager. These three domains include the knowledge, skill, and affective domains of competence. The latter of which is composed of the case manager's attitudes, philosophy, and values associated with the delivery of services to the consumer, which we have discussed earlier in this chapter.

Given the distinctions in case management definitions and models, an area where there appears to be a developing consensus in case management relates to the general process involved. For example, case management has been defined as a "collaborative process which assesses, plans, implements, coordinates, monitors, and evaluates options, and services to meet an individual's health needs through communications and available resources to promote quality, cost effective outcomes" (*The Case Manager*, 1994, p.59). In a similar view of process, Weil and Karls (1985) identified eight basic linear functions of case management, including (1) client identification and outreach; (2) individual assessment and diagnosis; (3) service planning and resource identification; (4) linking clients to needed services; (5) service implementation; (6) monitoring service delivery; (7) advocacy; and (8) evaluation. While these general process descriptions are helpful to understand the typical flow of functions and services across models of case management, they are not adequate to understand fully the specific functions, tasks, or knowledge and skills associated with case management practice.

To address this need there has been a series of nation-wide empirical studies (Leahy, 1994; Chan, Leahy, Downey, Lamb, Chapin, & Peterson 2000) undertaken to investigate the knowledge and skill competencies and functions and tasks associated with case management practices across the models that were described earlier in this chapter. Research in this area addressed two fundamental questions. First, what do case managers actually do in practice, or more specifically, what are the functions and specific tasks considered important by case managers in delivery of services to individual with disabilities and chronic health problems? The second question asks, what are the knowledge's and skills needed by the case manager in order to provide effective case management services?

In the first of these nation-wide competency studies, Leahy (1994) surveyed 14,078 Certified Case Managers (CCMs) to empirically validate common knowledge dimensions required for case management practice across the various models (e.g., role-based, organization-based). Leahy found five knowledge domains important to case management practice, they included (1) coordination and service delivery; (2) physical and psychosocial aspects of disability; (3) benefit systems/ cost benefit analysis; (4) case management concepts; and (5) community re-entry. In addition to validating the assumption that case managers share a common set of competencies, across disciplines, settings, and case management models, these findings were used as the basis for the content design and test specifications for the first empirically grounded Certified Case Manager examination in the mid 1990's.

Following up on this effort, Chan et al. (2000) surveyed a 20% random sample of CCMs in their nation-wide study to determine the underlying work-role dimensions (functions and tasks) and knowledge domains in case management, across models, disciplines, and settings. Their findings included the identification of four major job functions that included, in rank order of

35

importance (1) monitoring care and follow-up; (2) healthcare management; (3) program management and evaluation; and (4) disability case management. They also identified six major knowledge domains required of case managers for effective service delivery. These empirically derived knowledge domains, in rank order, are as follows (1) interpersonal communication; (2) healthcare management; (3) community resources and support; (4) managed care concepts; (5) psychosocial intervention; and (6) rehabilitation case management. In order to provide more specificity and substance in relation to our understanding of both the functions and tasks, and knowledge and skills considered important to the delivery of case management services, Tables I and II are provided below.

Table I
MAJOR JOB FUNCTIONS AND SPECIFIC TASKS

Factor 1: Monitoring Care and Follow-up
- Determining whether a client will benefit from case management services.
- Following up with the client and provider regarding treatment status.
- Determining the potential for a positive case outcome.
- Discussing alternative treatment plans with the providers when the client is not responding to the prescribed treatment plan.
- Monitoring and evaluating client response to treatment and revising treatment plans as needed.
- Obtaining written reports regarding client progress.
- Requesting and reviewing medical information from physicians and therapists (occupational, physical, and speech) to assess the client's medical status.

Factor 2: Healthcare Management
- Attending team conferences.
- Completing a thorough initial evaluation to assess the client's medical, psychological, social, environmental, vocational, and financial status.
- Preparing discharge plan.
- Acting as an advocate for the client and family with third-party payers and service providers.
- Researching and securing funding, community resources, and support needed for community re-entry.
- Meeting with the physician to discuss the client's medical status and

- Providing education, information, direction, and support to clients related to care goals.
- Evaluating and selecting facilities that provide specialized care services for clients.
- Discussing client care needs with service provider and furnishing rationale for needed services to obtain payment approval.
- Coordinating acquisition of medical equipment (including assessment, negotiation, proper use, and follow-up).
- Learning about resources for clients.
- Synthesizing assessment information to prioritize care needs and develop treatment plans.
- Implementing care and treatment plans.
- Conducting a home visit with the client.
- Monitoring and evaluating client response to treatment and revising treatment plans as needed.
- Contacting vendors in order to purchase adaptive/accommodative equipment.

Factor 3: Program Management and Evaluation
- Performing administrative functions related to the operation of a case management program.
- Providing consultation in health education.
- Providing consultation in accident prevention and wellness.
- Developing procedures for early intervention programs.
- Preparing cost-benefit analyses of case management programs.
- Promoting and marketing the case management program.
- Performing program evaluations and research functions to document improvements in client outcomes, cost savings, client compliance, and return to productivity.
- Determining and monitoring individual case management outcomes.
- Educating other stakeholders regarding the value and role of case mangers in health care delivery.

Factor 4: Disability Case Management
- Discussing return-to-work options with the employer.
- Obtaining a release for a return to work from the treating physician.
- Reviewing job analyses with the treating physician.

(table continues)

Table I (Continued)

- Developing individualized return-to-work plans.
- Meeting with the employer to discuss return to work options at the job site.
- Educating employers, payers, and health care providers regarding return-to-work issues.
- Obtaining functional capacity evaluations.
- Providing job modification and job accommodation services for the client.
- Providing follow-up support and consultation upon client's return to work.
- Developing and implementing transitional work programs.
- Conducting job analyses.
- Collecting and reviewing employment-related information from the client.
- Obtaining written reports regarding client progress.
- Performing utilization reviews.

Table II
MAJOR KNOWLEDGE AND SKILL DOMAINS

Factor 1: Interpersonal Communication
- Interpersonal communication.
- Interpersonal relationship.
- Case recording and documentation.
- Clinical problem-solving and critical-thinking skills.
- Case management process and tools.
- Psychosocial aspects of chronic illness and disability.
- Basic interviewing skills.
- Negotiation and conflict resolution strategies.

Factor 2: Healthcare Management
- Medical case management.
- Medical aspects of acute and chronic illness and disability.
- Goals and objectives of case management.
- Health care ethics.

- Assessment of physical functioning.
- Legal aspects of case management.
- Medical and allied health professions.

Factor 3: Community Resources and Support
- Levels of care (e.g., hospital, extended care facility, sub acute facility, home).
- Community resources and support programs.
- Health care benefits.
- Rehabilitation service delivery systems.
- Public benefit programs (e.g., SSI, SSDI, Medicare, Medicaid).
- Assistive technology.

Factor 4: Managed Care Concepts
- Managed care concepts.
- Cost-containment procedures and strategies.
- Health care benefits.
- Critical pathways, standards of care, practice guidelines.
- Health care delivery systems.
- Health care and disability-related legislation.
- Public benefit programs (e.g., SSI, SSDI).
- Cost-benefit analysis.
- Wellness and illness prevention concepts and strategies.
- Case management models.
- Utilization management.
- Program evaluation and research (e.g., outcome, satisfaction).
- Risk management and insurance principles.
- Integrated benefit systems.

Factor 5: Psychosocial Intervention
- Family dynamics.
- Multicultural issues and health behavior.
- Clinical pharmacology.
- Psychological and neuropsychological assessment.
- Mental health and psychiatric disability concepts.
- Substance use/abuse/addiction.
- Managed behavioral health care.

(table continues)

39

Table II (Continued)

Factor 6: Rehabilitation Case Management
- Disability compensation systems (e.g., workers' compensation, auto insurance,
- LTD, STD, accident, and health).
- Job analysis, job modification, and job accommodation.
- Work adjustment and work transition.
- Vocational aspects of chronic illness and disability.
- Work-hardening resources and strategies.
- Ergonomics.
- Vocational assessment.
- Job development and placement.
- Barrier-free architectural design.
- Life care planning

While these research efforts (Leahy, 1994; Chan, Leahy, Downey, Lamb, Chapin, & Peterson 2000) studied case managers from across disciplines (e.g., Nurses, Social Workers, Rehabilitation Counselors, Mental Health Counselors) and models (e.g., brokerage, clinical, role-based, strengths and rehabilitation, organization-based, and intensive case management models) to identify critical functions and knowledge requirements for case management, there is another extensive body of research over the past 40 years that specifically studied the role and competencies of the Rehabilitation Counselor, that is an excellent example of viewing role-based case management within the context of an overall professional role.

For example, the most recent national study of the Rehabilitation Counselor across service delivery settings, conducted by Leahy, Chan, and Saunders (2003) identified seven major functions: which included (1) vocational counseling and consultation; (2) counseling interventions; (3) community-based rehabilitation service; (4) case management; (5) applied research; (6) assessment; and (7) professional advocacy. In addition to these functions, Leahy et al., (2003) identified the following six knowledge domains required of rehabilitation counselors in performing their role: (1) career counseling, assessment, and consultation services; (2) counseling theories; techniques, and applications; (3) rehabilitation services and resources; (4) case and caseload management; (5) health care and disability systems; and (6) medical, functional, and environmental implications of disability. Tables 3 and 4 below provide a more specific look at the case management function and associated tasks, and the required knowledge to deliver effective case management services from a Rehabilitation Counseling perspective.

Table III
CASE MANAGEMENT FUNCTIONS AND TASKS FOR REHABILITATION COUNSELORS

- Compile and interpret client information to maintain a current case record.
- Perform caseload management activities.
- Consult with medical professionals about functional capacities, prognosis, and treatment plans for clients.
- Obtain written reports regarding client progress.
- Collaborate with other providers so that services are coordinated, appropriate, and timely.
- Write case notes, summaries, and reports so that others can understand the case.
- Determine and monitor individual case management outcomes.
- Monitor client progress.
- State clearly the nature of the clients' problems for referral to service providers.
- Develop rapport/network with physicians and other rehabilitation professionals.
- Use effective conflict resolution strategies when providing case management services.
- Report to referral source regarding progress of cases.
- Make sound and timely financial decisions within the context of caseload management in your work setting.
- Coordinate activities of all agencies involved in a rehabilitation plan.
- Interview the client to collect and verify the accuracy of case information.
- Refer clients to appropriate specialists and/or for special services.
- Use effective time management strategies.
- Abide by ethical and legal considerations of case communication and recording (e.g., confidentiality).
- Assess the significance of the clients' disabilities in consideration of medical, psychological, educational, and social support status.

Table IV
KNOWLEDGE DOMAINS OF CASE MANAGEMENT FOR REHABILITATION
COUNSELORS

- Case management processes and tools.
- Case recording and documentation.
- Principles of caseload management.
- Professional roles, functions, and relationships with other human service providers.
- Critical problem solving and critical thinking skills.
- Negotiation and conflict resolution strategies.
- Case management process, including case finding, service coordination, referral to and use of other disciplines, and client advocacy.
- Techniques for working effectively in teams across disciplines.

CULTURAL COMPETENCE IN CASE MANAGEMENT

In addition to the competency areas already discussed, rehabilitation and health-related organizations are attempting to meet the challenges and opportunities to respond effectively to the needs of individuals with disabilities from racially, ethnically, culturally, and linguistically diverse backgrounds. The incorporation of culturally competent approaches remains a challenge for the individual counselor, case manager, and the organization. In rehabilitation, the importance of multicultural issues and counselor competence is manifested through several internal and external perspectives, including changing demographics and globalization, issues of social justice, and professional obligation (Mason, 1999).

The make-up of the American population is changing as a result of immigration patterns and significant increases among racially, ethnically, culturally, and linguistically diverse populations residing in the United States. According to the US 2000 Census, the chance of two randomly chosen U.S. residents being ethnically different is 49%. Currently, traditional minorities are in the majority in 48 out of 100 largest US cities, with Hispanics representing the fastest growing majority group.

Interwoven in the discussions of changing demographics and rehabilitation is the concept of social justice. Sue (2001) argues that multicultural counseling competence must be about social justice, "providing equal access and opportunity, being inclusive, and removing individual and systemic barriers to

42

fair services" (p. 801). Several recent studies have found a disparity in access to services, provision of services, and outcomes in the public vocational rehabilitation program for individuals with disabilities from diverse racial and ethnic backgrounds (Bellini, 2002; Feist-Price, 1995; Wheaton, Wilson, & Brown, 1996; Moore, 2002). The perception of inequity in the provision of services to individuals with disabilities from diverse racial and ethnic backgrounds continues to challenge the rehabilitation counseling profession, the field of rehabilitation, and related health care delivery systems.

Another reason justifying the need for cultural competence is professional obligation. Practicing counselors may be legally vulnerable when defined and accepted competencies are violated. Multicultural counseling competence has been addressed by several professional rehabilitation organizations (Jenkins, Ayers, & Hunt, 1996). For example, the Commission for Rehabilitation Counselor Certification (CRCC) added a series of questions on multicultural issues for inclusion in the national certification examination. In addition, there have been multiple competency standards adopted by the Council on Rehabilitation Education (CORE) and the Council for Accreditation of Counseling and related Education Programs (CACREP) endorsing the obligation to increase counselor's multicultural knowledge, skills and awareness (Byington, Fischer, Walker, & Freedman, 1997).

DEFINING CULTURAL COMPETENCE
In defining multicultural competence, the emphasis is placed on "best practice" rather than the special interests of any group. Multicultural counseling competence refers to the counselor's attitudes/beliefs, knowledge, and skills in working with individuals from diverse backgrounds (Constantine & Ladany, 2000). If inappropriate cultural assumptions are made, accurate assessments, meaningful understandings, or appropriate interventions will not be made, regardless of the skills, training, or intelligence of the counselor.

The framework of a multicultural competence was developed by D. W. Sue (Sue, Arredondo, & McDavis, 1992; Sue et al., 1982) and was based on a three-stage continuous learning process of awareness, knowledge, and skills. The framework is depicted in Table V with a 3 x 3 matrix resulting in 31 different competencies (Sue et al., 1992). This same framework was used in the development of the multicultural rehabilitation competencies (Middleton et al., 2000) and in the development of many multicultural training programs (Sue, 2001; Trevino, 1996).

The dimension of awareness encompasses cultural self-awareness and other-awareness, and is achieved through introspection, self-monitoring, and reflective self-evaluation (Sodowsky, 1996). Others have described this dimension as developing a deep-cultural self-empathy where the individual can look at their own culture by stepping outside of it (Pedersen, 2000).

The knowledge dimension encompasses theoretical knowledge of multicultural counseling issues including racial and cultural concepts such as racial and ethnic identity, worldviews, and acculturation. Awareness helps the counselor ask the right questions and knowledge helps them answer those questions (Pedersen, 2002). For example, meaningful knowledge may assist a rehabilitation counselor to understand how race, culture, and ethnicity may affect help-seeking behavior or vocational choices.

Table V
COMPONENTS OF CULTURAL COMPETENCE

Belief/Attitude	Knowledge	Skill
1. Aware and sensitive to own heritage and valuing/ respecting differences.	1. Has knowledge of own racial/cultural heritage and how it affects perceptions.	1. Seeks out educational, consultative, and multicultural training experiences.
2. Aware of own background/ experiences and biases and how they influences psychological	2. Possesses knowledge about racial identity and development.	2. Seeks to understand self as racial/cultural being
3. Recognizes limits of competencies and expertise.	3. Knowledgeable about own social impact and communication styles.	3. Familiarizes self with relevant research on racial/ ethnic groups.
4. Comfortable with differences that exist between themselves and others.	4. Knowledgeable about groups one works or interacts with.	4. Involved with minority groups outside of work role: community events.

44

Beliefs/Attitudes	Knowledge	Skills
5. In touch with negative emotional reactions toward racial/ethnic groups and can be nonjudgmental.	5. Understands how race/ethnicity affects personality formation, vocational choices, psychological disorders, and so forth.	5. Able to engage in a variety of verbal/nonverbal helping styles.
6. Aware of stereotypes and preconceived notions.	6. Knows about socio-political influences, immigration, poverty powerlessness, and so forth.	6. Can exercise institutional inter-vention skills on behalf of clients.
7. Respects religious and/or spiritual beliefs of others.	7. Understands culture--bound, class-bound, and linguistic features of psychological help.	7. Can seek consultation with traditional healers.
8. Respects indigenous helping practices and community networks.	8. Knows the effects of institutional barriers.	8. Can take responsibility to provide linguistic competence for clients.
9. Values bilingualism.	9. Knows bias of assessment.	9. Has expertise in cultural aspects of assessment.
	10. Knowledgeable about minority family structures, community, and so forth.	10. Works to eliminate bias, prejudice, and discrimination.
	11. Knows how discriminatory practices operate at a community level.	11. Educates clients in the nature of one's practice.

Note. Adapted from D.W. Sue, Arredondo, & McDavis (1992) as cited in Sue (2001).

Finally, the Skills dimension addresses strategies and techniques used in working with clients from diverse cultures. Studies reveal that counseling effectiveness is improved when counselors use appropriate modalities and define goals consistent with the life experiences and values of clients (Pedersen et al, 1998). The ability to use both verbal and nonverbal responses appropriately is one competency included in the Skill dimension. For example, counselors are often taught to expect clients to establish good eye contact, discuss inner feelings, or verbalize concerns. Someone who is from an American Indian or Asian culture might not display these behaviors.

DEVELOPING MULTICULTURAL COMPETENCE
In developing professional multicultural competence, it is necessary that the rehabilitation counselor must be or become well trained in the conventional theories and strategies of counseling (Pedersen, 2002). A first step in developing multicultural counseling competence is an assessment in the areas of awareness, knowledge, and skill (Pedersen, 2002). Assessments can be achieved through the use of instruments such as the Multicultural Inventory (Sodowsky, Taffe, Gutke, & Wise, 1994) or the Multicultural Counseling Awareness Scale or MCAS-FORMB (Ponterotto, Gretchen, Utsey, Rieger, & Austin, 2002). Less formal methods can be achieved through individual assessments of one's abilities in each of the competency areas.

The competency-based approach has been articulated in a set of guidelines and explanatory statements for each competency within Sue's framework (Arredondo et al., 1996). This effort was expanded upon for rehabilitation counselors by Middleton (Middleton et al., 2000). The explanatory statements can be used as learning objectives, as outcome statements, or as behaviors that manifest a degree of competency (Arredondo, 1999). These are excellent resources available for use by individual counselors, case managers, and organizations in developing multicultural competence.

MULTICULTURAL PERSPECTIVE IN CASE MANAGEMENT

The professional multicultural competence perspective in case management is based on the acquisition of the awareness, knowledge, and skills needed for working effectively with individuals with disabilities from diverse backgrounds. Based on the work of Sue (Pedersen et al., 1998) developing professional multicultural competence for rehabilitation counselors and other case managers should include the following propositions:
1. Recognizing that traditional rehabilitation counseling practice is culture-bound and reflects a Euro-American worldview.

2. Acquiring culture-specific information about the life experiences, values, assumptions, and histories of culturally different groups within our communities.
3. Understanding oneself as a racial/cultural being and the potential impact on the rehabilitation counseling relationship.
4. Being able to use culturally relevant intervention strategies as a means of expanding helping responses in effective multicultural counseling.
5. Playing alternative helping roles maximizes the opportunities of providing appropriate services to individuals with disabilities from diverse cultures.
6. Acknowledging, respecting, and using non-Western indigenous healing methods and approaches.

The learning process to achieve cultural competence in rehabilitation counseling and case management involves the cognitive, affective, and behavioral levels. Professional multicultural development requires a commitment to a life long learning process to acquire the awareness, knowledge, and skills needed in working effectively with individuals with disabilities from racially, ethnically, culturally, and linguistically diverse backgrounds.

CONCLUSION

In summary, this chapter has provided an overall review of the various contemporary models of case management in today's rehabilitation and health care delivery systems. These models included the role-based, organization-based, responsibility-based, brokerage, clinical, strengths, rehabilitation-orientated, assertive community treatment, and intensive case management models. In addition to describing the models employed in delivering case management services, 8 general guiding principles and 20 principles of rehabilitation philosophy were presented to provide a useful framework for structuring the working alliance and to guide the counselor in providing case management services to the consumer.

To acquaint the reader more fully with the functions and tasks, and knowledge and skills associated with providing case management services across settings, empirical research was reviewed from two recent national studies (Leahy, 1994, Chan et al., 2000). Furthermore, as an example of role-based case management, recent research on Rehabilitation Counselor (Leahy et al., 2003) competencies were presented with a particular focus on the case management functions and tasks, and resulting knowledge and skill requirements for Rehabilitation Counselors providing these services. Finally, diversity issues and cultural competence were explored within the context of

47

providing effective case management services for both the Rehabilitation Counselors and other Case Managers within the rehabilitation and health related service delivery environments.

In the chapters that follow, additional foundational knowledge will be reviewed that is critical for the delivery of effective case management services across models, as well as a review of specific disability populations and service delivery settings that present unique issues and challenges to the case management process.

REFERENCES

Arredondo, P., Toporek, R., Brown S. P., Jones, J. Locke, D. C., Sanchez, J., & Stadler, H. (1996). Operationalization of the multicultural competencies. *Journal of Multicultural Counseling and Development, 24*, 42-78.

Bellini, J. (2002). Correlates of multicultural counseling competencies of vocational rehabilitation counselors. *Rehabilitation Counseling Bulletin, 45*, 66-75.

Byington, K., Fischer, J., Walker, L., & Freedman, E. (1997). Evaluating the effectiveness of a multicultural counseling ethics and assessment training. *Journal of Applied Rehabilitation Counseling, 28*, 15-19.

Case Management Society of America (1994). CMSA proposes standards of practice. *The Case Manager*, 59-70.

Chan, F., Leahy, M. J., Downey, W., Lamb, G., Chapin, M., & Peterson, D. (2000). A work behavior analysis of certified case managers. *Care Management, 6*(4), 50-62.

Constantine, M. G. & Ladany, N. (2000). Self-report multicultural counseling competence scales: Their relation to social desirability attitudes and multicultural case conceptualization ability. *Journal of Counseling Psychology, 47*, 155-164.

DiMichael, S. E. (1969). The current scene. In D. Malikin & H. Rusalem (Eds.), *Vocational Rehabilitation of the Disabled: An overview.* New York: New York University Press.

Feist-Price, S. (1995). African Americans with disabilities and equity in vocational rehabilitation services: One state's review. *Rehabilitation Counseling Bulletin, 39, 119-129.*

Hall, J. A., Carswell, C., Walsh, E., Huber,D. L., & Jampoler, J. S. (2002). Iowa case management: Innovative social casework. *Social Work, 47*, 132-141.

Huber, D. (2002). The diversity of case management models. *Nursing Case Management*, 7(6), 212-220.

Intagliata, J. (1982). Improving the quality of community care for the chronically mentally disabled: The role of case management. *Schizophrenia Bulletin, 8,* 655-674.

Leahy, M. J., Chan, F., & Saunders, J. (2003). Job functions and knowledge requirements of Certified Rehabilitation Counselors in the 21st century. *Rehabilitation Counseling Bulletin, 46*(2), 66-81.

Leahy, M. J. (1994). *Validation of essential knowledge dimensions in case management.* Chicago, IL: Foundation for Rehabilitation Certification, Education and Research.

Jenkins, A. E., Ayers, G .E., & Hunt, B. (1996). Cultural diversity and rehabilitation: The road traveled. *Rehabilitation Education, 10,* 83-103.

Mason, J. (1999). Vocational rehabilitation and cultural competency: Considering accountability. *Chapter Four, Switzer Monograph* (pp. 55-66). Alexandria, VA: National Rehabilitation Association.

Middleton, R. A., Rollins, C. W., Sanderson, P. L., Leung, P., Harley, D. A., Ebener, D., & Leal-Idrogo, A. (2000). Endorsement of professional multicultural rehabilitation competencies and standards: A call to action. *Rehabilitation Counseling Bulletin, 43,* 219-240.

Moore, C. L. (2002). Outcome variables that contribute to group differences between Caucasians, African Americans, and Asian Americans who are deaf. *Journal of Applied Rehabilitation Counseling, 33,* 8-12.

Muesner, K. T., Bond, G. R., Drake, R. E., & Resnick, S. G. (1998). Models of community care for severe mental illness: A review of research on case management. *Schizophrenia Bulletin, 24,* 37-74.

Parker, R. A., & Syzmanski, E. M. (2000). *Rehabilitation counseling: Basics and beyond* (3rd ed.). Austin: Pro-Ed.

Pedersen, P. B. (2002). The making of a culturally competent counselor. In W. J. Lonner, D. L. Dinnel, S. A. Hayes, & D. N. Sattler (Eds.), *Online Readings in Psychology and Culture* (Unit 10, Chapter 2), (http://www.wwu.edu/~culture), Center for Cross-Cultural Research, Western Washington University, Bellingham, Washington USA.

Pedersen, P. (Series Ed). (1998). *Multicultural Counseling Competencies: Individual and organizational development.* Thousand Oaks, CA: Sage Publications.

Pedersen, P. (2000). *A handbook for developing multicultural awareness* (3rd ed.). Alexandria, VA: American Counseling Association

Ponterotto, J. G., Gretchen, D., Utsey, S. O., Rieger, B. P., & Austin, R. (2002). A revision of the multicultural counseling awareness scale. *Multicultural Counseling & Development, 30,* 153-180.

Ridgely. M. S., & Willenbring, M. (1992). Application of case management to
    drug treatment: Overview of models and research issues. In R. Ashery
    (Ed.). *Progress and issues in case management* (Vol. 127, pp.12-33)
    Rockville, MD: US Department of Health and Human Services, Alcohol,
    Drug Abuse and Mental Health Administration.
Shaw, L., Leahy, M., & Chan, F. (2005). Case management: Historical
    foundations and current trends. In F. Chan, M. J. Leahy, & J. L.
    Saunders, (Eds.), *Case management for rehabilitation health
    professionals* (pp. 3-27). Osage Beach, MO: Aspen Professional
    Services.
Simpson, A., Miller, C., & Bowers, L. (2003). Case management models and
    the care programme approach: How to make the CPA effective and
    credible. *Journal of Psychiatric & Mental Health Nursing, 10*, 472-483.
Sodowsky, G. R. (1996). The Multicultural Counseling Inventory: Validity and
    applications in multicultural training. In G. R. Sodowsky & J. C. Impara
    (Series Eds.) & J. C. Impara (Vol. Ed.), *Multicultural assessment in
    counseling and clinical psychology: Buros-Nebraska series on
    measurement and testing* (pp. 325-343). Lincoln, NE: Buros Institute of
    Mental Measurements.
Sodowsky, G. R., Taffe, R. C., Gutkin, T. B., & Wise, S. (1994). Development
    of the Multicultural Counseling Inventory: A self-report measure of
    multicultural competencies. *Journal of Counseling Psychology, 41*, 137-
    148.
Sue, D. W. (2001). Multidimensional facets of cultural competence. *The
    Counseling Psychologist, 29*, 790-821.
Sue, D. W., Arredondo, P., & McDavis, R. J. (1992). Multicultural counseling
    competencies and standards: A call to the profession. *Journal of
    Counseling and Development, 70*, 477-486.
Sue, D. W., Bernier, J. E., Durran, A., Feinberg, L., Pedersen, P., Smith, E. J.,
    & Vasquez-Nuttal, E. (1982). Position paper: Cross-cultural counseling
    competencies. *The Counseling Psychologist, 10*, 45-52.
Trevino, J. G. (1996). Worldview and change in cross-cultural counseling.
    Counseling Psychologist, 24, 198-212.
Weil, M., & Karls, J. M. (1985).*Case management in human service practice*.
    San Francisco: Jossey-Bass.
Wheaton, J. E., Wilson, K. B., & Brown, S. M. (1996). The relationship
    between vocational rehabilitation services and the consumer's race,
    gender, and closure status. *Rehabilitation Counseling Bulletin, 40*, 116-
    133.
Woodside & McClam (2003). *Generalist case management: A method of
    human service delivery* (2nd ed.). Pacific Grove, CA: Brookes/Cole.

Wright B. A. (1983). *Physical disability: A psychosocial approach* (2nd ed.). New York: Harper & Row.

This page intentionally left blank

Section 2

Foundational Knowledge Related to Case Management

In This Section

Section 2, *Foundational Knowledge related to Case Management*, contains seven chapters. In Chapter 3, Rosenthal and colleagues provide a brief overview of the rise of managed care organizations examining their economic successes, political restructuring, and service shortcomings. New paradigms and trends in managed health care are also highlighted. The authors contend that the confluence of economic and management trends with societal trends highlights the immediate and future needs for a new, multi-disciplinary case manager. Trends in medical and vocational case management education are also examined.

Chapter 4 describes the new disability law and policy framework as it impacts labor force strategies and employment opportunities for the emerging workforce of persons with disabilities. Schmeling, Schartz, and Blanck highlight the historical evolution of national employment policy toward persons with disabilities from a civil rights perspective. They examine contemporary efforts toward a national employment policy, including legislation, litigation, and relevant policymaking.

Interpersonal communication skills for case managers is presented and discussed in Chapter 5 by Koch and Rumrill. The authors provide a framework for facilitating cooperative interactions with emphasis on interpersonal communication strategies for building collaborative relationships and suggest strategies for establishing bonds, setting goals, and accomplishing tasks. A negotiation/conflict resolution model for case managers is presented and discussed.

In Chapter 6, Tarvydas, Peterson, and Michaelson present information and discuss clinical decision-making and ethical issues encountered by case managers who practice within the health care and rehabilitation delivery systems. The authors discuss the various models available and processes recommended in working through and resolving ethical dilemmas in case management, as well as the identification of particularly significant ethical issues that may be encountered in practice.

Chapter 7 provides a comprehensive overview of essential community resources (medical and vocational case management) used by nurses and rehabilitation counselors to serve their clients effectively. Chapin also discusses the importance of resource utilization and provides information on community resource development as part of the case manager's role.

Merbitz and colleagues discuss assistive technology for case managers in Chapter 8. The authors survey the area of assistive technology

(AT), discuss some basic issues, organizing principles, AT service delivery models, and review different specific AT areas.

In Chapter 9, by Reid and colleagues, life care planning (LPC) is presented as a significant tool in guiding the provision of quality care and services throughout the lifespan of a catastrophically injured individual. The authors present LCP as a method to organize the multidimensional information that must be considered for effective case management. They present a comprehensive and detailed case study to emphasize the importance of this methodology for practicing case managers who work with the catastrophically injured clients.

$$\approx$$

3

The Restructuring of Managed Care: The Importance of Choice

David A. Rosenthal
John Lui
Fong Chan
Steve R. Pruett

Chapter Highlights

- Managed health care concepts

- Managed health care and case management

- Integrated health care systems

- Implications for case management education and training

- Demonstrating effectiveness

- The future

- Summary

The American health care system has undergone considerable change over the past several decades, moving from provider-driven health care of the 1970s and early 1980s; to the managed care, payer-driven systems in the late 1980s and 1990s (Chan, Lui, Rosenthal, Pruett, & Ferrin, 2002); to emerging models that increasingly include the consumer as part of the system of care (Morath, 2003). The traditional cost-containment measures used by managed care include primary care gate keeping, utilization review, preauthorization of referrals and procedures, practice guidelines, case management, profiling of providers, pharmaceutical restrictions, co-payments, and disease management (Dudley & Luft, 2001). Although efficiencies and cost effective procedures introduced by managed care concepts may have initially reduced overall health care expenditures, critics have maintained that much of the health care service delivery within managed care has been fragmented, has employed short-term incentives, and has lacked consumer/patient collaboration (Merry & Crago, 2001). Managed care has been successful in controlling some health care costs, but it also has been recognized as a political failure (Chan et al., 2002); restrictions to treatment access through utilization review processes have infuriated both consumers and physicians (Robinson, 2001).

In this chapter, the authors provide a brief overview of the rise of managed care organizations (MCOs), examining their economic successes, political restructuring, and service shortcomings; additionally, we highlight new paradigms and trends in managed health care, such as consumerism, willing provider care, proactive care, and consumer education. The confluence of economic management trends with societal trends highlights the immediate and future needs for a new, multi-disciplinary case manager. A final exploration of trends in medical and vocational case management education reveals ways in which the educational system is meeting (and failing to meet) those needs.

Harris, Ripperger, and Horn (2000) suggested that, by many economic and health-related measures, managed care has been a huge success. The authors argue that healthcare cost trends have moderated and that the overall health of the U.S. population has continued to improve, as reflected by increased life expectancy and reduced infant mortality. However, other economic indicators reveal that costs of health care have not moderated under managed care. The health care consulting firm Hewitt Associates issued a report projecting a 15.4 percent increase for health care costs in 2003, higher than the reported increase of 13.7 percent in 2002 and, in fact, the highest jump in health care costs since the early 1990s (Hayne & Zagata-Meraz, 2003). The health care consulting firm Watson Wyatt Worldwide reported that health care costs increased more than 14 percent in 2002 and anticipated increases of 14-15 percent in 2003. Both Hewitt Associates and Watson Wyatt Worldwide have predicted that health care costs will double by 2007 (Hayne & Zagata-Meraz, 2003; Watson Wyatt Worldwide, 2003).

Managed care has been criticized for limiting consumer choice and, by doing so, decreasing consumer satisfaction (Bruner, 2002). In order to maintain control of the cost of health benefits, MCOs have traditionally limited a consumer's choice of physician, hospital, therapist, and pharmacy to those providers that have contracts stipulating capitation and utilization review. While this has been effective in keeping medical costs from rising in the past, the reduced freedom to choose a provider runs counter to the American consumer's expectation of freedom of choice in medical care. This has led to not only low consumer satisfaction but also to the perception that MCOs provide inferior care (Boenheimer, Lo, & Casalino, 1999; Reschovsky, Hargraves, & Smith, 2002) or deny needed services (Harris, Ripperger, & Horn, 2000).

Health care plans change as they grow and adapt to market forces and as their networks of preferred providers become broader. Within the past few years, MCOs have developed multi-tiered plans that incorporate HMOs, PPOs, and out-of-network systems (Dudley & Luft, 2001). In the mid-1990s, MCOs began to restructure the role of the primary care provider. The *gatekeeper* role of the primary care provider was used to reduce the number of patient referrals to specialists, thereby reducing costs. This restrictive function led to consumer mistrust (Donelan, Blendon, Benson, Leitman, & Taylor, 1996; Goldberg, 1999) and uneasiness among primary care providers with their new role (Grobman, 1997). Since 1996, many MCOs have dropped the gatekeeper role of the primary care provider and allowed consumers *open access* to specialists who belong to the MCO (Koco, 1996; Kreier, 1996; West, 1997). These changes have muddled the distinctions among HMOs, PPOs, and other types of plans (Draper, Hurley, Lesser, & Struck, 2002). This is not to say the gatekeeper role has been discarded by all MCOs, but rather that it is being repackaged into a coordination and facilitative function to avoid its being perceived as an impediment to consumers seeking care (Draper et al., 2002).

Health care cost inflation has reached double-digit percentages. With *open access* policies in place, MCOs are no longer able to control access to expensive specialty care (Bruner, 2002). While the cost containment techniques used by managed care have been useful, they seem inadequate given the persistent rise in health care costs. According to a commissioned study prepared by PriceWaterhouseCoopers (April 2002), the factors responsible for the current rise in health care costs are:

- advances in medical treatment, diagnosis, and rising costs of prescription drugs;
- general inflation;

- higher payments to providers;
- government regulations and mandates;
- consumer demands given an aging population, advances in diagnostic procedures and preventive care, and demands for procedures due to direct marketing;
- risk management and litigation;
- fraud, abuse, and other forms of deception.

Although the effects of managed care activity on health care prices have been well studied, managed care's relationship to access and its broader effects across different insurance categories have not been (Litaker & Cebul, 2003). In a recent study investigating the association between managed care activity and individuals' access to care, Litaker and Cebul (2003) found that greater managed care activity was associated with unfavorable patterns of health care access regardless of an individual's insurance status: this suggests more pervasive and deleterious effects of managed care systems. Scheckler (2000) characterized HMOs as highly variable in quality and scope of service, highlighting two primary factors in consumer and physician satisfaction: 1) whether the plan involved salaried, single-plan physicians (staff model) or physicians employed by medical agencies and hospitals that contract with multiple plans (the former described their MCOs as more committed to quality patient care); and 2) the time allotted for each patient visit (with more time allotted associated with higher satisfaction). In addition, the findings of the 1996 Household Survey of the Community Tracking Study, drawn from 22 metropolitan statistical areas across the United States ($n = 19,672$), indicated that consumer satisfaction with HMOs is influenced as much by individual characteristics, such as a patient's health and socio-economic status, as by characteristics of the HMO itself (Ahern & Hendrix, 2003). The authors note that an HMO's social capital within a community affects its consumers' perceptions, emphasizing that, by encouraging trust and collaboration in a community, HMOs can inspire trust in their physicians and increase community access to quality health care.

The issue of maintaining affordable health care is of vital interest not only to consumers but also to employers and health care organizations. Employers generally provide health care coverage for their employees. With costs rising, many employers are either reducing the quality of benefits or requiring their employees to make larger contributions toward health care (Chan et al., 2002). Jacobs (2003) projected that even if health care cost increases are reduced to 8 percent per year, by the year 2030 the costs of health care benefits will exceed salary expenditures (based on a projected 2.5 percent per year increase in salary). The rise of health care premiums is also of concern for the MCOs, as many employers aggressively shop for the best deal to meet the needs of their employees.

In order to control costs and to provide freedom of choice, MCOs are providing consumers with more plan options (Parmenter, 2003). Strategies for containing costs by choice include *defined contribution* and *consumer-directed* health plans. *Defined contribution* plans cap an employer's fixed contribution to an employee's health insurance. The employee is responsible for costs beyond that cap (with a typical provision for catastrophic events). Given a menu of health plans, the employee may choose a plan with lower costs (e.g., an HMO). Resultant competition among plans for employee enrollment may lower overall health care costs. *Consumer-directed* health plans entail a larger role for employees in selecting benefits and providers. In order for this method to succeed in lowering costs, consumers need access to quality medical information and must be able to communicate their choices without excessive paperwork, for example by using an internet-based program (Gabel, Lo Sasso, & Rice, 2003).

Consumer choice can create problems as well. For instance, the elderly may purchase too much health coverage for fear of contracting diseases or conditions such as cancer or Alzheimer's, while younger people will choose less coverage since they are healthy. In this case, the young and healthy would no longer subsidize older people's health care. In reaction to public criticism of the managed care industry, 46 states have enacted comprehensive laws governing managed care and 21 states have passed laws requiring MCOs to contract with any willing health care provider (State Policy Watch, 2003). Such legislative initiatives typically require all health insurers to be "ready and willing at all times" to enter into service agreements with all health care providers who are qualified under state laws. As new management strategies successfully increase consumer choice, increased consumer responsibility will also be expected.

MANAGED HEALTH CARE CONCEPTS

BASIC INSURANCE CONCEPTS

The underlying principle of insurance is the concept of risk sharing. In the case of health insurance, the carrier provides the mechanism for a large group of people to share the risk of economic loss (medical expenses) because of illness or injury. Each person in the group pays a premium (a small amount relative to the potentially huge cost of illness or injury) to the insurer. In exchange, the carrier pays benefits to cover the medical cost when a loss occurs. This mechanism works because a significant portion of the contributing group will not incur an economic loss over some duration.

Indemnity health plans traditionally were the coverage choice for Americans because they offered the most flexibility. Indemnity coverage reimburses an insured person for the loss of money paid to cover medical expenses. Members of such plans can choose almost any hospital or doctor for treatment. To combat the rising cost of medical care, some cost-containment features, such as pre-hospitalization certification and catastrophic case management, were built into these traditional plans. The term *managed care* referred initially to such efforts. Today, the definition of managed care has broadened and can be described more accurately as "the integration of both the financing and the delivery of health care within a system that seeks to manage the accessibility, cost, and quality of that care" (Mullen, 1995, p. 22).

In addition to health insurance, some employers provide disability insurance as part of their employee benefit package. This type of insurance covers non-occupational illnesses and injuries. It does not cover medical expenses. The purpose of disability insurance is to replace a significant portion of income lost as a result of a worker's non-occupational illness or injury. There are two types of coverage: short-term disability (STD) plans are designed for short duration illnesses and injuries (e.g., 13 or 26 weeks), while long-term disability (LTD) plans cover illnesses and injuries that are more serious in nature (CIGNA Corporation, 1988). Employees eligible for STD or LTD benefits are usually paid approximately two thirds of their pre-disability earnings during their convalescence, the total not to exceed a dollar amount specified in the contract. Rehabilitation case management is a service used by LTD carriers to control costs by helping the claimant return to work. Essentially, rehabilitation case managers use rehabilitation technologies (e.g., vocational assessment, functional capacity evaluation, job analysis, job accommodation, and job placement) to help determine and document the claimant's degree of functional capacity and employability and to return client to work comparable to his or her previous level of employment.

Managed care models are increasingly being used by other forms of third-party insurance, including workers' compensation (WC) insurance (Powell, 1996). Workers' compensation laws vary from state to state. In general, WC benefits are designed to pay for injuries or diseases incurred at work or caused by work. Eligible workers receive money to replace lost wages at a fixed rate, medical expenses, and, in some states, vocational rehabilitation (Welch, 1994). Case managers need to know the terms of coverage, applicable state regulations, and other plans that may cover their clients in order to best serve clients' interests (Mullahy, 1995).

THE MANAGED HEALTH CARE CONTINUUM

Health maintenance organizations (HMOs), individual practice associations (IPAs), preferred provider organizations (PPOs), and point-of-service (POS) plans are some of the managed care models in the health services industry. Kongstevedt (1995) defined PPOs as "entities through which employer health benefit plans and health insurance carriers contract to purchase health care services for covered beneficiaries from a selected group of participating providers" (p. 26). Members of a traditional PPO plan are free to choose any of the physicians within the PPO network. Participating providers are subject to utilization management and reimbursement structures established by their PPOs. As an incentive to participate, the number of participating providers is optimized to maximize referrals.

A POS plan is a hybrid between traditional group health insurance and an HMO or PPO. Group members in a POS plan are allowed, at the point of service, to seek medical care within or outside the plan's network. Better coverage, however, is usually offered for health care services provided within the network; high deductibles and coinsurance payments are required for medical care received out of the network. There are two major types of POS plans: open-ended HMOs and gatekeeper PPOs. Open-ended HMOs are simply add-ons to existing HMO plans that cover expenses for health care received outside the network at reduced benefit levels. This add-on function allows some HMOs to be more competitive with other managed care organizations. Unlike traditional PPOs, gatekeeper PPOs requires members to choose a primary care physician (PCP) from within the PPO's network. PCPs serve as the gatekeepers to control utilization of services and referrals to specialists within the network. They are generally compensated on a *capitation* basis, i.e., paid fixed amounts per month per subscriber.

HMOs are responsible for providing a comprehensive range of health services to voluntarily enrolled populations at a fixed annual premium. HMOs, therefore, can be considered a combination of a health insurer and a health care delivery system. HMO physicians share the profits as well as the risks of financing and providing health care to groups of subscribers. They are offered a choice between billing and collecting a fee-for-service from the patient or having the HMOs pay them directly based on a capitation agreement (Kongstevedt, 1995). Because capitation payments are not related to the cost in time and resources of physician care, they encourage physicians to provide preventive care that benefits both the physicians and consumers within HMOs.

HMOs can be classified as either open-panel or closed-panel. In an open-panel HMO, any physician or provider meeting the organization's specific standards can be contracted as a provider. In a closed-panel HMO, a physician or provider must belong to a special group of physicians or providers that has contracted with the organization or must be a direct employee of the HMO. An individual practice association (IPA) and direct-contract HMO are examples of open-panel HMOs. Staff-model and group-model HMOs are examples of closed-panel HMOs. Finally, a network-model HMO can be either open- or closed-panel.

An IPA is to a group of physicians in independent practice who contract with an HMO to provide health care services for its members. Because IPA physicians provide services from their own offices to both HMO and non-HMO patients, the start-up capital required for this model is lower than for other types. The HMO usually pays the IPA based on a capitated structure. In turn, the IPA is responsible for compensating the physicians within the association. PCPs are frequently paid on a capitation basis, while specialists are paid on a discounted fee-for-service basis. In a direct-contract HMO, another type of open-panel model, the HMO contracts directly with individual physicians (PCPs and specialists) to provide health care services for its members. Payment methods are similar to those within the IPA structure, with capitation the preferred method of payment.

The staff-model is an example of a closed-panel HMO. In this arrangement, the HMO has its own facilities and hires its own health care staff. This affords the HMO greater control over how services are delivered. However, the HMO also bears all of the financial risk of providing health care services to its members. The start-up costs for this type of HMO are very high. The group-model, another closed-panel HMO, is similar to the IPA structure, except that physicians are employees (not members) of a physicians' group and practice together in a common facility. These physicians are paid based on their performance, areas of expertise, and administrative responsibilities. The HMO contracts with the physicians' group for a negotiated capitation rate. Kaiser Permanente is one of the most well known group-model HMOs in the U.S.

MANAGED HEALTH CARE AND CASE MANAGEMENT

Managed care is supposed to change the behavior of individual providers as well as health care delivery systems and patients by integrating an entire system of patient care that can lower costs, maintain quality, and improve patient health. Negotiated provider fees, utilization management, and risk-sharing agreements are key cost-control mechanisms of managed care (Mullen, 1995). In the managed care system, case managers are hired to serve as intermediaries, ensuring that assessments of illnesses, expected outcomes, and the payment processes of the providers are linked to performance standards. These practitioners help manage the care of patients experiencing chronic illnesses and disabilities throughout their recovery processes.

Consequently, practitioners must understand both medical and vocational case management to coordinate the care of individual patients effectively across the full spectrum of the rehabilitation processes (Choppa, Shafer, Reid, & Siefker, 1996). The main purpose of this section is to provide an overview of the managed care concepts related to case management services. Case managers provide both utilization review and case management services. Utilization review (UR) serves to prevent inappropriate or unnecessary hospitalizations. The three basic components of UR are managing utilization before treatment (pre-admission certification and pre-admission testing), managing utilization during treatment (concurrent review and discharge planning), and managing utilization after treatment (retrospective review). UR case managers are responsible for determining (for non-emergency cases) whether hospitalization or some other type of care is more appropriate, identifying the appropriate length of a hospital stay, and offering pre-admission certification. In the case of an emergency, the UR staff must be notified within 48 hours of hospitalization. To minimize hospital stays, UR staff may also arrange for patients to undergo diagnostic tests in an outpatient facility prior to hospitalization. During a patient's hospitalization, the UR staff concurrently reviews the patient's progress and may contact the patient's physician to discuss treatment, prognosis, and discharge planning. During discharge planning, the UR staff makes arrangements for at-home care, medical equipment and services, and other community support services. Retrospective review, then, focuses on uncovering erroneous charges or billing errors and spotting trends and excessive cost areas (Mullen, 1995).

Case management, on the other hand, can provide for alternative treatments or solutions for the medical care of patients with severe illnesses or injuries requiring lengthy or expensive treatment (e.g., AIDS, amputations, brain injuries, cancer, and spinal cord injuries). Case management aims to coordinate the treatment and rehabilitation efforts provided by a myriad of health care and rehabilitation professionals, making the best use of the patient's coverage and other resources.

MANAGED CARE AND WORKERS' COMPENSATION

Despite the political rhetoric, that has fueled campaign cries for health insurance reform during the past decade; the "health care crisis" has not come and gone. Rather it has come and grown, producing both substantial concerns about the rising costs of workers' compensation benefits and increased payer interest in the use of managed care strategies to help control those costs. In the remainder of this section, we examine the parallels between the rising costs associated with health insurance plans and workers' compensation systems, the growing need to apply the managed care strategies now characteristic of health

64

insurance programs to control workers' compensation expenditures, and the expanding career options available to case and disability managers with payer efforts to control and coordinate health insurance and workers' compensation benefits.

Here are some definitions as they apply to the health insurance and workers' compensation discussion that follows:

- **Client**: The person who sustained a loss (illness, injury, or other type of disability) and is, therefore, eligible to receive health insurance or workers' compensation benefits.

- **Health insurance**: Those plans under which workers and their dependents are provided with health care services. While most individuals receive their health insurance benefits under employer-sponsored programs, policies can also be purchased privately. The majority of such benefits are paid by insurance carriers (third-party payers), although larger sponsors may elect to fund their benefit plans themselves (self-insurers).

- **Workers' compensation**: Government-mandated plans designed to provide benefits to workers who sustain some type of job-related loss. These plans are administered on a state-by-state basis and the governing provisions will vary based on the jurisdiction. Two of the more important distinctions between workers' compensation (WC) and employer-provided health insurance (HI) are: 1) there is no dependent coverage available under WC; and 2) the types and extent of the benefits available to the worker (client) as well as the criteria for eligibility under a WC plan are set by statute, whereas an HI sponsor has substantially more freedom with respect to plan design, benefits, and eligibility. Most employers elect to provide their WC coverage through insurance carriers, although organizations that meet specific state criteria may elect to self-fund their WC plans. Some states include *second injury* funds in their WC systems to encourage employers to hire individuals who have already sustained some type of on-the-job loss.

- **Payers**: For the most part, HI and WC benefits are paid to or on behalf of covered individuals (clients) by insurance carriers (third parties). The premiums paid by the employer (sponsor) can increase substantially based on the amount of the benefits paid by the insurer.

- **Disability or case managers**: The primary obligation of the case or disability manager is to act as an advocate for the client when working with various components of that individual's health care delivery system. These practitioners, who come from a variety of professional disciplines within the health care field, are also responsible for

65

coordinating and monitoring available health care resources in order to ensure appropriate, cost-effective use. Case and disability managers will be found working in a variety of settings throughout the continuum of care (from initial loss through rehabilitation) to see that each client receives individualized, cost-effective health services in a way that does not compromise the quality of care being provided by the treatment team.

With these definitions in mind, we can describe parallels between health insurance and workers' compensation expenditures. In the 1960s and 70s, comprehensive benefit packages (health care and pensions) were one of the ways employers used to attract and retain career employees while attempting to hold down direct compensation expenditures (salaries or wages). Starting in the mid-70s, the health care costs associated with such packages began an upward spiral, matched by a similar growth in the cost of providing medical care to injured workers. For example, a study on medical trends (National Council on Compensation Insurance [NCCI], 1995) estimated growth in WC medical costs to be one and a half times greater than medical costs in general.

In the mid-80s, a decision by the Financial Accounting and Standards Board (FASB) made it imperative for employers to track and control their health care expenditures. Under the new rules, instead of carrying employer and employee contributions to pension plans as an asset on their balance sheets, organizations would have to project the potential cost of paying benefits to retirees and show the results as a liability. One of the most immediate results was a rush by employers to switch from defined benefit plan designs (e.g., 80% of the cost of a semi-private room) to defined contribution structures (e.g., $100 a day toward the cost of a semi-private room). Another result was an even greater use of managed care techniques to control health insurance expenditures. Yet employers were still failing to see the parallel between the growth in their HI costs and WC expenditures. In the early 1990s, the use of formal managed care techniques by workers' compensation systems was rare. By 1995, this situation had changed dramatically. As many as 50% or more of WC claims were thought to be handled though some kind of managed care arrangement, while 29 states had introduced some type of managed care or 24-hour coverage provisions into their WC laws or regulations (NCCI, 1995).

Because of the greater internal visibility of benefit plan costs, most employers turned their attention to growing corporate expenditures for health insurance. In addition to forming employer coalitions to negotiate discounts with a growing number of *provider networks*, employers tried various plan design strategies to achieve the following cost containment objectives:

- **Choice of provider**: limits employee choice of provider as a cost containment strategy.
- **Change of provider**: limits the employee's ability to change providers after an initial selection.
- **Authorized providers and liability for unauthorized care**: designates certain practitioners as treating providers and requires that services from others be authorized by a treating provider.
- **Medical fee schedules**: features fee schedules listing maximum reimbursements for health care procedures. The specifics can vary considerably.
- **Regulation of hospital charges**: statutory authority to regulate hospital charges.
- **Bill reviews for proper charges**: uses medical fee schedules through a mandated audit of bills for proper charges.
- **Managed care**: Although the use of managed care techniques is not new to workers' compensation, the regulation and mandating of managed care arrangements are relatively recent developments.
- **Utilization review**: UR tactics such as managing utilization before treatment (pre-admission certification and pre-admission testing), managing utilization during treatment (concurrent review and discharge planning), and managing utilization after treatment (retrospective review) have been increasingly used to control WC costs.
- **Treatment guidelines**: The inclusion of treatment guidelines in WC systems is a new but fast-growing phenomenon. The most prominent use of guidelines is in relation to low back injuries or pain.

Similar cost containment efforts were being made by the health care industry itself, in which growing competition was forcing existing structures into new, more cost-effective configurations. Traditional hospital-doctor relationships and fee-for-service approaches were being scrapped in favor of Health Maintenance Organizations (HMOs), Preferred Provider Networks (PPNs), and similar organizations that enable providers to reduce their operating costs and offer attractive discounts to payers. Gate keeping, risk sharing, and capitation arrangements were some of the other strategies offered by providers as financial incentives to discourage overuse or inappropriate use of health care resources. The need for trained professionals to coordinate and monitor health care use made case and disability managers a significant part of these efforts in health insurance managed care.

As evidence accumulates that shows the need to coordinate HI and WC expenditures and to apply managed care techniques to workers' compensation programs, the need for case and disability managers with experience in this area will grow, offering even more career opportunities for qualified practitioners.

RESEARCH FINDINGS – MANAGED CARE AND WORKERS' COMPENSATION

It appears that workers' compensation insurers pay considerably more than health insurers for the treatment of similar injuries. The first study of this problem was conducted in Minnesota in 1987. Another study compared the Minnesota model to 1991-93 data on health care charges and payments in California. Conducted by Johnson, Baldwin, and Burton (1996), the study indicated that the differences in workers' compensation charges in California were primarily due to service utilization levels rather than price discrimination. Of the four injury groups analyzed in the California study, the average medical care payment for work-related injuries was higher than that for similar injuries sustained off the job. The authors suggested that payment differences across injury types might reflect the degree of uncertainty among medical professionals about optimal treatment methods. For example, injuries for which providers did not agree on a common standard of treatment (e.g., back injuries) seemed to offer the greatest potential for an overuse of services. The data indicated that workers' compensation patients in the group with back injuries averaged 11 visits to physicians and 13 to chiropractors, compared to 1 physician visit and 4 chiropractor visits for health insurance patients. While the results were not conclusive, the question deserves additional study.

According to the same study, duplications of service might also account for some of the differences in utilization rates. For example, workers' compensation patients were more than twice as likely as health insurance patients to receive care from multiple physicians (35% vs. 15%). The use of both more services and more providers to treat work-related injuries appears to be the most important reason for higher WC health care costs. The potential savings would appear to be considerable if the treatment of work-related injuries was managed similarly to the treatment for off-the-job injuries, assuming that the WC patients receive the same care at the same cost as HI patients.

Studies in the mid-1990s indicated that some of the cost containment mechanisms adapted to control WC costs were working. In an article in *John Burton's Workers' Compensation Monitor* on "Industrial and Occupational Variations in Workers' Compensation Costs" (1996), the author cited the following data from the Bureau of Labor Statistics of the U.S. Department of Labor: in 1995, the national average for employers' WC costs for all workers in the private sector was 2.82% of gross earnings. Expenditures in the goods-producing and manufacturing sectors were higher than this average, while costs in the service and non-manufacturing sectors were lower. Another article in the same issue ("Workers' Compensation, 24-Hour Coverage," 1996) indicated that the growth in workers' compensation costs in the 1990s had slowed to less than 3% per year, a significant decrease compared to the period from 1984 to 1990, when the annual rate of increase averaged more than 13% per year. In the same article, the author attributed the increase in WC managed care and 24-hour coverage to the fact that the WC cost to employers was $57.3 billion nationally in 1993, compared to $2.1 billion in 1960. Medical benefits in 1993 accounted for 41.9% of all WC benefits. Of the 45 states for which it was possible to compare the dollar amounts in benefits paid per 100,000 workers, those states paid on average $54.6 million in total benefits per 100,000 workers, ranging from $110.3 million in Rhode Island to $19.7 million in Indiana ("Workers' Compensation Benefits Paid," 1996).

Another article in *John Burton's Workers' Compensation Monitor* summarized mid-1990s developments in workers' compensation as follows ("Workers' Compensation Benefits, Costs," 1996):

- **Statutory benefits**: Actuarial evaluations of legislative changes in WC statutes, combined with changes in medical fees and hospital reimbursement rates, showed a decline in WC compensation experience of 0.3% per year during the 1990s.
- **Benefits paid to workers**: Total cash and medical benefits increased at a rate of 1.4% per year during the decade.
- **Employers' costs of workers' compensation**: Measured in dollars per hour, this expenditure for all non-federal employees increased 3.6% per year since 1991.
- **Profitability for workers' compensation insurers**: Measured in terms of overall profitability, this ratio increased 4.7% per year during the 1990s. (Workers' Compensation Benefits Costs, 1996, p.1)

In a recent study (November, 2003), the Workers Compensation Research Institute (WCRI) conducted a survey to identify the medical cost containment strategies being used by state WC systems. The following are from Victor's (2003) brief summary of the findings:

- There is a growing body of empirical knowledge about the impact of price regulation on costs but little on price regulation and worker outcomes.
- The strongest area of empirical evidence in workers' compensation involves the impact of medical networks. There are a number of solid studies covering diverse states and time periods. All find that networks reduce medical costs. A few examine the impact on duration of disability or recovery of health, finding that workers who receive care

from network providers are equally healthy and do not have longer durations of disability. Several studies also find that workers report higher levels of satisfaction with non-network care.

- There are a few studies of the impact of provider choice laws on costs. The evidence is mixed, although recent studies suggest that network penetration is lower in states where the employee controls the selection of providers. As discussed above, lower network penetration means higher medical costs.

- Studies of utilization review and treatment guidelines in workers' compensation provide sketchy evidence of their impact. Combined with evidence from Medicare and group health, the studies suggest fewer hospital admissions, shorter lengths of stay, and fewer surgeries. A survey of physicians highlights a major limitation on the effectiveness of utilization review: 39 percent of physicians report that, at least sometimes, physicians do not provide accurate information for utilization review. One recent Australian study found that compliance with treatment guidelines led to better outcomes for workers with acute low back pain in terms of better-perceived physical health and reduced pain.

Interestingly, little evidence was found on the effectiveness of case management (Victor, 2003, p. 3).

INTEGRATED HEALTH CARE SYSTEMS

As previously discussed, during the mid-1990s managed care strategies moved from the group health arena into workers' compensation systems (Daiker, 1995; Lui, 1993; Tabak, 1995). During that time, trends in health care moved toward integrating health-care delivery systems, wherein multiple insurance lines, levels of care, and populations are integrated into a single system of care (Aron, 1996). Many rehabilitation counselors and case managers who once dealt solely in workers' compensation have had to diversify into other product lines. The integration of group health and workers' compensation health care benefits is also known as *24-hour care*. There is a clear parallel between growth of HI costs and WC expenditures. Managed care programs are increasingly being used as a way to control these costs. As a result, one sees a trend toward the use of integrated benefits systems (24-hour coverage) to link workers' compensation with traditional insurance, blurring the line between income security and treatment management issues. Employers have also chosen to bind the workers' compensation portion of their benefit costs together with health insurance and to manage both HI cost and WC expenditures internally, using select physicians and hospitals (DeMarco & Wolfe, 1995). Projections indicate that 24-hour medical coverage and team approaches in managing health care patients and/or industrially injured workers will become more common in the next century (Chan, Lui, Rosenthal, Pruett, & Ferrin, 2002).

In general, the term *24-hour care* indicates that an employee is covered around-the-clock under a single managed care package, whether or not an accident or illness is job-related (Knight, 1997). Knight (1997) suggested group health case managers and workers' compensation case managers have much to learn from each other. She cited back injury as an example of how the same injury may be approached very differently from the two sides. WC case managers often recommend therapy that is more frequent and move aggressively to other methods, whereas group health case managers may stay with a treatment for a much longer time. She argued that return-to-work techniques would also help contain group health costs. In addition, 24-hour care would help identify duplicate claims. For example, the use of a single provider to treat an employee's occupational and non-occupational injuries would prevent duplicate claims and services. Ultimately, 24-hour care will help reduce costs and produce better outcomes.

Figure 1 depicts the relationship between occupational and non-occupational injuries and illnesses, the roles of case managers in the intervention process, and a continuum of case management interventions.

Figure 1. **Case Management Interventions in an Integrated Health Care System**

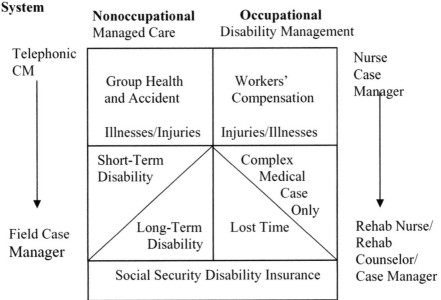

Under this model, a 24-hour care plan can benefit from both the advent of case management interventions developed for managed care (group health) and disability management (workers' compensation). A disability manager is defined by the Certification of Disability Management Specialists Commission (CDMSC) on its web site (www.cdms.org) as "one who contributes to workplace productivity by providing services to accommodate the medical and vocational needs of ill and injured workers and minimize the cost impact of disabilities and absences for employers." Akabas, Gates, and Galvin (1992) define disability management more specifically as a "workplace prevention and remediation strategy that seeks to prevent disability from occurring or, lacking that, to intervene early following the onset of disability, using coordinated, cost-conscious, quality rehabilitation service that reflects an organizational commitment to continued employment of those experiencing functional work limitations" (p. 2).

At the highest level, employers are concerned chiefly with the physical and mental health of their employees. Case management interventions at this level include wellness programs, health education, stress-management training, and employee assistance programs that foster a healthy life style. Safety education and the design of an ergonomically sound workplace can help prevent work-related injuries. Nursing case managers, rehabilitation counselors, and case managers are responsible for prevention activities in such a scenario. A rehabilitation case manager who is a Certified Rehabilitation Counselor or licensed clinical counselor can also provide in-house vocational and psychosocial adjustment counseling.

Case management interventions at the time of illnesses and injuries focus on early medical intervention and conflict resolution in order to avoid an adversarial relationship between the employee and the employer. Early intervention requires the cultivation of easy access to a network of quality providers who understand occupational health and return-to-work issues. Telephonic case management is appropriate for most situations. The compressed time frame in medical management reduces a number of cases from becoming lost-time cases. Field-based case management may be required for catastrophic injuries or complicated medical cases. Examples of catastrophic cases include amputations, traumatic head injury, spinal cord injuries, severe burns, multiple facture, and crushing injuries. Other indicators that a field-based case manager intervention may be needed include:

- a physician report indicating that the injured worker is unlikely to return to his or her former job;
- a physician report labeling the period of disability as indefinite;
- prolonged physical therapy;
- prolonged, excessive chiropractic treatment;

- the lack of a specific treatment plan;
- an unclear medical diagnosis or prognosis;
- medical complications that develop in addition to injury;
- co-existing medical problems (e.g., epilepsy); and
- an employee unhappy with the treatment program, failing to follow the treatment plan, or seeking a second medical opinion.

McMahon et al. (2000) documented the progression of disability benefits (PODB), a phenomenon in which workers with work-limiting disabilities migrate through a system of economic disability benefits and ultimately are placed in the Social Security Disability Insurance (SSDI) system. In this context, one could argue that health care and disability case management be construed as one form of service intervention. The Social Security Administration is currently exploring innovative ways (e.g., the Ticket-To-Work initiatives) to return SSDI recipients to gainful employment. It is clear that rehabilitation counselors can play a significant role in providing upstream services—such as disability prevention, disability management, and disruption of PODB—and downstream services, such as vocational rehabilitation for recipients of short-term disability, long-term disability, or SSDI benefits.

ROLES AND FUNCTIONS OF REHABILITATION COUNSELORS IN THE INTEGRATED HEALTH CARE SYSTEMS

Because of the paradigm shift in private sector rehabilitation, the roles and functions of rehabilitation counselors have changed: additional knowledge and skills are required for effective performance. In recent years, Chan and his associates have conducted a series of professional competency studies to identify changing job functions and knowledge requirements of certified rehabilitation counselors and certified disability management specialists (Chan, Leahy, McMahon, Mirch, & DeVinney, 1999; Chan et al., 2003; Chan et al., 2000; Chan et al., 2001; Currier, Chan, Berven, Habeck, & Taylor, 2001; Leahy, Chan, & Saunders, 2003; Leahy, Chan, Shaw, & Lui, 1997; Leahy, Chan, Taylor, Wood, & Downey, 1998). They found that private rehabilitation specialists with disability management practices engage mainly in case management activities and design and implement early return-to-work interventions. To a lesser degree, these practitioners also perform some vocational rehabilitation (counseling, assessment, and job placement) and mid-level management responsibilities. The knowledge base required to perform these functions effectively includes psychosocial intervention skills, vocational aspects of disability, case management techniques, human resources and business knowledge, and managed care and managed disability concepts.

In a role and function study of certified case managers (CCM), Chan et al. (2000) identified monitoring care and follow-up, health care management, program management and evaluation, and disability case management as central job functions. Knowledge in the areas of processes and relationships, health care management, community resources and support, service delivery, psychosocial interventions, and disability case management were found to be essential to the professional practice of case management in today's health care and disability service systems. Chan et al. suggested that there is a convergence of medical case management and vocational case management. Thus, the blending of nursing, rehabilitation counseling, and social work roles in health care and disability case management will continue (Shaw, Leahy, & Chan, 1999). Increasingly, nurse case managers are working with employers on return-to-work issues and vocational and social work case managers increasingly perform medical case management duties. Due to the rapid changes in the manner in which health care services are provided, case managers have had to expand their roles beyond traditional disciplinary lines. Such blurring is seen as a positive step by leaders in the profession, who note that, although nurses, vocational rehabilitation counselors, and others have unique skills and backgrounds, they must all begin to identify as *case managers* in order to lobby together for a secure foothold in the changing field of health care. In the coming years, cross training will become essential for health care professionals seeking careers in case management in order to acquire the requisite skills. The need for cross training was reported by Shaw, McMahon, Chan, Taylor, and Wood (1997), as rehabilitation counselor respondents in their study revealed that they did not feel sufficiently prepared to handle medical management issues. Additionally, private sector rehabilitation professionals must become more familiar with medical treatment modalities and early return-to-work interventions in the workplace.

IMPLICATIONS FOR CASE MANAGEMENT EDUCATION AND TRAINING

Leahy, Chan, and Shaw (1999) provided a thorough discussion of the roles and functions of, and the education and training requirements for, health care and disability case managers. They indicated that successful case managers share a common understanding of

- the coordination and delivery of services,
- the physical and psychosocial aspects of disability,
- benefit systems and cost benefit analysis,
- case management concepts, and
- principles of community re-entry.

74

A comparison of the findings of two surveys regarding case management education in nursing (Haw, 1996) and rehabilitation counseling education (RCE) programs (Shaw, McMahon, Chan, Taylor, & Wood, 1997) revealed some important commonalities and trends.

- Twelve graduate nursing programs were identified that had entire programs or majors devoted to case management. One additional program had a 13-credit-hour, post-baccalaureate program and a doctoral program with a major focus in case management. There are no rehabilitation counseling programs with this level of commitment to case management training.

- Only 20% of graduate and 4% of undergraduate nursing programs had one or more case management courses available. The figure for RCE programs is 66%.

- However, 89% of graduate and 95% of undergraduate nursing programs included content on case management in their required courses. Content beyond a basic level was much more likely in graduate programs. This same figure for graduate RCE programs is 78%.

- Clinical case management experience was required for 24% of graduate and 12% of undergraduate nursing programs, compared to 16% of RCE programs. Clinical experience was optional for 38% of graduate and 22% of undergraduate nursing programs, compared to 26% of RCE programs.

- Both nursing and RCE programs had similar problems with respect to the availability of educational materials (70% vs. 61%) and the difficulty of finding good role models (67% vs. 57%). Difficulty finding good clinical placements appeared more problematic for nursing programs (55% vs. 28.5%).

- Generally speaking, nursing faculty members have high levels of case management education themselves, although it appears less intensive than for RCE program faculty (e.g., self-study or continuing education vs. graduate course work). RCE faculty members appear to have more case management work experience. Scholarly activity in the case management arena is similarly low for both groups.

Shaw et al. (1997) reported that the climate surrounding the job of a disability case manager in the early 1980s was significantly different from today's environment, which includes practice standards, capitation, and integrated health care systems. Indeed, most of those case management content areas that receive minimal exposure in rehabilitation counseling education programs have emerged as critically important activities within only the past few years. For example, they reported that those areas where content was adequately addressed by the majority of RCE programs tend to represent traditional requirements (e.g., vocational assessment, job placement, coordination of services, and plan development). Those areas that were relatively neglected have emerged only recently as important developments (e.g., case management credentialing, utilization review and management, cost containment, and case management software).

Currier, Chan, Taylor, and Wood (1998) conducted a study to examine the roles, functions, and the knowledge requirements for disability case managers. They adopted Habeck and Kirchner's (1999) two-level concept of disability management (see Chapter on disability management). Level I disability management is conceptualized as managerial or administrative in nature, with practitioners having little direct contact with disabled or injured workers. Level I practice occupies an organizational level and is more business oriented, requiring analytic, design, evaluation, and organizational development knowledge and skills. The Level I practitioner must possess expertise in benefit plan design, management information systems, and organizational behavior.

The Level II practitioner, on the other hand, appears to be more human-services oriented, requiring clinical and rehabilitation skills and case management expertise, including job analysis and return-to-work (RTW) functions. The knowledge required to perform level II functions overlaps considerably with the knowledge required for insurance rehabilitation practice as identified by Leahy, Chan, Taylor, Wood, and Downey (1998). This includes understanding vocational assessment and planning, case management and reporting, expert witness testimony, employment and disability-related legislation and regulations, community resources, psychosocial and functional aspects of disability, and job analysis and modification. Currier et al. (1998), however, underscored in their report that knowledge in the areas of disability management concepts, principles of insurance, benefit plans, medical case management, ergonomics, managed care concepts, and business practices and operations appears to be additional and warrants attention in the training and credentialing of disability management specialists. Furthermore, the middle ground of the continuum between level I and level II involves program development, service coordination, education and training, and organizational development. It may be worthwhile to consider the knowledge and skills required for these functions as well as those specific to disability management practitioners.

Lastly, Chan, Leahy, Downey, Lamb, Chapin, and Peterson (2000) surveyed certified case managers (CCMs) and identified monitoring care and follow-up, health care management, program management and evaluation, and

76

disability case management as central job functions. Knowledge in the areas of processes and relationships, health care management, community resources and support, service delivery, psychosocial interventions, and disability case management were found to be essential to the professional practice of case management in today's health care and disability service systems. Again, this research supported the need for cross training to prepare case managers to work effectively in both health and employment arenas (Shaw, Leahy, & Chan, 1999).

DEMONSTRATING EFFECTIVENESS

QUALITY AND BENCHMARKS

The use of clinical practice guidelines to control unexplained variations in health care services and to standardize clinical problem-solving behavior in similar circumstances in order to control costs is becoming increasingly important in the managed care system (Gosfield, 1997). For example, many health care facilities have formed clinical pathway committees to streamline the procedures used in treating different diseases (e.g., cardiac and orthopedic cases). Today, clinical pathways are helping health care teams to define treatment roles clearly and to trim excessive testing and other procedures. By making most common procedures more efficient and using a streamlined package of care and services, teams can treat uncomplicated cases more economically and smoothly (Gosfield, 1997). According to the American Association of Health Plans (cited in Gosfield, 1997), 87% of HMOs currently use clinical practice guidelines to standardize clinical behavior. Case managers are also concerned with this development. As a result, the Case Management Society of America (CMSA) has produced its Standards of Practice, while the Individual Case Management Association (ICMA) has collaborated with Aetna Health Plans to develop the Case Management Practice Guidelines. Strictly speaking, the CMSA standards are more concerned with professional conduct, while the Guidelines are more similar to the clinical practice guidelines developed by other health professionals. The Institute of Medicine (IOM, part of the National Academy of Sciences) provided the following bases for developing clinical practice guidelines.

- Practice guidelines must be systematically developed statements to help practitioners and patients make decisions about appropriate health care for specific clinical circumstances.
- Medical review criteria must be systematically developed statements that can be used to assess the appropriateness of specific health care decisions, services, and outcomes.
- Standards of quality must be authoritative statements of minimum levels of acceptable performance or results, excellent levels of

performance or results, or the range of acceptable performance or results.

The Office of the Forum on Quality and Effectiveness of the Agency for Health Care Policy and Research (created by Congress in 1989) has the statutory responsibility to publish clinical practice guidelines, medical review criteria, performance measures, and standards of quality and thus could be a valuable resource for case managers regarding clinical practice guidelines (Gosfield, 1997).

OUTCOME MEASUREMENT AND REPORT CARDS

In a consumer-based market, assessments of quality of service must be supported by empirical data. The development of appropriate outcome measurements for different illnesses and disabilities and treatment modalities is important.

If case managers are to perform effectively in determining appropriate sources for services, they must have a way to get information about the quality of the care being provided. Medical report cards can provide case managers with a more objective rationale to use in directing clients to one facility rather than another. For example, the National Committee for Quality Assurance (NCQA) has created the Health Plan Employer Data and Information Set (HEDIS) in order to provide guidelines to measure the quality of care provided by health care plans. Case managers themselves could become the subjects of such medical report cards in order to ensure that the practitioner's skills match the user's expectations.

A pertinent research question for providers in today's climate of accountability and cost-effectiveness is this: "Which approach works best for a given individual under his or her particular conditions?" If we can identify the underlying principles, resources, and processes used by effective case managers to serve consumers who represent a range of illnesses and disabilities of different severities and case complexities, we can identify the best practices and develop service standards for managing prototypical cases.

Pransky and Himmelstein (1996a, b) provided an excellent model for conceptualizing the outcomes of workers' compensation medical care that is also useful for evaluating health care outcomes. They defined medical outcomes as the results or effects of medical care on quality of life, including social functioning, mental health and personal well-being, and general perceptions of health, functional, and physical status. Workers' compensation outcomes include resolution of symptoms, return to normal functioning at home, and return to full and long-term functional and earning capacity. The authors suggested that outcomes be evaluated from a multi-stakeholder

78

perspective. For example, workers are probably more concerned about relief of symptoms, the reduced need for ongoing medical care, and improving their ability to meet job requirements. Employers, on the other hand, likely hold more important the work status of the employee, his or her work performance at pre- and post-injury levels, the disruption of the workplace, indirect costs, and the injured worker's satisfaction with his or her care. Pransky and Himmelstein also suggested that, in measuring health care and workers' compensation outcomes, it is important to consider a range of outcomes. In their opinion, the more restricted the range of outcomes, the less credible the results. The following list presents the domains of successful outcomes considered important by employers, workers, and society.

Table I
IMPORTANT OUTCOMES IN WORKERS' COMPENSATION MEDICAL CARE

Resolution of the Condition
- Symptoms – especially pain
- Function in daily activities – compared with pre-injury levels
- Household and family responsibilities
- Transportation/driving
- Sexual activity
- Sleep
- Social and recreational activities
- Health perceptions and self-esteem
- Mood
- Ongoing medical care requirements – number of visits/case

Vocational Status
- Work status (full/part-time, same/different job, employer) – lost time per case, restricted duty days
- Quality of work (psychosocial and other aspects of work)
- Quality of work life
- Function at work – physical and psychosocial dimension
- Interpersonal relationships
- Conflicts – late decision to retain attorney
- Comparison of the post-injury job with pre-injury job function, tasks (physical and mental) versus post-discharge tasks

(table continues)

Table I (Continued)

- Short- and long-term job retention
- Productivity, quality, and flexibility at work
- Appropriate advancement and skill acquisition

Total costs (by case, by diagnosis, by company)
- Direct: WC payments for indemnity and medical care
- Indirect: Employer's additional costs – retraining, accommodations
- Patient: financial burden (income change, health care, other costs)
- Cost shifting to other systems: especially short-term disability plans and group health

Patient and employer satisfaction
- Communication
- Appropriateness of care
- Opportunity for input in decisions; perceptions of control over outcome

Prevention
- How the job where the injury occurred was changed to reduce risk of injury to other workers; include level of exposure prior to injury
- Modification to decrease injury risk for co-workers

Adopted from Pransky and Himmelstein (1996b).

Finally, Pransky and Himmelstein (1996b) argued on behalf both of measuring efforts to prevent workplace injury from occurring in the first place and of evaluating the effectiveness of medical and rehabilitation intervention in preventing re-injury. Case managers can play an important role in health promotion, disability prevention, and disability management activities. Case managers can also be active participants in conducting research to determine optimal practice standards and the effectiveness of various case management interventions as they relate to the patient, employer, and society.

THE FUTURE

Trends indicate that the present revolution in health care is the movement from the current payer-driven system to a more consumer-driven, market-based system (Boenheimer, Lo, & Casalino, 1999; Harris, Ripperger, & Horn, 2000; Reschovsky, Hargraves & Smith, 2002). The paradigm of managed care has shifted the competitive advantage of health care organizations from prestige to price and accelerated the conversion of health care entities from not-for-profit to for-profit structures. At the same time, managed care encourages risk-based competition (designing plans to attract low-risk populations), with the result that high-risk groups (e.g., people with disabilities) may be underserved, excluded, or simply priced out of the market (Scism, 1994). The focus of some managed care organizations on profits has also compromised the quality of care in selected cases, resulting in consumer complaints and increased attention from politicians. In a market-based environment, consumer choice, consumer satisfaction, and health outcomes will drive the success of managed care organizations, while the monitoring of quality will receive increased attention.

Some employers have moved beyond integration of benefits issues, focusing on overall productivity and enhanced employee value. In turn, this leads management to pay attention to all forms of work interruptions and incidental absence such as sick pay, unauthorized time off, and absences allowed by the Family and Medical Leave Act (FMLA) (Chajewski, Parry & Molmen, 1999). This new thrust, referred to as "Absence Management," is generally defined as the process of tracking and attempting to control the use both of unscheduled paid time off and of the Family and Medical Leave Act (FMLA). Early identification of the reasons for absence from work enables appropriate and immediate intervention, which in turn reduces the risks of disability and other forms of work interruptions. "Disability prevention is the primary goal of absence management" (Douglas, 2000, p. 201). All of these trends have increased the need to coordinate services and have driven the growth and elaboration of case management activities. In turn, increased case management entails more effective use of employer resources in disability care, so that the need to rehabilitate has actually decreased. These dynamics account for the shift from reactive to proactive service paradigms.

The convergence of health care case management and rehabilitation case management provides both an opportunity for growth of private sector rehabilitation as well as increased competition among multiple allied health care service providers as roles (e.g., nurse, physical therapist, occupational therapist, medical social worker, and rehabilitation counselor) begin to blur. The presentation of a case management model in a 24-hour care plan provides a framework for conceptualizing better the role of private rehabilitation practitioners in this rapidly changing practice environment.

AN AGING WORKFORCE
The baby boomer generation—what remains of some 76 million people born in the United States between 1946 and 1964—presents two complementary challenges to a rapidly changing managed care system. This population represents a significant portion of the labor force in the United States, and as

retirement age approaches for its members, the gap its retirees leave behind could be difficult to fill. Moreover, as large numbers of baby boomers retire and live increasingly long lives, they will increase the ratio of people aged 65 years and older to those aged 20 to 64 (known as the old-age dependency ratio) from about 22 percent currently to nearly 50 percent by 2050 (Hursh, 2003). The health care system must prepare for an older, fixed-income population often reliant on government assistance programs that expects the latest and best in diagnostic, pharmaceutical, and restorative medical care.

Simultaneously and contrastingly, the health care and workers' compensation systems must prepare for an older workforce as many baby boomers postpone retirement, in part to maintain their health care benefits. According to an AARP study (2002), a growing proportion of workers over the age of 45 consider health care a reason to remain employed: today, more than half (56%) of older workers say the need to pay for health care costs is a major factor in their decision to be working. This statistic has increased 15 percent since 1985. Nor are the barriers to remaining employed beyond retirement age what they once were: mandatory retirement ages are decreasingly enforced, the age of eligibility for Social Security benefits has increased and will likely continue upward while the earnings test for reducing those benefits has been eliminated by amendment (Clark & Quinn, 2002). Advances in medical technology and greater awareness of healthy lifestyle practices allow many older workers to lead healthier and longer lives (Crimmins, Reynolds, & Saito, 1999; Rix, 2002). Alternatively, many older workers who become injured or experience chronic disability remain in their employers' workers' compensation systems as a result of stricter definitions of Permanent and Partial Impairment. An older workforce means a workforce more prone to chronic conditions and disease that often takes longer to recover from on-the-job injuries. Health insurance and workers' compensation systems will face both strains on presently defined resources and the need to develop novel approaches to cope with the unique medical problems of the elderly.

INTERNET-BASED HEALTH CARE SERVICES

As it has with many other industries, the Internet has left its mark on managed care. Insurers are using the Internet to educate consumers about the health care providers and services within their network. This way, consumers are able to use the Internet to locate a provider near their residence with a particular set of qualifications. Consumers can often use the health care provider's web site to research a particular treatment and the costs associated with that treatment (Zagata-Meraz, 2003). Health care programs also use the Internet to give consumers quick, convenient access to their personal accounts, permitting enrollment or modifications to their plans through a secure web site. Cyber case managers may obtain information and advise their client by email when their plan may require medical case management.

SUMMARY

Case managers can play an important role in the managed care environment. The use of case managers for utilization management, intensive case management, health promotion, and disability prevention can help control health care and workers' compensation costs. Most importantly, the use of case managers as educators, patient advocates, problem-solvers, and negotiators will promote a better working relationship between patients and health care service providers that will prove vital as we move from a payer-driven health care system to a consumer-based managed care system.

REFERENCES

AARP. (2002). *Staying ahead of the curve: The AARP work and career study.* Washington, DC: AARP.

Akabas, S. H., Gates, L. B., & Galvin, D. E. (1992). *Disability management: A complete system to reduce costs, increase productivity, meet employee needs, and ensure legal compliance.* New York: AMACOM.

Aron, L. J. (1996). Integrating health and disability: 24 hour coverage. *Case Review, 2,* 15-16.

Beckley, N. J. (1995). Case management and integrated delivery. *Case Review, 1,* 25-30.

Bruner, J. (2002). The next big thing in health benefits: Consumer choice. *Benefits Quarterly,* 49-52.

Chan, F., Leahy, M. J., Downey, W., Lamb, G., Chapin, M., & Peterson, D. (2000). A work behavior analysis of certified case managers. *Care Management, 6*(4), 50-62.

Chan, F., Leahy, M., McMahon, B. T., Mirch, M., & DeVinney, D. (1999). Foundational knowledge and major practice domains of case managers. *Journal of Care Management, 5*(1), 10-18, 26-30.

Chan, F., Leahy, M., Saunders, J., Tarvydas, V., Ferrin, M., & Lee, G. (2003). Training need of certified rehabilitation counselors for contemporary practice, *Rehabilitation Counseling Bulletin, 46*(2), 82-91.

Chan, F., Lui, J., Rosenthal, D., Pruett, S. R., & Ferrin, J. M. (2002). Managed care and vocational rehabilitation. *Journal of Rehabilitation Administration, 26,* 85 –97.

Chan, F., Taylor, D., Currier, K., Chan, C. H., Wood, C., & Lui, J. (2001). Disability management practitioners: A work behavior analysis. *Journal of Vocational Rehabilitation, 5* (1), 47-56.

CIGNA Corporation (1988). *LTD training manual.* Atlanta, GA: Author.

Chajewski, Parry & Molmen (1997). *Turning to benefit integration: Results from a survey of employers.* Integrated Benefits Institute. July, 1997.

Choppa, A. J., Shafer, K., Reid, K. M. & Siefker, J. M. (1996). Vocational rehabilitation counselors as case managers. *The Case Manager, 7*, 45-50.

Clark, R. L., and Quinn, J. F. (2002). Patterns of work and retirement for a new century. *Generations: Journal of the American Society on Aging, 26*(2), 17-24.

Currier, K., Chan, F., Taylor, D., & Wood, C. (1998). *Disability management specialists: An investigation of major practice domains and associated knowledge areas* (Technical Report#98-001). Rolling Meadows, IL: Foundation for Rehabilitation Education and Research.

Currier, F., Chan, F., Berven, N., Habeck, R., & Taylor, D. (2001). Job functions and knowledge domains for disability management practice: A Delphi study. *Rehabilitation Counseling Bulletin, 44*, 133-143.

Crimmins, E., Reynolds, S., and Saito, Y. (1999). Trends in Health and Ability to Work Among the Older Working-Age Population. *Journal of Gerontology, 54*(1), 531-540.

Daiker, B. (1995). Managed care in workers' compensation. *AAOHN Journal, 43*, 422-427.

DeMarco, J. W., & Wolfe, K. (1995). Managed care concepts in the delivery of disability management services to industry. In D. E. Shrey & M. LaCerte (Eds.), *Principles and practices of disability management in industry* (pp. 519-554). Winter Park, FL: GR Press, Inc.

Douglas, J. (2000). Integrated disability management: An employer's guide. International Foundation of Employee Benefit Plans, Inc. 2000.

Draper, D. A., Hurley, R. E., Lesser, C. S., & Struck, B. C. (2002). The changing face of managed care. *Health Affairs, 21*(1), 11-23.

Dudley, R. A., & Luft, H. S. (2001). Managed care in transition. *New England Journal of Medicine, 344*, 1087-1092.

Gabel, J. R., Lo Sasso, A. T., & Rice, T. (2003). Consumer-driven health plans: Are they more than talk now? *Health Affairs* (need to get other info).

Gosfield, A. G. (1997). Guidelines in case management. *The Case Manager, 8*(3), 103-108.

Habeck, R. V., & Kirchener, K. (1999). Case management issues within employer-based disability management. In F. Chan & M. Leahy (Eds.), *Health care and disability case management* (pp. 239-264). Lake Zurich, IL: Vocational Consultants Press.

Harris, G. E., Ripperger, M. J., & Horn, H. G. (2000). Managed care at the crossroads, *Health Affairs, 19*(1), 157-164.

Hayne, R. & Zagata-Meraz, S. (2003). Health care costs driving major plan changes. *Hewitt Press Release.* Retrieved September 21, 2003. from http://was4.hewitt/resource/newsroom/pressrel/2003/.

Hursh, N. (2003) *Pro-Work Strategies for Older Workers with Disabilities: A Disability Management Approach.* Presented at the 24th Switzer Seminar Series, Washington, DC, October 18, 2003

Industrial and occupational variations in workers' compensation costs. (1996, January/February) *John Burton's Workers' Compensation Monitor, 9*(1), 1-10.

Jacobs, A. (2003). *The Health Care Cost Crisis.* A presentation to the National Association of Legislative and Political Specialists for Education, November 23, 2003, Madison, WI., Wisconsin Education Association Trust. Madison, WI.

Johnson, W. G., Baldwin, M. L., & Burton, Jr., J. F. (1996). Why is the treatment of work-related injuries so costly? New evidence from California. *Inquiry, 33*(Spring). Blue Cross and Blue Shield Association and Blue Cross and Blue Shield of the Rochester Area.

Knight, H. (1997). 24-hour care today. *The Case Manager, 8*(1), 39-42.

Kongstevedt, P. R. (1995). *Essentials of managed health care.* Gaithersburg, MD: Aspen Publications.

Koco, L. (1996, September 16). United expands market for "open access" plan. *National Underwriter Life & Health-Financial Services Edition,* 13-14.

Kreider, J. (1996). All lines case management coverage. *The Case Manager, 7*(4), 47-52.

Leahy, M., Chan, F., Taylor, D., Wood, C., & Downey, W. (1998). Evolving knowledge and skill factors for practice in private sector rehabilitation. The *NARPPS Journal, 6*(1), 34-43.

Leahy, M., Chan, F. & Saunders, J. (2003). Job functions and knowledge requirements of certified rehabilitation counselors in the 21st century, *Rehabilitation Counseling Bulletin, 46*(2), 66-81.

Leahy, M., Chan, F., Shaw, L., & Lui, J. (1997). Preparation of rehabilitation counselors for case management practice in health care settings. *Journal of Rehabilitation, 63*(2), 53-59.

Leahy, M., Chan, F., Taylor, D., Wood, C., & Downey, W. (1998). Evolving knowledge and skill factors for practice in private sector rehabilitation. *The NARPPS Journal, 6*(1), 34-43.

Lui, J. (1993). Trends and innovations in private sector rehabilitation for the 21st century. In L. E. Perlman and C. E. Hansen (Eds.), *Private sector rehabilitation: Trends and issues for the 21st century* (pp. 47-50). Alexandria, VA: National Rehabilitation Association.

McMahon, B. T., Danczyk-Hawley, C. E., Reid, C., Flynn, B. S., Habeck, R.V., Kregel, J., & Owens, P. (2000). The progression of disability benefits. *Journal of Vocational Rehabilitation, 15*, 3-15.

Merry, M., Crago, M. G. (2001). The past present and future of health care quality: Exploring three avenues to improve patient care, *Physician Executive, 27*(5), 30-35.

Morath, J. (2003). Changing the health care culture: The consumer as part of the system of care. *Frontiers of Health Service Management, 19*, (4), 17-28.

Mullahy, K. M. (1995). *The case manager's handbook.* Gaithersburg, MD: Aspen Publications.

Mullen, J. K. (1995). *Introduction to managed care: Fundamentals of managed care coverage and providers.* New York: Life Office Management Association.

Parmenter, E. M. (2003). Controlling health care cost: Components of a new paradigm. *Journal of Financial Service Professionals, 57*(4), 59-68.

Pransky, G, & Himmelstein, J. (1996a). Outcome research: Implications for occupational health. *American Journal of Industrial Medicine, 29*, 573-583.

Pransky, G., & Himmelstein, J. (1996b). *Evaluating outcomes of workers' compensation medical care.* University of Massachusetts Medical Center, Worchester, MA: Occupational Health Program and the New England Center for Occupational Musculoskeletal Disorders (NECOMD).

PriceWaterhouseCoopers (2002, April). *The factors fueling rising health care costs.* Retrieved September 29, 2003 from the PriceWaterhouseCoopers health care website: http://www.pwchealth.com.

Reschovsky, J. D., Hargraves, J. L., & Smith, A.F. (2002). Consumer beliefs and health plan performance: It's not whether you are in an HMO but whether you think you are. *Journal of Health Politics, Policy and Law, 27*, 353-377.

Rix, S. E. (2002). The labor market for older workers. *Generations: Journal of the American Society on Aging, 26*(2), 25-30.

Scism, L. (1994, September 20). Picking cherries: Health insurer profits by being very choosy in selling its policies. *Wall Street Journal*, p. A-1.

Shaw, L., Leahy, M. J., & Chan, F. (1999). Case management: Past, present, and future. In F. Chan & M. Leahy (Eds.), *Health care and disability case management* (pp. 39-60). Lake Zurich, IL: Vocational Consultants Press.

Shaw, L., McMahon, B. T., Chan, F., Taylor, D., & Wood, C. (1997). Survey of CORE-accredited programs in rehabilitation counseling regarding private sector case management. *Journal of Rehabilitation, 63*(2), 46-51.

State Policy Watch. (2003). *Health care Financial Management, 57*(6), p. 12-13.

Strickland, T. (1995). Moving toward 2000: Trends and tribulations in case management. *CCM Update*, 4-6.

Tabak, M. H. (1995, February). Merging managed care and workers' compensation. *Risk Management,* 16-19.

Taylor, H. (2002). How and why the health insurance system will collapse. *Health Affairs, 21*(6), 195-200.

Victor, R. A., *(2003)*. *Evidence of Effectiveness of Policy Levers to Contain Medical Costs in Workers' Compensation* – A WCRI Professional Paper. Richard A. Victor. November 2003. WC-03-08.

Watson Wyatt Worldwide (2003). *Creating informed health care consumers.*

Welch, E. M. (1994). *Employer's guide to workers' compensation.* Washington, DC: The Bureau of National Affairs, Inc.

West, D. (1997, January 13). Direct access becoming key feature of HMOs. *National Underwriter Property & Casualty-Risk & Benefits Management,* 23-24.

Workers' compensation benefits paid to workers. (1996, March/April). *John Burton's Workers' Compensation Monitor, 9*(2),

Workers' compensation benefits, costs, and profits: An overview of developments in the 1990s. (1996, November/December). *John Burton's Workers' Compensation Monitor, 9*(6), 1-7.

Workers' compensation, 24-hour coverage, and managed care. (1996, January/February). *John Burton's Workers' Compensation Monitor, 9*(1), 11-22.

Zagata-Meraz, S. (2003). Enrolling Online for Benefits Continues to be Number One Choice for US Employees. *Hewitt press release*, Retrieved February 4, 2003. http://was4hewitt.com/hewitt/resource/newsroom/pressrel/2003/02-04-03.

4

The New Disability Law and Policy Framework: Implications for Case Managers

James Schmeling
Helen Schartz
Peter Blanck

Chapter Highlights

- Evolving national employment policy

- ADA law and policy overview

- Applicability of the ADA

- Conclusion

Understanding the history of disability law and policy and its evolution toward a new framework are important for case managers. This knowledge will help case managers effectively implement the goals of the framework and obtain best outcomes for their clients, agencies, and communities at large. Case managers will be equipped to participate in the dialogue about the future direction of disability policy at local, state, and federal levels.

In the past fifteen years, disability laws and policies have attracted widespread attention from policymakers, courts, legal academics, rehabilitation professionals, researchers, employers, and disability advocates (Blanck, 1997; Blanck, Hill, Siegal & Waterstone, 2003; Blanck & Marti, 1997). Since its passage in 1990, the Americans with Disabilities Act (ADA, 2000) has become America's prominent national policy statement affecting the lives of persons with disabilities. Despite the far-reaching implications of the ADA and related policy developments, analysis of the new disability rights-based approach, and its effects on persons with disabilities and their service providers, has been limited (Blanck & Schartz, 2001).

To a remarkable degree, many contemporary employment, health care, and governmental and rehabilitation programs for persons with disabilities are modeled on outmoded and medicalized stereotypes about disabilities. These longstanding views date as far back as the Civil War pension system, which first linked the definition of disability to an inability to work and established physicians and bureaucrats as the gatekeepers of disability benefits (Blanck, 2001; Blanck & Millender, 2000; Blanck & Song, 2001; 2001/2002; 2003).

The medical model of disability focused on the individual, whose condition was seen as an infirmity that precluded participation in society. The medical model never considered the effects of the physical and social environment in which people with disabilities were forced to function. Instead, it countenanced the segregation and economic marginalization of individuals with disabilities (Drimmer, 1993; Hahn, 2000; Milani, 1999). Because the medical model aimed to address the needs of people with disabilities rather than recognize their rights, it led to government policies that viewed assistance for people with disabilities as a form of either charity or welfare.

Disability laws and policies have undergone a dramatic shift from a model of charity and compensation, to medical oversight, and then to civil rights (Blanck, 2000; Blanck & Millender, 2000). Contemporary employment policies and laws are focused on increasing the labor force participation of qualified persons with disabilities and reducing their dependence on government entitlement programs. Federal laws, such as the Workforce Investment Act of 1998 (WIA), the Rehabilitation Act of 1973 as reauthorized in WIA, the Ticket to Work and Work Incentives Improvement Act of 1999 (TWWIIA), and the

Americans with Disabilities Act of 1990 (ADA), illustrate public support for enhancing employment opportunities for working age adults with disabilities and preventing discrimination in the workplace (Blanck, 2000; Blanck et al., 2003).

This chapter describes the new disability law and policy framework as it impacts labor force strategies and employment opportunities for the emerging workforce of persons with disabilities. The disability framework affects employers and employees, the systems within which employers and employees work, and the rehabilitation professionals who work with them to navigate the systems.

The first part of the chapter highlights the evolution of national employment policy toward persons with disabilities to a civil rights perspective. The second part examines contemporary efforts toward a national employment policy, including legislation, litigation, and relevant policymaking. The third part identifies future challenges and approaches to employment policy initiatives.

EVOLVING NATIONAL EMPLOYMENT POLICY FOR INDIVIDUALS WITH DISABILITIES

The Social Security Disability Insurance (SSDI) program defines disability as an inability to engage in "substantial gainful activity" and requires a medical assessment of the disabling condition (Stone, 1984). The Rehabilitation Act of 1973 is also grounded in a medical approach to disability, promoting the conception of individuals with disabilities as impaired and needing to be cured through rehabilitation (Blanck & Millender, 2000).

By contrast, the disability rights model that first began to influence government policy in the 1970s conceptualized the disabled as a minority group entitled to the same legal protections for equality that emerged from the struggles of African Americans and women (Blanck & Millender, 2000). The rights model focuses on the environment that subordinates disabled persons and insists that government eliminate the legal, physical, economic, and social barriers to secure full involvement in society for persons with disabilities (Seelman, 2000; Scotch & Schriner, 1997).

Although, until recently, national employment policy conceptualized disability from a medical perspective, people with disabilities as individuals and in organized groups began to challenge these stereotypes. For instance, many applicants rejected for social security benefits in the 1950s appealed those decisions and hired lawyers to represent them in the appeals process (Berkowitz, 1987). Many applicants whose appeals were rejected sought redress in federal court. Federal courts often accepted expanded definitions of eligibility, including ruling in favor of applicants for SSDI who were capable of working but were unable to obtain jobs (Liebman, 1976).

Beginning in the 1970s, disabled individuals asserted their right to be independent in pursuing education and housing. A group of students with disabilities challenged the policies at the University of California at Berkeley (Shapiro, 1993). In New York, an advocacy group for the rights of disabled individuals was formed in 1971, called Disabled in Action (National Council on Disability, 1996).

During this period, concepts from the independent living philosophy were integrated into the national disability policy. Title VII of the Rehabilitation Act initiated funding for independent living services or Centers for Independent Living (CILs). Not only did the CILs provide services for individuals with disabilities, but also, they were to be operated by individuals with disabilities (ILRU, 2004; National Council on Disability, 1996).

The evolving policy of inclusion fostered federal and state laws from accessibility in voting and air travel, to independence in education and housing (National Council on Disability, 1996), culminating with passage of the ADA in 1990, and later supplemented by other disability-related legislation and generic legislation, which incorporates disability-related provisions.

In the ADA, Congress expressly recognized the minority status of disabled persons, finding that:

(2) historically, society has tended to isolate and segregate individuals with disabilities, and, despite some improvements, such forms of discrimination against individuals with disabilities continue to be a serious and pervasive social problem; . . . (7) individuals with disabilities are a discrete and insular minority who have been faced with restrictions and limitations, subjected to a history of purposeful unequal treatment, and relegated to a position of political powerlessness in our society . . . (ADA, 42 U.S.C. § 12101(a) (2000)).

CONTEMPORARY EFFORTS TOWARD A NATIONAL EMPLOYMENT POLICY

The ADA (2000) articulates the nation's goals for assuring "equality of opportunity, full participation, independent living, and economic self-sufficiency" for individuals with disabilities (§ 12101(a)(8)). Although the ADA was to remove discriminatory barriers facing individuals with disabilities, prominent barriers remain in federal and state government programs, including economic disincentives to work, reflected in the SSDI and SSI programs, and typically manifested by a lack of adequate and affordable health insurance for the working disabled (e.g., Blanck, Sandler, Schmeling, & Schartz, 2000; Brooks & Klosinski, 1999; Stapleton & Tucker, 2000).

Recent national policy initiatives have been aimed at diminishing the economic barriers to work for disabled persons who want to work and who are capable of working (Jensen & Silverstein, 2000; Silverstein, 2000). TWWIIA, for instance, expands the availability of health care coverage for individuals with disabilities in several ways. First, states may allow disabled people with incomes over 250% of poverty level to "buy into" Medicaid health insurance programs if they are otherwise eligible for SSI. Individuals, whose medical conditions have improved, making them ineligible for SSI or SSDI, may buy into Medicaid if they continue to have a severe determinable impairment. Under TWWIIA, Medicaid premiums and other cost shares are determined on a sliding scale. For those persons with incomes between 250% and 450% of poverty level, premiums may not exceed 7.5% of their income. As of February 2004, twenty-eight states have implemented and five more have authorized Medicaid Buy-In programs (Jensen, 2004).

TWWIIA extends Medicare coverage for people returning to work from SSDI to 8.5 years without payment of a Medicare Part A premium. After 8.5 years, four and one half years longer than previous eligibility, the individual may continue to receive Medicare by paying the premiums for both Part A and Part B. The changes in health insurance options are meant to stimulate SSDI beneficiaries to return to work (e.g., after being injured on the job) without risking the loss of health insurance coverage by retaining Medicare coverage (Blanck, Hill, Siegal & Waterstone, 2003).

TWWIIA and WIA were designed to reduce work disincentives that historically have limited employment options for disabled persons. TWWIIA allows for an expedited reinstatement of benefits for SSDI recipients whose benefits were terminated because of increased earnings from work and who are unable to work because of a disability. The beneficiary may receive SSDI for up to six months during the period that the Social Security Administration is considering the reapplication.

TWWIIA establishes the Ticket to Work and Self-Sufficiency Program (the Ticket Program). SSI and SSDI recipients use a "ticket" to obtain employment services from employment networks. The goal of the Ticket Program is to give beneficiaries choice and control over their employment services and to foster competition and innovation among employment service providers (Virginia Commonwealth University RRTC, 2000). As of March 2004, a total of 6,947,228 tickets had been issued to SSI and SSDI recipients. Of those, 3,936 have been placed with employment networks (Social Security

Administration, 2004). A total of 1,077 employment networks had been established at that time (Social Security Administration).

WIA establishes "one stop" employment and job training centers that provide accessible services to all individuals, including those with disabilities. WIA provides that recipients of SSI and SSDI are automatically eligible for Vocational Rehabilitation Services (Seelman, 2000). WIA mandates that partners work together in the workforce system, including welfare-to-work programs, and provides for optional partners such as the Temporary Assistance to Needy Families (TANF) program. Section 188 of WIA requires nondiscrimination on the basis of disability, supplementing obligations under the ADA (Silverstein, 2004).

The new employment policy framework reflects a significant change in acknowledging the rights of qualified individuals with disabilities to work (Seelman, 2000). The approach is in contrast to the medical model of disability that dominated American federal policy for most of the twenty-first century (Blanck & Millender, 2000).

THE NEW DISABILITY LAW AND POLICY FRAMEWORK

Disability policy guides practice and practice informs policy. It is important, therefore, for rehabilitation professionals and case managers to understand and apply policy, as well as to promote policy change when necessary. Advocacy for policy change has many sources, including CILs, people with disabilities, case managers, legislators, and other stakeholders.

Impetus for policy change often comes from the field and people working within the system who have first-hand knowledge of flaws or solutions. Effective integration of the state vocational rehabilitation systems with Medicaid, Medicare, TANF, Welfare to Work, Unemployment Insurance, Mental Health, and other service delivery systems is a goal of WIA. Not all of these systems, however, are designed in accordance with the needs of people with disabilities.

President George W. Bush, during his first month in office in 2001, announced the "New Freedom Initiative" (NFI) stating "Americans with disabilities should have every freedom to pursue careers, integrate into the workforce, and participate as full members in the economic marketplace" (White House, n.d.). The purpose of the NFI is to remove barriers to the workplace and promote access and integration. NFI proposes increasing access to assistive and universally designed technologies; expanding educational opportunities for Americans with disabilities; and promoting full access to community life.

Despite the new approach toward a national disability employment policy of inclusion, millions of disabled individuals who are capable of working remain unemployed or underemployed (e.g., National Organization on Disability, 2000; Schwochau & Blanck, 2000). Individuals with disabilities may be less prepared for competitive employment in the future (Seelman, 2000; U.S. Census Bureau, 2003).

Not all of the available information paints a dismal picture for individuals with disabilities. Kaye (1998) reports increases in employment among people aged 21–64 with severe functional limitations (i.e., a smaller group of individuals compared to those with severe disabilities) from almost 28% in 1991–1992 to 32% in 1994–1995. Kruse and Schur (2003) find that from 1990 to 1994, employment trends of disabled persons after the ADA differ depending on the disability category: employment rates declined among those reporting work disabilities, but improved among those reporting severe functional limitations without a work disability.

An analysis of SIPP information (McNeil, 2000) from 1994 to 1997 for persons with non-severe disabilities finds that employment rates increased from 77% to 81%. Although during 1994 to 1997 employment rates for those with severe disabilities declined from 34% to 29%, overall employment rates for younger individuals with severe disabilities were higher in 1997 compared to 1991.

Other evidence suggests that disabled individuals have been attaining higher levels of education over time. The 1998 N.O.D. / Harris Survey reported that 20% of disabled individuals responded they had not completed high school, compared to 39% in 1986 (Taylor, 1998). Education is the foundation for transition to higher education or work. New initiatives from SSA, such as the Youth Transition Process Demonstration, will assist youth with disabilities to maximize their economic self-sufficiency as they transition from school to work. Focused on people with disabilities from ages 14 to 25 who either receive SSI, SSDI, or Childhood Disability Benefits (CDB) or youth who could receive these benefits, the Youth Demonstration is intended to promote collaboration among state, local, and federal agencies for transition services and supports. WIA implements youth services in the One-Stop intended to improve employment and education for youth with disabilities. The U.S. Department of Labor funds a national center on youth with disabilities to provide technical assistance in this area (National Collaborative on Workforce and Disability Youth, 2004).

CHALLENGES AND OPPORTUNITIES

A cardinal question remains, how will policymakers, researchers, rehabilitation professionals, and people with disabilities assess the effectiveness of the new national disability policy? The ADA attempts to define these goals "to assure equality of opportunity, full participation, independent living, and economic self-sufficiency for individuals [with disabilities]" (ADA, 42 U.S.C. § 12101(a)(8) (2000)). Title IV of WIA amended the Rehabilitation Act of 1973 to reiterate the national employment goals of "empower[ing] individuals with disabilities to maximize employment, economic self-sufficiency, independence, and inclusion and integration into society" (Rehabilitation Act, 29 U.S.C. 701(b)(1) (2000)).

These national initiatives conceive employment as part of a broader concept of civil rights. Implementation and evaluation of these initiatives, therefore, must reflect and assess not only trends in labor market activity, but also advancements in self-sufficiency, independence, inclusion and integration (Blanck & Schartz, 2001). Rehabilitation professionals must understand the current research and apply the results of research to the practice of rehabilitation and case management.

States with progressive rehabilitation professionals may integrate new policy into practice to take advantage of granting opportunities from the various federal initiatives, and importantly, to comply with the requirements of new legislation and policy. More critical, though, is that the federal agencies responsible for new initiatives are increasingly turning to demonstration programs to field new programs and service delivery options.

These demonstration programs are evaluated for effectiveness, and then agencies use best practices from the field and replicate them nationwide in an effort to increase the integration and self-sufficiency of people with disabilities. There are several examples of new funding opportunities with which rehabilitation professionals must be familiar, such as Work Incentive Grants, Medicaid Infrastructure Grants, Customized Employment Grants, and Disability Program Navigator. These demonstration programs and grants have the potential to impact practice in their respective states (see Law, Health Policy & Disability Center, 2003, for an extensive listing for many states). Each may generate new knowledge and practice that may be replicated.

The WIA final regulations provide principles relevant to such projects: "The success of the workforce investment system is dependent on the development of true partnerships and honest collaboration at all levels among all stakeholders" and "the underlying notion of One-Stop is the coordination of programs, services, and governance structures so the customer has access to a seamless system of workforce investment services" (65 Fed. Reg. 49295). Rehabilitation and workforce professionals are at the core of both.

INTEGRATING DISABILITY LAW AND POLICY
Employment inclusion and integration require access to a range of workplace and non-workplace activities. Traditional economic outcomes need to be

augmented by examining a range of employment opportunities, including self-employment, entrepreneurial activities and temporary employment. A preliminary study of Iowa's Entrepreneurs with Disabilities (EWD) program describes how participants with disabilities progress through the program of technical and financial assistance, business development grants to establish or expand small-businesses with the goal of becoming self-sufficient, and the characteristics of successful participants (Blanck et al., 2000).

Similar approaches have been undertaken across the country. Changes have occurred in the past decade in self-employment, and more than thirty state agencies have developed self-employment policies since WIA was passed in 1998, and almost forty state agencies now have policies for self-employment (Arnold & Ipsen, 2003).

Technology has become an integral part of the workplace. Without effective access to technology (e.g., the Internet and computers), individuals with all types of disabilities (e.g., mobility, sensory, neurological, and learning impairments) will continue to face obstacles in work and in their daily lives (Blanck & Sandler, 2000). Achievement of the promise of full inclusion and labor force participation requires more than advancing technology. It requires legislative mandates and corresponding technology.

The Technology-Related Assistance for Individuals with Disabilities Act of 1988 and Assistive Technology Act of 1998 are disability-related laws that involve accessible technology; Section 508 of the Rehabilitation Act is another. Inclusion and labor force participation also require change in underlying attitudes and behaviors toward individuals with disabilities in all parts of American society.

Practitioners should consider environmental factors that contribute to and define disabilities. Scotch and Schriner (1997) consider disability as human variation in which an individual is disabled to the extent that their environment does not accommodate their needs. Building on this concept, the National Institute on Disability and Rehabilitation Research (NIDRR) (Seelman, 2000) has promoted the adoption of a conception of disability as "the product of an interaction between individual characteristics and the natural, built, cultural, and social environments" (p. 3).

NIDDR has funded research projects on "Technology for Independence" that address this interaction, as well as a resource center to provide technical assistance and training to these projects (see TI-CBRC, 2003, for descriptions of the projects). Rehabilitation professionals also need to address attitudinal and environmental factors that act as barriers to employment (Hahn, 2000). For instance, in what ways will the accessibility and universal design goals of WIA enhance employment opportunities for disabled individuals?

Increasing dialogue among corporations and government about disability and diversity is one strategy for increasing awareness of issues of importance to people with disabilities, and for promoting attitudinal change. Rehabilitation professionals, working with the local workforce system that is responsive to the needs of businesses, may dialogue with employers, local, state, or federal government, and people with disabilities.

ADA LAW AND POLICY OVERVIEW

In this part, we review the major legal cases decided under the ADA and their disability framework policy implications for case managers. The ADA is composed of six sections or titles. The beginning or the preface, § 12101, sets out Congress's "Findings and Purposes" (ADA, 42 U.S.C. § 12101 (2000)) and identifies people with disabilities as "a discrete and insular minority who have been faced with restriction and limitations, subjected to a history of purposeful unequal treatment, and relegated to a position of political powerlessness in our society." (§ 12101(a)(7)). The preface identifies the nation's goals of assuring "equality of opportunity, full participation, independent living, and economic self sufficiency" (§ 12101(a)(8)) for individuals with disabilities. Among the purposes of the ADA is to "provide a clear and comprehensive national mandate for the elimination of discrimination against people with disabilities," (§ 12101(b)(1)) and to ensure that the federal government plays a central role in enforcing these standards (§ 12101(b)(3)).

ADA TITLE I
Title I sets forth the antidiscrimination provisions for employment. "No covered entity shall discriminate against a qualified individual with a disability because of the disability of such individual in regard to job application procedures, the hiring, advancement, or discharge of employees, employee compensation, job training, and other terms, conditions, and privileges of employment" (§ 12112). Covered entities are defined as employers, employment agencies, labor organizations or joint-labor management committees (§ 12111). Although a covered entity is forbidden from discriminating, it is not required to make accommodations that create an "undue hardship," (§ 12111(10)) or create a situation where an employee is a significant risk to the health or safety of others in the workplace.

1. The Definition of Disability: *Sutton* Trilogy
In 1999, the U.S. Supreme Court rendered three important decisions in ADA employment cases. Known as the "*Sutton* trilogy," the cases interpreted the definition of disability under the ADA, including the extent to which mitigating

measures must be considered in determining if a person is disabled under the law.

The *Sutton* trilogy illustrates the ways in which rehabilitation professionals should be aware of changing definitions of disability under Title I of the ADA. It shows the interaction of the case law with DOT, OSHA, or other federal regulations that impact workplace health and safety. Case managers also need to assess the appropriateness of workplace accommodations. Complex assessments involve the degree to which individuals (1) self-compensate or mitigate orthopedic impairments in major life activities such as working; and (2) may be reasonably accommodated to work safely and productively in various settings.

The ADA prohibits employment discrimination for qualified individuals with a disability. To be covered by the law, the employee or perspective employee must be "an individual with a disability who, with or without reasonable accommodation, can perform the essential functions of the employment position that such individual holds or desires" (ADA, 42 U.S.C. § 12111(8)). A "disability" is defined as "a physical or mental impairment that substantially limits one or more of the major life activities of such individual" (§ 12102 (2)(A)). In the *Sutton* trilogy, the Supreme Court concluded that mitigating measures, things that could be done to help correct or mitigate an individual's impairment, must be considered when determining whether an individual has a disability under the ADA.

In *Sutton v. United Air Lines, Inc.* (1999), the court held that the determination of whether an individual has a disability within the meaning of the ADA should be made with reference to measures that mitigate the individual's impairment. United Airlines denied the plaintiffs, who suffered severe myopia, commercial airline pilot positions on the basis that the plaintiffs did not meet the minimum vision requirement. Without corrective lenses, the plaintiffs could not see to conduct numerous activities such as driving a vehicle, watching television, or shopping in public stores. With corrective measures such as glasses or contact lenses, however, the plaintiffs had vision of 20/20 or better.

The Court held that measures to correct for, or mitigate, a physical or mental impairment, must be taken into account when judging whether that person is 'substantially limited' in a major life activity and thus 'disabled' under the ADA" (*Sutton v. United Air Lines, Inc.*, 1999, p. 482). The majority held that one may still have a disability under § 12102(A) of the ADA if they are substantially limited in a major life activity despite the mitigating measures. Determining whether an individual is disabled under the ADA, therefore, requires an individualized inquiry.

In *Murphy v. United Parcel Service* (1999), the court extended the set of mitigating measures to be considered to medication used to treat impairments. Similar to *Sutton*, the court held that the determination of whether individuals are substantially limited must take into account the functioning of the individuals when they are medicated.

In *Murphy*, a plaintiff with hypertension was terminated from his job as a UPS mechanic because his high blood pressure disqualified him for a DOT health certificate. Although he had high blood pressure, the plaintiff's doctor testified that the plaintiff had normal functioning when medicated. The Court held that the plaintiff was not disabled under the ADA because, when medicated, his hypertension did not substantially limit major life activities.

In *Albertsons, Inc. v. Kirkingburg* (1999), the Court held that ADA plaintiffs are required to offer evidence that they are substantially limited in a major life activity to prove their disability and that an employer does not have to justify its enforcement of a safety regulation when the regulation may be waived under an experimental program in individual cases.

A truck driver for Albertson's Grocery Stores, Kirkingburg, was mistakenly certified as meeting the DOT vision standards, although he was monocular. A physician later correctly assessed that Kirkingburg did not meet the applicable DOT standards. Independent of the standards, the DOT had implemented an experimental waiver program for drivers with deficient vision who had recent commercial driving experience without incident. Although Kirkingburg applied for the waiver, Albertson's fired him for failure to meet the DOT standard. Kirkingburg sued Albertson's claiming that under the ADA he was a qualified individual with a disability because he was able to meet the standards of a waiver program that the DOT had in place.

The Court found that Kirkingburg was not an individual with a disability, and, that even if he were an individual with a disability, he would not have been qualified to perform the job in question. The Court noted that Kirkingburg had developed "self-correcting mechanisms" for coping with his visual impairment. The Court stated that these self-correcting measures, whether conscious or unconscious, might be considered a mitigating measure just like artificial aids, medications, or other devices.

The Court ruled that Albertson's was justified in firing Kirkingburg when he could not meet the DOT standard. The Court reasoned that because the waiver program was experimental and designed to collect data regarding the experiences of experienced drivers with visual acuity deficits, but not a change of the regulatory visual acuity standards, the waiver did not modify the DOT safety-related requirements. The *Sutton* Trilogy illustrates the importance of understanding factors that mitigate impairment in determining whether a person has a disability for purposes of the ADA.

2. Substantial Limitation of a Major Life Activity: *Toyota v. Williams*

The issue in *Toyota Motor Manufacturing v. Williams* (2002) was interpretation of the ADA's phrase "substantially limited." The court considered whether the plaintiff's impairments substantially limited her in the major life activity of performing manual tasks. The Court held that for a plaintiff to be substantially limited in performing manual tasks, the plaintiff must demonstrate an impairment that prevents or severely restricts her from activities of central importance to most people's everyday lives.

In *Toyota*, the plaintiff sued her former employer for failing to provide her with an accommodation when she became disabled with carpal tunnel syndrome from working on the automobile assembly line. The Court unanimously decided that "substantially" suggests "considerable" or "to a large degree" and precludes impairments that interfere in only a minor way with performing manual tasks (*Toyota Motor Manufacturing v. Williams*, 2002, pp. 196–197). Interpreting "major" as important was restricted to those activities that are of central importance to daily life.

The Court held that an individual must have an impairment that prevents or severely restricts the individual from doing activities that are of central importance to most people's daily lives and the impairment's impacts must be permanent or long term (*Toyota Motor Manufacturing v. Williams*, 2002, p. 197). Household chores, bathing, and brushing one's teeth are among the types of manual tasks of central importance to people's daily lives (*Motor Manufacturing v. Williams*, p. 202).

3. Direct Threat Defense: *Chevron v. Echazabal*

In *Chevron U.S.A., Inc. v. Echazabal* (2002), the Court interpreted the ADA defense that employers are not required to hire or retain employees who pose a direct threat to the health or safety of others in the workplace. The Court was asked whether the direct threat defense would apply to an employer who refuses to hire a job applicant with a disability because the job would endanger the *applicant's* own health. The Court held that the ADA allows an employer's refusal to hire a job applicant with a disability where the applicant's job performance would endanger his own health.

In this case, the plaintiff's physical examination showed liver abnormality or damage caused by Hepatitis C, which the employer's doctors said would be aggravated by exposure to toxins at the employer's refinery. The employer relied on the EEOC "direct threat to self" regulation, which allows an employer to screen out potential workers with disabilities for risks that they would pose to others in the workplace and for risks on the job to their own health or safety.

The direct threat determination is to consider, among other aspects, the potential imminence of the risk and the severity of the harm based on a reasonable medical judgment that relies on the most current medical knowledge or the best available objective evidence, and on an individual assessment of the individual's present ability to safely perform the essential functions of the job (Regulations to Implement the Equal Employment Provisions of the Americans with Disabilities Act, 29 C.F.R. § 1630.2(r) (2003)). The primary issue was whether the ADA permits the EEOC regulation allowing a threat-to-self defense. The Court decided that the ADA permits the EEOC regulation.

A major purpose of the ADA is to eliminate paternalistic attitudes by covered entities in dealing with qualified persons with a disability. Rehabilitation professionals should not declare an individual ineligible for programs and services based on the idea that it is best for the person with a disability if they do not participate. Persons with a disability should be encouraged to make their own informed decisions rather than have agencies make the decisions as to their best interests.

4. Reassignment and Workplace Accommodations: *U.S. Airways v. Barnett*

In *U.S. Airways, Inc. v. Barnett* (2002), the issue was whether the ADA requires an employer to reassign an employee with a disability to a position as an accommodation even though another employee is entitled to hold the position under the employer's bona fide and established seniority system. The Court held that when a requested accommodation conflicts with the rules of a seniority system, that fact will ordinarily make the accommodation unreasonable, entitling an employer to summary judgment. The plaintiff, however, may present evidence of special circumstances that make reasonable a seniority rule exception in the particular case.

In this case, the employee who injured his back while working requested assignment to a mailroom position as an accommodation. At least two other employees had seniority and, therefore, were entitled to the position. The employer decided not to make an exception to the seniority system, and the employee lost his job.

The Court reasoned that discrimination includes an employer's not making reasonable accommodations for a qualified employee, unless the employer "can demonstrate that the accommodation would impose an undue hardship on the operation of the business" (ADA, 42 U.S.C. § 12112 (b)(5)(A) (2000)). But, "[t]he simple fact that an accommodation would provide a 'preference'—in the sense that it would permit the worker with a disability to violate a rule that others must obey—cannot, in and of itself, automatically show that the accommodation is not 'reasonable'" (*U.S. Airways, Inc. v. Barnett*, 2002, p. 1521).

Because of the importance of seniority to employee-management relations, an employer's showing that a proposed assignment will violate the rules of a seniority system, by itself, will be sufficient to meet the "undue hardship on the operation of the business" requirement (*U.S. Airways, Inc. v. Barnett*, 2002, p. 1519). However, if specific circumstances have altered the employee expectations of fair, uniform treatment, a requested accommodation may be reasonable.

Because an accommodation may amount to a preference for a person with a disability does not mean that it is *per se* not reasonable and not required by the ADA. When working with clients, employers, and agencies, case managers should consider modifications to rules, policies, or practices as generally reasonable, even though persons not protected by the ADA would not necessarily be entitled to the same modification.

5. Social Security Benefits and Title I: *Cleveland v. Policy Management Systems*

In *Cleveland v. Policy Management Systems Corp.* (1999), the Court considered whether the receipt of Social Security Disability Insurance (which benefits persons with disabilities who are unable to do their previous work and incapable of engaging in any other kind of substantial gainful work) precludes the SSDI recipient from simultaneously pursuing an action for disability discrimination under the ADA. The Court held that an ADA plaintiff cannot defeat a defendant company's summary judgment motion when there are apparent contradictions between her ADA claim and SSDI claim, unless there is a sufficient explanation for the discrepancy.

Cleveland involves a plaintiff who suffered a stroke, and then sought and obtained Social Security Disability Insurance (SSDI) benefits. SSDI provides monetary benefits to every insured individual who "is under a disability" (Social Security Act, 42 U.S.C. § 423 (a)(1) (2000)). Disability is defined as an "inability to engage in any substantial gainful activity by reason of any . . . physical or mental impairment which can be expected to last for a continuous period of not less than 12 months" (§ 423 (d)(2)(A)). The individual's impairment must be "of such severity that she is not only unable to do her previous job but cannot, considering her age, education, and work experience, engage in any other kind of substantial gainful work which exists in the national economy" (§ 423 (d)(1)(A)).

In contrast, the ADA prohibits covered employers from discriminating "against a qualified individual with a disability because of the disability of such individual" (ADA, 42 U.S.C. § 12112 (a) (2000)). The ADA defines a "qualified individual with a disability" to include a person who can perform essential job functions with or without reasonable accommodation (§ 12111 (8)).

According to the Court, "when the SSA determines whether an individual is disabled for SSDI purposes, it does not take the possibility of 'reasonable accommodation' into account, nor need an applicant refer to the possibility of reasonable accommodation when she applies for SSDI" (*Cleveland v. Policy Management Systems Corp.*, 1999, p. 803). The Court decided that receipt of SSDI benefits did not bar the plaintiff from bringing an ADA claim when she had offered an adequate explanation that she could nonetheless "perform the essential functions of her job, with or without reasonable accommodation" (*Cleveland v. Policy Management Systems Corp.*, 1999, p. 807).

Case managers and other rehabilitation professionals may not rely on SSDI findings alone that a person is incapable of working to determine that person is not a qualified person under the ADA. The fact that a person is receiving SSDI compensation does not necessarily mean that that person is not capable of working if provided reasonable accommodations, entitled to reasonable modifications of services covered by Title II of the ADA, or capable of benefiting from the services and programs.

6. Arbitration Agreements and Title I: *EEOC v. Waffle House*

In *EEOC v. Waffle House* (2002), the issue was whether an agreement between an employer and an employee to arbitrate employment claims precludes the EEOC from pursuing victim specific judicial relief, such as back pay, reinstatement, and damages, in an enforcement action under Title I. The Court held that an arbitration agreement does not prohibit the EEOC from seeking victim-specific judicial relief on behalf of an employee subject to the arbitration agreement because the EEOC is pursuing a public interest.

In his employment application, the plaintiff agreed that disputes concerning his employment would be settled by arbitration (*EEOC v. Waffle House*, 2002, p. 282). After having a seizure at work, the plaintiff was discharged. The plaintiff filed a charge of discrimination with the EEOC alleging that he was discharged because of his disability. The EEOC filed an enforcement action against Waffle House, requesting specific relief to make plaintiff whole, including back pay, reinstatement, and compensatory damages.

The Court decided that the arbitration agreement, which barred the employee from seeking relief, did not bar the EEOC from pursuing make-whole relief specifically for the employee. The EEOC was seeking to vindicate a public interest, rather than simply providing make-whole relief for an employee, even when the EEOC pursued victim-specific relief.

Case managers should note that when they act as representatives for an employer, the EEOC might bring an ADA action against the case manager, employer, or agency independent of the employee's ADA claim. When acting as a representative of the employer or agency, the case manager takes on the employer's obligations of non-discrimination under the ADA. When acting as an advisor to clients in ADA matters, case managers and rehabilitation professionals may consider advising clients to seek enforcement assistance from the EEOC.

TITLE II AND PUBLIC ENTITIES

Title II of the ADA prohibits discrimination by state or local governments. Part A defines the antidiscrimination provisions, "no qualified individual with a disability shall, by reason of such disability, be excluded from participation in or be denied the benefits of the services, programs, or activities of a public entity, or be subjected to discrimination by any such entity" (ADA, 42 U.S.C. § 12132 (2000)). Part B is devoted to the special circumstances and requirements for non-discrimination in public transportation. A core element of Title II involves the "integration mandate."

Perhaps the most significant Title II case is *Olmstead v. L.C. ex rel. Zimring* (1999). In *Olmstead*, the Court held that Title II requires a state to place persons with mental disabilities in community settings rather than in institutions when the state's treatment professionals have determined that community placement is appropriate, the transfer is not opposed by the affected individual, and the placement may be reasonably accommodated, taking into account the resources of the state and the needs of others with mental disabilities.

The *Olmstead* plaintiffs had mental retardation and mental illness and had been voluntarily admitted to the psychiatric unit at Georgia Regional Hospital in Atlanta (GRH). Although their treatment professionals concluded that each could be cared for appropriately in a community-based program, plaintiffs remained institutionalized at GRH. Plaintiffs alleged that the State violated Title II in failing to place them in a community-based program once their treating professionals determined that such placement was appropriate. According to four Justices, undue institutionalization qualifies as discrimination "by reason of . . . disability" as advocated by the Department of Justice, and unjustified placement or retention of persons in institutions severely limits their exposure to the outside community, and therefore constitutes a form of disability based discrimination prohibited by Title II.

State rehabilitation and workforce programs are to provide programs and services to qualified persons with a disability in the most integrated setting possible. These programs should avoid discrimination against qualified persons with a disability by making all modifications in policies, practices, and procedures that do not result in undue financial and administrative burdens or fundamentally alter the nature of the service or program.

TITLE III AND PRIVATE ENTITIES

Title III of the ADA provides antidiscrimination requirements for public accommodations and services operated by private entities. The requirement is that "[n]o individual shall be discriminated against on the basis of disability in the full and equal enjoyment of the goods, services, facilities, privileges, advantages, or accommodations of any place of public accommodation by any person who owns, leases (or leases to), or operates a place of public accommodation" (ADA, 42 U.S.C. § 12182(a) (2000)).

A public accommodation must make reasonable modifications in its policies, practices, and procedures, unless that entity demonstrates that doing so would fundamentally alter the nature of its goods, services, or facilities. Older facilities must remove architectural barriers if it is "readily achievable" to do so (ADA, 42 U.S.C. § 12182(b)(2)(A)(iv) (2000)), while facilities (or alterations) that post-date the ADA must be designed to be readily accessible to individuals with disabilities to the "maximum extent possible" (§ 12183(a)(2)).

A. Asymptomatic Impairments, Definition of Disability, and Title III

In *Bragdon v. Abbott* (1998), the issue was whether asymptomatic HIV disease is a disability within the language of the ADA and whether the plaintiff's HIV disease posed a direct threat to the health or safety of the treating dentist. The Court held that asymptomatic HIV disease is a physical impairment that substantially limits the major life activity of reproduction, and thereby a disability under the ADA. In addition, the record did not support a determination, as a matter of law without a trial, that HIV infection did not pose a direct threat to the health and safety of others.

Although a public accommodation includes the "professional office of a health care provider" (ADA, 42 U.S.C. § 12181 (7)(F) (2000)), a public entity is not required to provide services to an individual who poses a direct threat to the health or safety of others (§ 12182 (b)(3)). The Court found that a private health care provider may refuse to treat a patient without violating title III when the patient's infectious condition "poses a direct threat to the health or safety of others" (§ 12182 (b)(3)).

A direct threat, as defined by the ADA is "a significant risk to the health or safety of others than cannot be eliminated by a modification of policies, practices, or procedures or by the provision of auxiliary aids or services" (§ 12182 (b)(3)). The Court held that lower courts must assess the direct threat risk with objective views of health care professionals without deferring to their individual judgments. Public rehabilitation programs that are operated by private entities are covered by Title III. The *Bragdon* court endorsed a broad reading of Title III antidiscrimination provisions.

B. Reasonable Accommodation: *PGA v. Martin*

PGA Tour, Inc. v. Martin (2001) involved whether Title III protects access to professional golf tournaments by a qualified entrant with a disability, and whether use of a golf cart by a contestant might be a reasonable accommodation. The Court held that the PGA's golf tours and their qualifying rounds fall within Title III of the ADA, protecting access by a qualified entrant with a disability. The walking requirement imposed by the PGA is not compromised by allowing Martin to use a cart—a modification that provides an exception to a peripheral tournament rule without impairing its purpose does not "fundamentally alter" the tournament.

The issue was whether the ADA protects access to professional golf tournaments by qualified entrants with a disability. The Court decided that golf courses constitute a type of place specifically identified as a public accommodation under the ADA. The ADA defines a public accommodation to include "a gymnasium, health spa, bowling alley, golf course, or other place of exercise or recreation" (*PGA Tour, Inc. v. Martin*, 2001, p. 677).

A second issue is whether a disabled contestant may be denied the use of a golf cart because it would "fundamentally alter the nature" of the tournament (*PGA Tour, Inc. v. Martin*, 2001, pp. 664–665). The Court found that the waiver of the walking rule for plaintiff would not work a fundamental alteration of the game. In addition, the waiver would not give plaintiff an advantage over others and fundamentally alter the character of the competition.

Martin endorses a policy of broad access for qualified persons with a disability to public accommodations covered by Title III. Privately operated rehabilitation programs should provide broad access to services, including by making reasonable accommodations.

APPLICABILITY OF THE ADA TO THE NEW DISABILITY LAW AND POLICY FRAMEWORK

This part highlights the applicability of the ADA to other disability laws and policies designed to enhance the independence and self-sufficiency of persons with disabilities.

WORKFORCE INVESTMENT ACT (WIA)
The Workforce Investment Act of 1998 establishes state and local Workforce Investment Boards responsible for developing a "one-stop" delivery system of accessible, innovative, and comprehensive employment services (Blanck & Schartz, 2001; Morris & Farah, 2002). The boards partner with local vocational rehabilitation agencies, businesses, and job training and education programs to assist local communities in increasing employment (Blanck et al., 2003).

Among the services provided by one-stop system are assistance in job search activities, career planning, job skill assessments and training, and childcare resources. One-stops provide resources for job and entrepreneurial training, transportation and housing assistance, and access to affordable health coverage (Morris & Farah, 2002).

WIA is designed to help individuals with disabilities achieve employment, economic independence, and inclusion into society (29 U.S.C. § 701(b)(1) (2000)). It is the federal funding vehicle for states to provide rehabilitation services and employment opportunities to people with disabilities (Frieden, 2003).

The programs and services supported by WIA are covered by the antidiscrimination provisions of the ADA and Section 504 of the Rehabilitation Act of 1973 (Hoff, 2000). The antidiscrimination provisions apply to state and local agencies supported with WIA funds, state and local workforce boards, one-stop operators, and employment providers (Silverstein, 2000).

"Disability" is defined under WIA consistently with the regulations implementing the ADA (Implementation of the Nondiscrimination and Equal Opportunity Provisions of the Workforce Investment Act of 1998, 29 C.F.R. § 37.4 (2003. Employees of private service providers are protected by Title I. State and local activities are covered under Title II. Title III's public accommodation provisions apply to private service providers receiving WIA funds from workforce boards.

A qualified person with a disability is entitled to effective benefits and services provided under WIA. One-stops and service providers must administer their programs in the most integrated setting possible (Implementation of the Nondiscrimination and Equal Opportunity Provisions of the Workforce Investment Act of 1998, 29 C.F.R. § 37.7(d) (2003)), and not impose criteria that screen out individuals with disabilities (§ 37.7(i)). They must provide reasonable accommodations to qualified applicants, participants, and employees with disabilities, unless doing so causes undue hardship. They also must make reasonable modifications to policies and practices to avoid discrimination (§ 37.8(a)–(b)).

TICKET TO WORK AND WORK INCENTIVES IMPROVEMENT ACT
(TWWIIA)
TWWIIA provides benefits to eligible individuals with disabilities who want to
and are capable of working (Ticket to Work and Self-Sufficiency Program, 20
C.F.R § 411.125(B) (2003)). One benefit allows working individuals with
disabilities the option of maintaining Medicaid health insurance coverage. This
promotes the ability of participants to return to work without the loss of
essential health care benefits. Another benefit is providing "tickets" for persons
with disabilities to choose, rather than be assigned to, service providers for
employment training.

One of the barriers to work for persons with disabilities has been the
inability to obtain health care coverage (Schartz, Schartz, & Blanck, 2002).
Disability-based payments often diminish incentives to work, particularly when
the attempt to work itself reduces eligibility for such benefits (Pacer Center,
2003). Cash benefits, for instance under the SSI and SSDI programs, primarily
have been available to individuals who could not engage in "substantial gainful
activity" (Blanck, Clay, Schmeling, Morris, & Ritchie, 2002).

TWWIIA's Ticket to Work and Self-Sufficiency Program provides
recipients of disability insurance with a "ticket" to purchase employment
training services from qualified Employment Networks (ENs) (see Ticket to
Work and Self-Sufficiency Program, 20 C.F.R. § 411.300 (2003), defining the
EN's purpose). The goal is to encourage individuals with disabilities to seek
rehabilitation services that aid in attaining employment and to reduce
dependence on governmental benefit programs (Ticket to Work and Self-
Sufficiency Program, 2001). Ticket program services include the provision of
case management, workplace accommodations, peer mentoring, job training,
and transportation assistance.

ENs receive payment from SSA when they succeed in placing the
participant in employment. Public and private organizations may apply to be
ENs, as may family and friends who meet the EN qualifications. More than
one-third of the states have implemented TWWIIA and others have passed
legislation creating similar programs (Folkemer, Jensen, Silverstein, & Straw,
2002).

Individuals with disabilities covered by TWWIIA likely are qualified
individuals with disabilities under the ADA. The applicability of the ADA to
ENs depends on the classification of the EN. ENs include individuals,
cooperatives, and public and private rehabilitation providers. Case managers
and other rehabilitation professionals are likely to encounter ENs in their
professional practice. It will be important to understand requirements of ENs
for compliance with the ADA and other non-discrimination provisions.

Although Title I protects employees of an EN, the relationship between an EN and its Ticket participants is governed by Title II provisions for public entities or Title III provisions for private entities as places of public accommodation. A state agency serving as an EN is a public entity governed by Title II. A private community rehabilitation provider is a public accommodation covered under Title III. Public and private ENs receiving federal grants or contracts also are subject to the antidiscrimination provisions of Section 504 of the Rehabilitation Act of 1973 (Nondiscrimination on the Basis of Disability by Public Accommodations and in Commercial Facilities, 1991).

Although a Ticket participant is a person with a disability for purposes of SSI or SSDI and likely covered under the ADA as an individual with a disability, as noted, the Supreme Court in *Cleveland* decided being "disabled" under SSA regulations does not necessarily mean an individual is disabled under the ADA. Title II requires that ENs not exclude a qualified individual with disabilities from their services and programs. These ENs must be physically and programmatically accessible (Ticket to Work and Self-Sufficiency Program, 20 C.F.R. § 411.315(a)(2) (2003)).

State or local government ENs, covered under Title II, must ensure that their programs, when viewed in their entirety, are accessible (Nondiscrimination on the Basis of Disability in State and Local Government Services, 28 C.F.R. §§ 35.149–150 (2003)). Title III requires that privately run ENs provide access to all persons with disabilities, not just those who are "qualified" for a particular program or service, which differs from Title I and II approaches (Parmet, 1993). An individual, family member, or friend of a Ticket participant who owns, leases, or operates a place of public accommodation as an EN is subject to Title III. Private ENs must remove barriers in existing buildings or provide services through alternative methods when "readily achievable" (ADA, 42 U.S.C. § 12181(9) (2000); Nondiscrimination on the Basis of Disability by Public Accommodations and in Commercial Facilities, 28 C.F.R. § 36.304 (2003)).

As ADA Title II or III entities, ENs must ensure effective communication with, and physical and programmatic access to, facilities and services for Ticket applicants, participants, their families, and the public (ADA, 42 U.S.C. § 12182(b)(2)(A)(iv) (2000); Blanck & Sandler, 2000)). ENs may not adopt program eligibility criteria that screen out people with certain disabilities (or individuals who have an association with people with disabilities) from programs or services, unless such criteria are necessary to program operation (§ 12182(b)(2)(A)(i)). Public and private ENs must reasonably modify their policies, practices, and procedures when necessary to allow people with disabilities to participate, unless doing so would fundamentally alter the program (Nondiscrimination on the Basis of Disability by Public Accommodations and in Commercial Facilities, 28 C.F.R. § 36.202 (2003); Nondiscrimination on the Basis of Disability in State and Local Government Services, 28 C.F.R. § 35.130(b)(7) (2003)).

Program participants may assign their Ticket to a public or private EN willing and able to provide services (Ticket to Work and Self-Sufficiency Program, 20 C.F.R. § 411.140 (2003)). The program encourages a range of service choices in which the participant and the EN choose their working partners (§§ 411.145; 411.150). Participants are able to choose their EN and deposit the Ticket to receive services from that EN or the state VR agency, and may choose to re-assign the Ticket to another EN (see § 411.150, placing limitations on Ticket reassignment).

There are sound reasons why ENs may specialize in services to particular groups of individuals (Ticket to Work and Self-Sufficiency Program, 2001, p. 67,399). Specialization can provide for greater efficiency and effectiveness in the delivery of services. Where an EN is not qualified to serve a particular individual, the ADA's undue burden provision does not require the EN to serve that Ticket holder. When accommodation is possible and reasonable, public or private ENs may not charge an individual to cover their costs (Nondiscrimination on the Basis of Disability by Public Accommodations and in Commercial Facilities, 28 C.F.R. §§ 36.301(c) (2003); Nondiscrimination on the Basis of Disability in State and Local Government Services, 35.130(f) (2003)).

Questions remain about TWWIIA implementation. What is an EN's responsibility under the ADA to serve individuals with multiple disabilities? In the case of a Ticket participant who is deaf and blind, does an EN specializing in serving deaf Ticket holders violate the ADA's nondiscrimination provisions by not providing materials in Braille, effectively excluding the blind and deaf individual from services?

Addressing such issues under the ADA, an EN's core obligation to Ticket holders is nondiscrimination in the provision of program access and services. An EN's decision not to provide service to a Ticket holder with multiple or secondary disabilities must be substantiated by evidence that such secondary disabilities require a service modification that would either fundamentally alter the program or pose an undue burden. An EN must ensure physical access to potential program participants and their families, for instance, by using alternative means of meeting with clients or their representatives (Ticket to Work and Work Incentives Advisory Panel, testimony of Blanck, 2002).

Another prominent question related to Ticket implementation is whether the ADA prevents ENs from choosing to provide services only to the pool of least disabled and "creamed" participants. Disability advocates' concerns about program implementation reflect the emergence of two separate and perhaps unequal markets for EN services, one served by private specialized ENs and another by state VR providers (Ticket to Work and Work Incentives Advisory Panel, testimony of Imparato, 2002).

The economic incentives in the Ticket Program encourage ENs to serve participants who need the fewest and least costly services (e.g. workplace accommodations and job training), and those who are able to return to work for an extended period of time (Ticket to Work and Work Incentives Advisory Panel, testimony of Imparato, 2002). Disability advocates are concerned that state VR agencies will bear a greater burden of serving individuals with more involved disabilities and costly service needs (Ticket to Work and Work Incentives Advisory Panel, testimony of Cebula, 2002).

Current trends suggest that most program participants either have not used their Tickets or have remained in the state VR system instead of assigning their ticket to an EN of their choice (Social Security Administration, 2002). Education that explains the Ticket Program is vital for beneficiaries and service providers, as well as for other stakeholders on the local, state, and federal levels (Social Security Administration). Ticket participants, moreover, must be knowledgeable about their rights and responsibilities under the program.

TEMPORARY ASSISTANCE FOR NEEDY FAMILIES (TANF)

In 1996, the Personal Responsibility and Work Opportunity Reconciliation Act created the Temporary Assistance for Needy Families program. TANF replaced the Aid to Families with Dependent Children program as a shift away from long-term welfare services and toward the requirement of employment for welfare recipients (Schoen, 1997).

Among other goals, the TANF program strives to promote job preparation and employment to help reduce dependency on government welfare (General TANF Provisions, 45 C.F.R. § 260.20(b) (2003)). TANF's work requirements encourage eligible recipients to seek employment and self-sufficiency. Recipients must begin working when the state determines they are ready for employment, or after twenty-four cumulative months of assistance (Schoen, 1997, p. 646). Families receiving TANF benefits must participate in work activities for at least twenty hours per week, with two-parent families required to work at least thirty-five hours per week. A state has the option to exempt single parents with a child under one year of age from these requirements (Schoen, pp. 647–648).

With a focus on reducing the number of welfare recipients, monetary benefits end after a total of sixty months, regardless of whether an individual has found gainful employment (Schoen, 1997, pp. 648–649). TANF agencies may reduce or terminate benefits if a recipient refuses to work (Social Security Act, 42 U.S.C. § 607(e)(1) (2000)). There are exceptions to the work term limit for personal hardship and situations involving family violence (Schoen, pp. 648–649).

TANF places requirements on the state administering agencies. The agency is responsible for developing an individual responsibility plan (IRP) for participants by assessing job skills, prior work experience, and prospects for employability (Schoen, 1997, pp. 648–649). The IRP is intended to help the individual achieve employment and to increase job responsibility over time (Social Security Act, 42 U.S.C. § 608(b)(2)(A)(3) (2000)). States are subject to declines in federal assistance if they do not satisfy minimum participation rates (Accountability Provisions—General, 45 C.F.R. § 262.1(a)(4) (2003)), comply with work term time limits (§ 262.1(a)(9)), or sanction recipients who refuse to work (§ 262.1(a)(14)).

In 2001, TANF services were provided to more than two million families comprising some five million individuals. Over four million of the recipients were children (Office of Family Assistance, 2003). Families typically end TANF services when they locate employment (Office of Family Assistance). Many families that have left the TANF program continue to rely on governmental programs such as Medicaid, Food Stamps, and the Earned Income Tax Credit (Welfare Reform Hearing, 2001).

The TANF program is not directed specifically towards individuals with disabilities. Yet, a substantially higher proportion of TANF recipients reported having physical or mental impairments than did adults in the non-TANF population (National Council on Disability, 2003). Many TANF families include a child with a disability or a member with an undiagnosed disability (LaCheen, 2001; National Council on Disability). Psychiatric disabilities and learning disabilities are prevalent in the TANF population (LaCheen, 2001). Many TANF recipients have undiagnosed disabilities, and their histories of disability do not establish a record of a substantially limiting impairment (LaCheen, 2001). As TANF agencies develop and maintain recipient profiles and track their progress, information about participants' records of disabilities may develop (LaCheen, 2001).

Programs and activities supported by TANF funds are subject to federal antidiscrimination laws such as the ADA, the Age Discrimination in Employment Act, Section 504 of the Rehabilitation Act of 1973, and Title VI of the Civil Rights Act of 1964 (General TANF Provisions, 45 C.F.R. § 260.35 (2003)). An individual with a physical or mental limitation receiving TANF benefits does not qualify automatically as an "individual with a disability" under the ADA (LaCheen, 2001, pp. 89–90).

Subject to restrictions, state TANF programs may establish exceptions to the mandatory work requirements (LaCheen, 2001). State programs have not ordinarily applied the ADA's definition of disability when defining exceptions (Thompson, Holcomb, Loprest & Brennan, 1998). For instance, California's TANF program (CalWORKs) exempts from work requirements individuals with a doctor's verification that the disability likely will last at least thirty days, and that it significantly impairs the ability to be employed or participate in welfare-to-work activities (CalWORKs, Cal. Welf. & Inst. Code § 11320.3(b)(3)(A) (2003)). New York's program exempts individuals who are "disabled or incapacitated" based on a determination by the welfare agency or a private doctor referred by the agency (Public Assistance and Food Stamp Employment Program Requirement, N.Y. Comp. Codes R. & Regs. tit. 12, § 1300.2(b)(4) (2002)). New York also exempts those who are ill or injured, when unable to engage in work for up to three months (§ 1300.2(b)(1)).

There are aspects to the applicability of ADA law to state TANF programs. If a claim of discrimination arises from lack of access to the application process, individuals with disabilities who are covered by the ADA need not qualify for TANF benefits to raise such a challenge (LaCheen, 2001). However, where a job-training program requires participants to have a certain diploma to participate, and the applicant with a disability does not have such a diploma, the ineligibility requirement for program participation may properly preclude an ADA challenge (LaCheen, 2001). Some states may argue that individuals who have not been compliant with TANF work requirements are not qualified individuals for purposes of an ADA challenge (LaCheen, 2001).

One unresolved issue is whether TANF program work requirements will have an unfair impact on persons with disabilities (LaCheen, 2001). No study has assessed whether TANF recipients with disabilities face more significant barriers to employment than nondisabled recipients (National Council on Disability, 2003). To strengthen protections for persons with disabilities in TANF programs, advocacy groups have recommended that states give assurances that participants with disabilities are screened with appropriate diagnostic tools, and that work activities include rehabilitation activities (e.g., as supported by TWWIIA) to help the individual attain work.

States may train their staffs who serve TANF recipients on issues related to disabilities to, for instance, aid in access to Medicaid or other health coverage when recipients move from welfare to work. Compliance may require regular reviews to ensure that TANF programs comply with the ADA and Section 504 requirements (National Council on Disability, 2003). Case managers must be familiar with the requirements of non-discrimination as they work with TANF programs and participants.

CONCLUSION

Before the ADA, there was not a comprehensive federal antidiscrimination protection framework for people with disabilities (Blanck, Hill, Siegel & Waterstone, 2003). Different states had laws covering nondiscrimination in employment, public accommodations, and state services. Many states covered one, but not the rest, of these areas. The passage of the ADA changed the federal landscape, and many states subsequently passed new or amended antidiscrimination laws modeled in part on the ADA.

This chapter has highlighted ways that the Supreme Court has interpreted the ADA and has discussed disability-related legislation. The ebb and flow between and among the federal and state laws is reflective of changing views about the role of the federal and state government in the lives of citizens (Noonan, 2002). With the narrowing by the Supreme Court of federal civil rights laws and the ADA in particular, states' laws take on renewed importance for the protection of people with disabilities from discrimination.

A complete treatment of the different states' laws is beyond the scope of this chapter, but several authors have given a more complete examination to these issues pre- and post-ADA. Blanck et al. (2003) discuss these issues in detail, covering the evolution of state disability laws in response to the ADA and to Supreme Court decisions interpreting the ADA.

Post-ADA, and particularly after various Supreme Court decisions limited the reach of the ADA, states have reacted by enacting or changing state anti-discrimination laws. California expanded on the protections of the ADA post-*Sutton* in the Fair Employment and Housing Act, requiring that mitigating measures not be used as factors in the determination of disability (Blanck et al., 2003). The Act provides greater protection for people with disabilities than the ADA, in many settings, and is indicative of the mandate that people with disabilities should be included in all settings in California. Other states have responded as well, and case managers must be familiar with relevant state legislation on anti-discrimination provisions.

Important issues are emerging about the new disability law and policy framework and its reach and applicability to American social and economic policy. The issues are compelling in light of the changes that have occurred in the areas of employment, welfare, and health care policy. Case managers will increasingly be called on to assess and advise their clients as to the application of these policies.

Authors' Note

The program of research described herein is supported, in part, by grants to Peter Blanck from The University of Iowa College of Law Foundation; the National Institute on Disability and Rehabilitation Research, U.S. Department of Education; the National Institutes on Health, National Institute on Aging; the Nellie Ball Trust Fund; and the Gail and Stan Richards Endowment. For details on grant funding and related studies, see Law, Health Policy & Disability Center (2003), http://disability.law.uiowa.edu.

REFERENCES

Accountability Provisions—General, 45 C.F.R. Part 262 (2003).

Albertsons, Inc. v. Kirkingburg, 527 U.S. 555 (1999).

Americans with Disabilities Act of 1990, 42 U.S.C. §§ 12101–12213 (2000).

Arnold, N., & Ipsen, C. (2003). *State self-employment policies: A decade of change.* Missoula, MT: University of Montana Rural Institute, RTC on Disability in Rural Communities. Retrieved March 24, 2004, from http://rtc.ruralinstitute.umt.edu/SelEm/FinalReport/StateSelfEmploymentP olicies.htm.

Berkowitz, E. D. (1987). *Disabled policy: America's programs for the handicapped.* New York: Cambridge University Press.

Blanck, P. (1997). The economics of the employment provisions of the Americans with Disabilities Act: Part I—workplace accommodations. *DePaul Law Review, 46,* 877–914.

Blanck, P. (Ed.) (2000). *Employment, disability, and the Americans with Disabilities Act: Issues in law, public policy, and research.* Evanston, IL: Northwestern University Press.

Blanck, P. (2001). Civil war pensions and disability. *Ohio State Law Journal, 62,* 109–249.

Blanck, P., Clay, L., Schmeling, J., Morris, M., & Ritchie, H. (2002). Applicability of the ADA to "Ticket to Work" employment networks. *Behavioral Sciences and the Law, 20,* 621, 625–627.

Blanck, P., Hill, E., Siegal, C., & Waterstone, M. (2003). *Disability civil rights law and policy.* St. Paul, MN: Thomson/West.

Blanck, P., & Marti, M. W. (1997). Attitudes, behavior, and the employment provisions of the Americans with Disabilities Act. *Villanova Law Review, 42,* 345–408.

Blanck, P, & Millender, M. (2000). Before disability civil rights: Civil war pensions and the politics of disability in America. *Alabama Law Review, 52*, 1–50.

Blanck, P., & Sandler, L. A. (2000). ADA title III and the internet: Technology and civil rights. *Mental & Physical Disability Law Reporter, 24*, 855–859.

Blanck, P., Sandler, L. A., Schmeling, J. L., & Schartz, H. A. (2000). Emerging workforce of entrepreneurs with disabilities: Preliminary study of entrepreneurship in Iowa. *Iowa Law Review, 85*, 1583–1670.

Blanck, P., & Schartz, H. A. (2001). Toward researching a national employment policy for persons with disabilities. In *22nd Mary E. Switzer Memorial Seminar: Emerging workforce issues: WIA, Ticket to work, and partnerships*. Alexandria, VA: National Rehabilitation Association.

Blanck, P., & Song, C. (2001). "With malice toward none, with charity toward all:" Civil war pensions for native and foreign-born union army veterans, *Transnational Law and Contemporary Problems, 11*, 1–74.

Blanck, P., & Song, C. (2001/2002). Civil war pension attorneys and disability politics. *University of Michigan Journal of Law Reform, 35*, 137–217.

Blanck, P., & Song, C. (2003). "Never forget what they did here": Civil war pensions for Gettysburg union army veterans and disability in nineteenth-century America, *William and Mary Law Review, 44*, 1109–1171.

Bragdon v. Abbott, 524 U.S. 624 (1998).

Brooks, R. A., & Klosinski, L. E. (1999). Assisting persons living with HIV/AIDS to return to work: Programmatic steps for AIDS service organizations. *AIDS Education and Prevention, 11*(3), 212–223.

CalWORKs (California Work Opportunity and Responsibility to Kids Act), Cal. Welf. & Inst. Code §§ 11200–11215 (West 2003).

Chevron U.S.A., Inc. v. Echazabal, 536 U.S. 73 (2002).

Cleveland v. Policy Management Systems Corp., 526 U.S. 795 (1999).

Drimmer, J. C. (1993). Cripples, overcomers, and civil rights: Tracing the evolution of federal legislation and social policy for people with disabilities. *UCLA Law Review, 40*, 1341–1410.

EEOC v. Waffle House, 534 U.S. 279 (2002).

Folkemer, D., Jensen, A., Silverstein, R., & Straw, T. (2002). *Medicaid buy-in programs: Case studies of early implementer states*. Retrieved March 24, 2004, from http://aspe.hhs.gov/daltcp/reports/EIcasest.htm.

Frieden. L. (2003, March 18). Letter to the Honorable John A. Boehner, Chair, Education and the Workforce Committee. Retrieved March 25, 2004, from http://www.ncd.gov/newsroom/correspondence/boehner_03-18-03.html.

General Temporary Assistance for Needy families (TANF) Provisions, 45 C.F.R. Part 260 (2003).

Hahn, H. (2000). Accommodations and the ADA: Unreasonable bias or biased reasoning? *Berkeley Journal of Employment and Labor Law, 21*, 166–192.

David Hoff. The Workforce Investment Act: Opportunities and Issues for the Disability Community (Nat'l Ctr. On Workforce and Disability, Dec. 1, 2000), Retrieved March 29, 2004, from http://www.onestops.info/print.php?article_id=119.

ILRU (2004). ILRU Directory of Independent Living Centers & SILCs, Vol. 26, Houston, TX: Author.

Implementation of the Nondiscrimination and Equal Opportunity Provisions of the Workforce Investment Act of 1998, 29 C.F.R. Part 37 (2003).

Jensen, A., & Silverstein, R. (2000, February). Improvements to the SSDI and SSI work incentives and expanded availability of health care services to workers with disabilities under the Ticket to Work and Work Incentives Improvement Act of 1999. *Policy Brief, 2.* Retrieved March 24, 2004, from http://www.communityinclusion.org/publications/text/pb2text.html.

Jensen, A. (2004). State Medicaid Buy-In Programs Summary Table: Implementation, Authorization, Studies and Enrollments – February 23, 2004 update. Retrieved March 29, 2004, from http://www.uiowa.edu/~lhpdc/work/summary_tables/StateMedBuyIn_summarytable.doc.

Kaye, H. S. (1998). Is the status of people with disabilities improving? *Disability Statistics Abstract, 21*, 1–4.

Kruse, D., & Schur, L. (2003). Employment of people with disabilities following the ADA. *Industrial Relations, 42*, 31–66.

LaCheen, C. (2001). Using title II of the Americans with Disabilities Act on behalf of clients in TANF programs. *Georgetown Journal of Poverty Law and Policy, 8*, 1–215.

Law, Health Policy & Disability Center. (2003). *State resources for disability program navigators to coordinate systems change activities.* Iowa City, IA. Retrieved March 25, 2004, from http://disability.law.uiowa.edu/lhpdc/projects/dol_wigs/index.html.

Liebman, L. (1976). The definition of disability in Social Security and Supplemental Security Income: Drawing the bounds of social welfare estates. *Harvard Law Review, 89*, 833–853.

McNeil, J. M. (2000, July 3). *Employment, Earnings, and Disability.* Paper presented at the 75th Annual Conference of the Western Economic Association International, Vancouver, British Columbia. Retrieved March 25, 2004, from http://www.census.gov/hhes/www/disable/emperndis.pdf.

Milani, A. A. (1999). Living in the world: A new look at the disabled in the law of torts. *Catholic University Law Review, 48*, 323–417.

117

Morris, M., & Farah, L. (2002). *Building relationships at a community level: Lessons learned from work incentive grantees (WIGs)* (Rep. No. 1). Iowa City, IA: University of Iowa College of Law, Law, Health Policy & Disability Center. Retrieved March 25, 2004, from http://disability.law.uiowa.edu/lhpdc/projects/dol_techdocs/PolicyBrief_L essons_Learned.doc.

Murphy v. United Parcel Service, 527 U.S. 516 (1999).

National Center on Workforce and Disability. (2000). *The Workforce Investment Act: Opportunities and issues for the disability community.* Boston: Hoff, D. Retrieved March 24, 2004, from http://www.onestops.info/print.php?article_id=119.

National Collaborative on Workforce and Disability / Youth. (2004). Retrieved on March 29, 2004 from http://www.ncwd-youth.info/.

National Council on Disability. (2003). *TANF and disability—importance of supports for families with disabilities in welfare reform.* Washington, DC. Retrieved March 25, 2004, from http://www.ncd.gov/newsroom/ publications/pdf/familysupports.pdf.

National Council on Disability (1996). Achieving independence: The challenge for the 21st century: A decade of progress in disability policy: Setting an agenda for the future. Washington, D.C.

National Organization on Disability (2000). *The 2000 N.O.D. / Harris survey of Americans with disabilities.* Washington, D.C.

Nondiscrimination on the Basis of Disability by Public Accommodations and in Commercial Facilities, 56 Fed. Reg. 35544, 35552 (July 26, 1991).

Nondiscrimination on the Basis of Disability by Public Accommodations and in Commercial Facilities, 28 C.F.R. Part 36 (2003).

Nondiscrimination on the Basis of Disability in State and Local Government Services, 28 C.F.R. Part 35 (2003).

Noonan, J. T., Jr. (2002). *Narrowing the nation's power: The Supreme Court sides with the states.* Berkeley, CA: University of California Press.

Office of Family Assistance, U.S. Dep't of Health and Hum. Servs., Temporary Assistance for Needy Families Program: Fifth Annual Report to Congress X184-230. Retrieved February 3, 2003 from http://www.acf.dhhs.gov/programs/ofa/annualreport5/.

Olmstead v. L.C. *ex rel.* Zimring, 527 U.S. 581 (1999).

Pacer Center (2003). Work Incentives for Persons with Disabilities, Retrieved July 31, 2003, from http://www.pacer.org/text/employ/workinc.htm.

Parmet, W. E. (1993). Title III–Public accommodations. In L. Gostin & H. Beyer (Eds.) *Implementing the Americans with Disabilities Act; Rights and responsibilities of all Americans.* 123. Baltimore, MD: P. H. Brookes Publishing.

PGA Tour, Inc. v. Martin, 532 U.S. 661 (2001).

Public Assistance and Food Stamp Employment Program Requirements, N.Y. Comp. Codes R. & Regs. tit. 12, Part 1300 (2002).

Regulations to Implement the Equal Employment Provisions of the Americans with Disabilities Act, 29 C.F.R. Part 1630 (2003).

Rehabilitation Act of 1973, 29 U.S.C. §§ 701–796*l* (2000).

Schartz, K., Schartz, H., & Blanck, P. (2002). Employment of persons with disabilities in information technology jobs: A literature review for 'IT Works.' *Behavioral Sciences & the Law, 20*, 637–657.

Schoen, L. M. (1997). Working welfare recipients: A comparison of the Family Support Act and the Personal Responsibility and Work Opportunity Reconciliation Act. *Fordham Urban Law Journal, 24*, 635–662.

Schwochau, S., & Blanck, P. D. (2000). The economics of the Americans with Disabilities Act: Part III – Does the ADA disable the disabled? *Berkeley Journal of Employment and Labor Law, 21*(1), 271–313.

Scotch, R. K., & Schriner, K. (1997). Disability as human variation: Implications for policy. *Annals of the American Academy of Political and Social Science, 549*, 148–159.

Seelman, K. D. (2000, July 17). *Employment of individuals with disabilities—opportunities and challenges—The best of times/the worst of times.* Paper presented at the Employment and Disability Policy Summer Institute, Cornell University, Ithaca, NY.

Shapiro, J. P. (1993). *No pity: People with disabilities forging a new civil rights movement.* New York: Times Books.

Silverstein, R. (2000, March). Provisions in the Workforce Investment Act relating to nondiscrimination on the basis of disability and the development by the governor of a written methods of administration. *Policy Brief,* 2. Retrieved March 25, 2004, from http://www.communityinclusion.org/publications/text/pb4text.html.

Silverstein, R. (2004). What policymakers need and must demand from research regarding the employment rate of persons with disabilities. Manuscript in preparation.

Social Security Act, 42 U.S.C. §§ 301–1397jj (2000).

Social Security Administration. (2004, March 3). *Ticket to work: Ticket tracker.* Washington, DC. Retrieved March 25, 2004, from http://www.ssa.gov/work/Ticket/ticket_info.html#TicketTracker.

Stapleton, D. C., & Tucker, A. F. (2000). Will expanded health care coverage for people with disabilities increase their employment and earnings? Evidence from an analysis of the SSI work incentive program. In D.S. Salkever & A. Sorkin, *Research in Human Capital and Development: Vol. 13, The Economics of Disability.* Stamford, Conn.: JAI Press.

Stone, D. A. (1984). *The disabled state.* Philadelphia: Temple University Press.

Sutton v. United Air Lines, Inc., 527 U.S. 417 (1999).

Taylor, H. (1998, October 14). *The Harris poll #56: Americans with disabilities still pervasively disadvantaged on a broad range of key indicators.* Rochester,   NY.   Retrieved   March   25,   2004,   from http://www.harrisinteractive.com/harris_poll/printerfriend/index.asp?PID= 152.

Technology for Independence: Community-Based Resource Center (TI-CBRC). (2003). The technology for independence projects. Iowa City: IA. Retrieved   March   25,   2004,   from http://disability.law.uiowa.edu/cbrc/research/ti_projects.htm.

Thompson T.S., Holcomb, P.A., Loprest, P., & Brennan, K. (1998). The Urb. Inst. and the U.S Dep't of Health & Hum. Servs., State Welfare-to-Work Policies for People with Disabilities: Changes Since Welfare Reform; Executive   Summary).   Retrieved   March   29,   2004   from http://aspe.hhs.gov/daltcp/reports/wel2wkes.htm.

Ticket to Work and Self-Sufficiency Program, 66 Fed. Reg. 67,370, 67,370 (Dec. 28, 2001).

Ticket to Work and Self-Sufficiency Program, 20 C.F.R Part 411 (2003).

Ticket to work and work incentives advisory panel: Hearings before committee, 107th Cong. 35–37 (2002) (testimony of Peter Blanck).

Ticket to work and work incentives advisory panel: Hearings before committee, 107th Cong. 20-21 (2002) (testimony of Ray Cebula).

Ticket to work and work incentives advisory panel: Hearings before committee, 107th Cong. 26 (2002) (testimony of Andrew Imparato).

Social Security Administration. (2002). *Ticket to Work and Work Incentives Advisory Panel, Annual Report to the President and Congress: Year Two* (SSA Pub. No. 63-011). Washington, DC.

Ticket to Work and Work Incentives Improvement Act of 1999, 42 U.S.C. §§ 1320b-19–1320b-22, 42 U.S.C. § 434, 26 U.S.C. § 1260 (2000).

Toyota Motor Manufacturing v. Williams, 534 U.S. 184 (2002).

U.S. Airways, Inc. v. Barnett, 535 U.S. 391 (2002).

U.S. Census Bureau. (2003). *Disability labor force status—work disability status of civilians 16 to 74 years Old, by educational attainment and sex: 2003.* Washington, DC. Retrieved March 25, 2004, from http://www.census.gov/hhes/www/disable/cps/cps203.html.

Virginia Commonwealth University Rehabilitation Research and Training Center (RRTC). (2000). Ticket to work and self-sufficiency program. *Connections, Spring/Summer*, 3.

Welfare reform: Hearing before the Subcommittee on Human Resources, Committee of Ways and Means, 107th Cong. (2001) (testimony of Christine Devere). Retrieved March 26, 2004, from http://waysandmeans. house.gov/legacy/humres/107cong/3-15-01/107-5final.htm.

White House. (n.d.). Fulfilling America's promise to Americans with disabilities. Washington, DC. Retrieved March 25, 2004, from http://www.whitehouse.gov/news/freedominitiative/freedominitiative.htm.

Workforce Investment Act of 1998, Pub. L. 105-220, 112 Stat. 936 (codified in scattered sections of 20 and 29 U.S.C. (2000)).

Workforce Investment Act; Final Rules, 65 Fed. Reg.49295 (Aug. 11, 2000) (to be codified at 20 C.F.R. pts. 652 et al.).

5

Interpersonal Communication Skills for Case Managers

Lynn C. Koch
Phillip D. Rumrill

Chapter Highlights

- The working alliance

- The intake interview

- Expectations about the working alliance

- Putting the working alliance into action

- A negotiation/conflict resolution model

- Summary

Case managers working in managed disability and health care arenas represent an array of professional backgrounds (e.g., nursing, social work, rehabilitation counseling, mental health counseling, physical therapy, occupational therapy, speech therapy). Regardless of professional background, case managers must be able to facilitate effective working relationships among clients, family members, and other professionals if quality services are to be provided and successful outcomes are to occur. This can prove to be an extremely challenging task, particularly when one considers the diversity of interests and values that are represented by stakeholders in the case management process.

The purpose of this chapter is, therefore, to provide a framework for facilitating cooperative interactions. Recognizing that because of their diverse professional backgrounds, case managers have varying levels of interviewing/counseling skills training, an emphasis is placed on interpersonal communication strategies for building collaborative relationships. Many examples presented in this chapter are derived from a rehabilitation counseling/case management perspective. The concepts, however, are directly applicable to case management in health care settings as well.

THE WORKING ALLIANCE: A FRAMEWORK FOR BUILDING COLLABORATIVE RELATIONSHIPS

"True rehabilitation seeks to build inner strength and self-respect in the client; such values are fostered by a relationship in which the [person with a disability] feels that he or she has an important role in planning his or her life, and that what he or she says and feels are respected" (Rubenfeld, 1988, p. 41). The effective coordination of client-centered case management services requires the active participation of *all* members of the rehabilitation/treatment team (i.e., case managers, clients, family members, vendors, payers, health care providers, other service providers, employers). This collaborative effort in which all stakeholders contribute equally to the rehabilitation process is similar to what Bordin (1979) referred to as the "working alliance."

The concept of the working alliance is rooted in the psychoanalytic tradition. In the field of psychoanalysis, Zetzel (1956) introduced the term "therapeutic alliance" to describe the patient's attachment to the psychoanalyst. This alliance was viewed by Zetzel as a form of transference or, more specifically, as a repetition of the positive aspects of the mother-child relationship. Greenson (1967) originated the term "working alliance" and defined it as "the relatively nonneurotic, rational relationship between the patient and analyst which makes it possible for the patient to work purposefully in the analytic situation" (p. 46). Greenson also viewed the psychoanalytic relationship as a form of transference.

Bordin (1979) "reconceptualized the notion of the working alliance to encompass all change-inducing relationships" (Horvath & Greenburg, 1989, p. 224). According to Bordin, the working alliance is facilitated when a collaborative effort is present that provides opportunities for all members of the alliance to make equal contributions to the relationship. The three necessary components of the working alliance are bonds, goals, and tasks (Bordin, 1979).

Bonds can be described as the compatibility that develops as a result of collaboration in a shared activity. Bonds incorporate mutual trust, respect, and acceptance as manifested by "a sense of common commitment and shared understanding in the activity" (Bordin, 1994, p. 14). The change goal is a mutually agreed upon target of intervention. In rehabilitation settings, the change goal refers to objectives such as return to employment, increased independence, or improvement in functioning. Tasks include "specific activities that the partnership will engage in to instigate or facilitate change" (Bordin, 1994, p. 14). For the working alliance to be effective, all its members must perceive the tasks as relevant and share responsibility for the completion of tasks (Horvath & Greenberg, 1989). Mutual agreement between all partners regarding bonds, goals, and tasks is required in order for the alliance to be productive and for positive outcomes to result. In addition to mutual agreement regarding the components of the working alliance, the *equality* of all partners must be recognized and a *shared responsibility* for planning and outcomes must be maintained (McAlees & Menz, 1992).

Although rehabilitation researchers are only beginning to consider the impact of the working alliance on the rehabilitation process, Chan, Shaw, McMahon, Koch, and Strauser (1997) noted that this construct should be granted greater attention because of its potential relevance to establishing active participation between rehabilitation clients and service providers. In one recent study, Lustig, Strauser, Rice, and Rucker (2002) examined the relationship between the working alliance and rehabilitation outcomes and found that, within a sample of 2,732 vocational rehabilitation clients, positive ratings of the working alliance were related to successful rehabilitation outcomes (employment), job satisfaction, and positive perspectives regarding future employment opportunities. Because the depiction of the counseling relationship as a collaborative enterprise is consistent with rehabilitation philosophy and legislation, additional research on the working alliance in rehabilitation is clearly warranted.

The next section provides a discussion of how the intake interview can be used as a tool for structuring the working alliance. The third section addresses the need to clarify the expectations of all members of the rehabilitation/treatment team as an initial step in developing effective alliances. In the fourth section, strategies for establishing bonds, setting goals, and accomplishing tasks are suggested. This chapter concludes with a negotiation/conflict resolution model that can be used to resolve any differences that may occur among members of the working alliance.

THE INTAKE INTERVIEW: AN ALLIANCE BUILDING TOOL

The intake interview is conducted in *every* rehabilitation setting. In fact, it has been described as the most widely used assessment tool in rehabilitation and related health care settings (Berven, 2001). Interviewing is a method of gathering data about an individual to describe the individual and make predictions. Interviews require the skillful use of verbal and nonverbal responses to elicit relevant information from clients that is used for the purposes of clinical decision-making and rehabilitation planning. Some of the information gathered through interviewing (e.g., client expectations, behavioral observations, and client reactions to current situation) may be unobtainable through other means and can serve as a check for the validity of other assessment measures (Groth-Marnat, 1997).

The interview most often occurs during the initial contact(s) between the case manager and the client. The manner in which the interview is conducted, therefore, has major implications for establishing effective working alliances and laying the groundwork for positive client outcomes.

The function of the intake interview varies by setting. According to Groth-Marnat (1997), the general objectives of the intake or assessment interview are to (a) gather client data that cannot easily be obtained through other means of assessment; (b) create a trusting relationship that is conducive to obtaining sensitive information; (c) develop a greater understanding in both the interviewer and interviewee regarding client concerns; and (d) provide direction and support in helping the interviewee deal with his or her concerns. Power (2000) summarized the following purposes of the intake interview in rehabilitation settings:

1. to establish rapport between the counselor or case manager and the client;
2. to provide the client with information about the role and function of the agency or program, available services, counselor or case manager responsibilities, and client responsibilities;
3. to facilitate the self-understanding of client strengths, weaknesses, personality traits, and aptitudes;
4. to ease potential anxiety about the rehabilitation process; and

5. to provide the client, case manager, and other rehabilitation/treatment team members with preliminary planning information.

Interview approaches range from highly unstructured to highly structured (Berven, 2001; Groth-Marnat, 1997). Unstructured interviews do not follow any specific format or guidelines. The interviewer determines what questions to ask, and interviewees have freedom to drift from one topic to the next. Structured interviews, on the other hand, are highly directive and usually follow a format that determines the specific questions to be asked and the order in which they are to be presented. The unstructured interview has the advantages of being highly flexible and conducive to establishing rapport. Unstructured interviews have been criticized due to their relative subjectivity. Structured interviews have, however, sounder psychometric qualities (e.g., reliability and validity) but may be viewed as highly impersonal (Berven, 2001; Groth-Marnat, 1997). Most intake interviews conducted in clinical and rehabilitation settings tend to be semi structured. Intake forms and initial interview guides provide some degree of structure and they are commonly used in a variety of different rehabilitation settings to collect basic client information (e.g., name, address, phone number, birth date, referral source, diagnosis). These tools have the added benefit of freeing the counselor or case manager to investigate other aspects of the client's situation in a more flexible manner (Groth-Marnat, 1997). Checklists can also be used to guide the case manager in identifying client issues of concern that should be addressed in the interview.

In addition to its function as a data-gathering tool, the initial interview provides an opportunity for the client to receive an orientation to services. However, the amount of information that is relayed to clients during the interview can be overwhelming. For this reason, many agencies provide clients with handbooks that can be taken home with them after the interview is completed. These handbooks describe what clients can expect to happen, educate them about their rights and responsibilities, and address frequently asked questions.

Interviews are typically centered on specific themes (e.g., independent living, vocational planning, life care planning, and medical issues) relevant to the professional role of interviewers and the functions of the program or agency that they represent. Regardless of the degree of structure, effective interviewing occurs when specific issues pertinent to rehabilitation planning are adequately addressed. The general categories of client information that are addressed by case managers include:

1. **Identifying Information** (name, address, phone number, age, gender, ethnicity, reason for referral, prior receipt of services, employment status, sources of financial support);

2. **Nature of the Problem** (diagnosis, cause and onset of disability, barriers to employment and/or independent living, functional assets and limitations, disability-related treatment, results of recent evaluations, medications and side effects, general health status);
3. **Personal and Family History** (marital status, number of dependents, sources of emotional support, living arrangements, means of transportation, primary source of income, other sources of financial support, medical insurance);
4. **Educational/Vocational History** (level of education completed, certificates or degrees earned, academic performance, job seeking skills, most recently held positions, length of employment in each position, transferable skills, reasons for termination of employment, reasons for significant interruptions in work history, accommodations made at places of employment);
5. **Client Expectations** (desired services, preferred service providers, anticipated client/case manager roles and responsibilities, preferred outcomes, independent living and/or career goals, level of family involvement expected in planning);
6. **Observations** (comfort level, client strengths, decision-making abilities, affect, communication skills, punctuality, appropriateness of client expectations and understanding of agency or program, other behavioral observations); and
7. **Action Steps** (tasks to be completed by each member of the treatment team, additional documentation needed to determine eligibility, evaluations to be scheduled, referrals to other agencies or programs, next appointment).

According to Groth-Marnat (1997), the success of an interview is determined by the attitude expressed by interviewers rather than the techniques they use. Consistent with this observation, three facilitative conditions have been identified as crucial to the establishment of effective working alliances (Bordin, 1979). These conditions—*empathy, warmth,* and *genuineness* are derived from person-centered therapy and have been described as "necessary and sufficient" factors for therapeutic gain (Rogers, 1957; Raskin & Rogers, 1989). It is unlikely that the goals of the interview will be achieved in the absence of these conditions. Furthermore, the principles underlying the three conditions are applicable to other relationships. The case manager's interactions with all members of the rehabilitation/treatment team can be optimized by communicating in a manner that reflects empathy, warmth, and genuineness. These conditions will be operationalized in subsequent sections of this chapter.

EXPECTATIONS ABOUT THE WORKING ALLIANCE

The quality of the working alliance is influenced by four factors: (a) client needs and characteristics; (b) counselor/case manager characteristics; (c) counselor/case manager technical skills and activities; and (d) degree of fit between counselor/case manager resources and client needs and characteristics (Al-Darmarki & Kivligham, 1993). The construct of expectations operates as both a client *and* a counselor/case manager factor with major implications for the quality of the working alliance. The influence of client and counselor expectations on the quality of the working alliance has been extensively addressed in counseling research and practice. Expectations have also been examined in terms of their impact on the counseling process and therapeutic outcomes (Al-Damarki & Kivlighan, 1993; Galassi et al., 1992; Tinsley, Tokar, & Helwig, 1994; Tracey & Dundon, 1988). In the field of rehabilitation, this construct has been accorded less attention. The effect of expectations on the rehabilitation case management relationship must be addressed if effective working alliances are to be established and if positive client outcomes are to result. As McCarthy and Leirer (2001) noted, a mutual understanding and negotiating of client expectations and counselor/case manager capacities for fulfilling them is a prerequisite for effective co-management. Furthermore, the construct of expectations must be expanded to incorporate the perspectives of *all* members of the rehabilitation/treatment team (Koch, Williams, & Rumrill, 1998).

Expectations can be categorized as those that occur initially and those that occur during the relationship-building and treatment processes (Bergin & Garfield, 1994). Distinguishing between these two dimensions is necessary because expectations are likely to change over the course of treatment. Goldstein (1981) differentiated between prognostic expectations and role expectations. Whereas prognostic expectations refer to an assessment of the likelihood of treatment success, role expectations refer to the behaviors of each participant in the working alliance.

Goldstein (1981) also identified three distinct role expectations with regard to the counselor's function: nurturant, model, and critic (Goldstein, 1981). The nurturant counselor is expected to function in a non-directive, non-critical, caring manner and to provide substantial   guidance to the client. The model counselor is one who is expected to serve as a well-adjusted diplomat that sets an example for the client. The critical counselor is expected to behave in an analytical manner and to encourage clients to assume considerable responsibility for the counseling process.

In a factor analysis of client expectations regarding the counselor's role, Berzins (1971) identified four dimensions: (a) approval-seeking (expectations for counselor support and emotional guidance); (b) advice-seeking (expectations for cognitive guidance and evaluation from the counselor); (c) audience-seeking (expectations for assuming personal initiative while the counselor acts as a "sounding board"); and (d) relationship-seeking (expectations for spontaneous self-disclosure in the context of a collaborative relationship).

McCarthy and Leirer (2001) examined the expectations of rehabilitation clients regarding ideal counselor characteristics. "Commitment to advocacy for the client" was the most desired counselor characteristic among the participants in their study. "Nurturing traits" was the second most commonly desired counselor characteristic. "Factual knowledge with which to assist client's rehabilitation" was the third most commonly desired characteristic, but it was mentioned much less often than the other two.

In addition to prognostic and role expectations, expectations about the concrete aspects of counseling have been identified (Gladstein, 1969; Koch, 2001). Examples of concrete aspects relevant to rehabilitation case management include scheduling of appointments, case manager's availability, office location, types of services, and timely delivery of services.

Expectations have also been conceptualized as consisting of two separate and distinct components—preferences and anticipations. Whereas preferences reflect what one wants or hopes will occur, anticipations reflect what one thinks, with a degree of certainty, will occur (Duckro, Beal, & George, 1977). A person's preferences may be very different from his or her anticipations. For example, a client may express a strong preference for certain case manager behaviors but have weaker anticipations that the desired behavior will actually occur. In fact, in a qualitative investigation of the preferences and anticipations of individuals referred to a vocational rehabilitation agency, Koch (2001) discovered that, not only did applicants report differences in their preferences and anticipations, but, in many cases, they had no idea what to anticipate. This uncertainty was expressed despite the fact that most of the research participants reported fairly clear ideas about what they preferred. Discrepancies between preferences and anticipations obviously must be resolved if positive outcomes are to result.

Each rehabilitation/treatment team member is also likely to enter the working alliance with his or her own unique set of expectations (preferences and anticipations). Al-Darmaki and Kivlighan (1993) reported that congruence in client-counselor expectations of the counseling relationship is positively related to ratings of the working alliance. Studies (e.g., Tinsley et al., 1988) have also indicated that client decisions to discontinue therapy after the first few sessions may result largely from a discrepancy between the client's expectations for counseling and what actually occurs in therapy. The early identification of *each* rehabilitation/treatment team member's expectations is crucial so that any discrepancies can be resolved and a mutually agreed upon set of expectations can be established.

Throughout the rehabilitation/treatment process, the case manager can ensure a productive working alliance that will result in positive client gain by:

1. Addressing expectations as a routine component of the intake process;
2. Clarifying expectations about the case management process, services to be provided, the roles and responsibilities of each partner, and goals or outcomes;
3. Identifying discrepancies between preferences and anticipations and initiating an approach for increasing consistency between preferences and anticipations;
4. Determining if there are differential expectations among members of the working alliance and establishing a process for moving toward a *mutual* set of expectations; and
5. Reassessing expectations at various stages of rehabilitation planning (Koch et al., 1998).

PUTTING THE WORKING ALLIANCE INTO ACTION: STRATEGIES FOR FORMING BONDS, SETTING GOALS, AND ACCOMPLISHING TASKS

The working alliance is an interdisciplinary mechanism for achieving the ultimate objective of case management—to provide responsive and cost-effective client services. With that outcome in mind, case managers must also attend to "process" factors that influence how effectively rehabilitation/treatment teams work together. Specifically, case management skills related to the operation of working alliances involve (a) establishing bonds among alliance members (b) setting appropriate goals, and (c) negotiating the tasks that each member will perform to attain those goals.

BONDS

Although case managers and counselors represent distinct professional orientations, they share a priority on relationship-building skills (Roessler & Rubin, 1998). A counselor's effectiveness is determined, in large measure, by his or her ability to "connect with" clients, and the successful case manager is one who can establish bonds—not only between him or her and individual members of the working alliance but also among other members of the team (Rumrill & Scheff, 1996). Lustig, Strauser, Rice, and Rucker (2002) underscored the importance of establishing bonds early in the rehabilitation process due to the brief, intermittent nature of rehabilitation and the limited

130

amount of time that counselors and case managers have to devote to each individual client because of the large caseloads they often manage. Borrowing from the counseling literature with these shared priorities in mind, the core conditions of therapeutic rapport—empathy, warmth, and genuineness (Truax & Carkhuff, 1967)—can be applied to the bonding process that case managers facilitate as the first step in the working alliance.

Empathy, the act of "coming to know a person from his (or her) internal frame of reference, gaining some flavor of his (or her) moment-by-moment experience" (Truax & Carkhuff, 1967, p. 42), is a construct that is well known to anyone who has taken a beginning course in counseling or psychotherapy. As a core element of effective case management, however, its importance is often underestimated. To build effective working alliances that meet clients' stated needs, case managers must show empathy for both the client and professional team members.

Professional empathy (Rumrill, 1996), is especially important in the modern era of managed care, increased professional specialization, and cross referrals. Never before has it been more important for nurses to understand occupational therapy, for social workers to understand vocational evaluation, and for physicians to understand psychotherapy. To empathize with the political, practical, and ethical realities of each professional team member's field, the case manager must:

1. Concentrate with intensity on the person's expressions (both verbal and non-verbal).
2. Concentrate upon responses that are interchangeable with those of the person.
3. Formulate responses in language that is most attuned to the person.
4. Respond in a feeling tone similar to that communicated by the person.
5. Move toward clarifying and expanding the person's experiences.
6. Employ the person's behavior as the best guideline to assessing the effectiveness of the case manager's responses (Carkhuff, 1969; Rumrill & Scheff, 1996).

Warmth. The case manager who demonstrates warmth to clients and professional team members alike will facilitate a working alliance marked by reciprocal positive regard and acceptance. The key ingredient in warmth is the communication of respect (Pietrofesa, Hoffman, Splete, & Pinto, 1978)—respect for the client, respect for the expertise of each member of the working alliance, and respect for an interdisciplinary process whose whole, truly, exceeds the sum of its parts. Methods of engendering respect for all members of the working alliance include (a) praising individual team members for their efforts and accomplishments, (b) expressing appreciation to the entire team at the beginning and/or end of meetings, and (c) paying deference to the expertise and perspective of each team member (including the client).

Genuineness. Being real, honest, and authentic is a quality that enables the case manager to quickly establish the bonds that are needed for effective working alliances. In the words of Gazda (1973, p. 58), "the genuine counselor employs no facades. Defenses are reduced, and he or she is open to, and integrated into, the human experience." The same is true for case managers; members of the working alliance who respect one another as people first will be much more likely to accord appropriate respect for each other's professional or consumer status. Techniques for demonstrating genuineness include appropriate humor, self-disclosure, and taking responsibility for mistakes. Another important element of genuineness for case managers is communicating at a language level that is understandable to all members of the working alliance. Professional jargon and acronyms should be kept to a minimum, and members' reactions to the case manager's statements should be regarded as a vehicle for corrective change (Roessler & Rubin, 1998). In other words, the genuineness of one's presentation is best reflected in the expressions of others.

Basic interviewing/counseling skills. In order to promote the establishment of bonds, the case manager must relate to all members of the working alliance in a manner that communicates empathy, warmth, and genuineness. Basic attending skills that convey these core conditions are summarized as follows:

1. Posture the body in an open, non-defensive manner that communicates interest in what the other person is saying. Lean slightly forward with relaxed arms and both feet on the floor. Avoid crossing the arms and legs because such a posture may communicate unavailability to the other person.
2. Maintain appropriate eye contact. In North American culture, this consists of a fairly steady gaze without staring. Other cultures, however, have different norms regarding what is considered appropriate eye contact, and a steady gaze may be considered disrespectful. It is important, therefore, for the case manager to acknowledge and respect individual differences and cultural norms regarding eye contact.
3. Pay attention to both the verbal and nonverbal communications of the other person. Observe whether verbal and nonverbal cues are consistent. Sometimes facial expressions, bodily movements, and voice quality can communicate more than mere words. For example, people may verbally state that they are relaxed, but nonverbal cues such as fidgeting, a knitted brow, and hesitancy in speech may suggest otherwise.

132

4. Restate, in one's own words, what the other person says. This gives the case manager an opportunity to verify that what the other person intended to communicate is what was heard. It also gives the other person a chance to correct misinterpretations. Phrases such as "What I hear you saying is...In other words...It sounds to me like...Let me see if I understand correctly...." are effective lead-ins for paraphrasing.

5. In addition to paraphrasing, ask questions to obtain more specific information about what is being said (e.g., "What was that experience like? How did you feel when that happened?"). Asking questions, or clarifying, helps to sharpen listening skills by getting beyond vague generalities. It also communicates a willingness to work at knowing and understanding the other person from his or her frame of reference. Clarifying also involves gently informing the other person when inconsistencies between verbal and nonverbal behaviors are noted (e.g., "You say everything is okay, but I see tears in your eyes.").

6. Supportive silence is another technique for communicating empathy, warmth, and genuineness. Silence provides the opportunity for the other person to organize his or her thoughts when attempting to communicate painful feelings or difficult ideas. It may seem unnatural to remain silent at these times, and the case manager may feel the need to say something to alleviate the other person's discomfort. However, when someone is experiencing emotional turmoil, the best support is sometimes to simply be with that person, without talking.

7. At the end of each interaction with members of the working alliance, summarize what transpired and what the next steps to be taken will be. This, again, provides opportunities to clarify miscommunications and ensures that everyone leaves the interaction with the same understanding of what occurred (Egan, 2000; Ivey & Ivey, 2003; McKay, Davis, & Fanning, 1995).

GOALS

Once the case manager has set a tone of empathy, warmth, and genuineness among members of the working alliance, the next step involves establishment of short-term, intermediate, and long-term goals. Lustig et al. (2002) suggested that goals be established early in the process since members of the working alliance may only meet intermittently. Each team member brings needs and priorities to the goal-setting process, but the working alliance exists primarily to serve the client. Hence, the needs of other team members (e.g., vendors' needs to make a profit, sponsors' needs to control costs, and rehabilitation counselors' needs to close cases) must be viewed as factors that help to clarify and, in some cases, modify the client's goals—not as outcomes in and of themselves.

Short-term client goals are best reflected in a clear description of the purpose of each meeting of, or correspondence with, members of the working alliance. The case manager should develop a specific agenda for each meeting and make every effort to adhere to the list of topics and time frames. To carry the sense of purpose forward in every interaction, case managers must ensure that all team members know why they are there and what their role will be. This is especially important when new or replacement members are added to the rehabilitation/treatment team.

In setting intermediate and long-term goals, case managers are reminded that clients are their own "best expert" and most eloquent advocate (Roessler & Rumrill, 1995; Rumrill, 1996). Clients play a super ordinate role in asserting what outcomes they expect from the working alliance. The foremost role of the case manager is to find ways to actualize those expectations. If and when the client's expectations exceed the alliance's ability to help, the case manager must (a) help the client to formulate goals that are more realistic or (b) add members to the team whose services and resources are compatible with the client's expectations.

Specifically, facilitating the goal-setting process can be viewed from a problem-solving perspective (D'Zurilla, 1999). In this context, the problem is considered an opportunity for change or a need for services. The goal is the desired outcome of the working alliance, as stated in the client's terms. The tasks that each team member will perform to assist the client in attaining the goal constitute solutions. Preliminary goal-setting steps can be outlined as follows:

1. Understand the client's perception of the need for services. To what extent are they aware of the need? Do their perceptions coincide with the assessments of referral sources and other team members?

2. Consider the clients' need attributions. Why were they referred for services? What circumstances led the clients to seek help from the working alliance?

3. Assess the clients' appraisal of the opportunities that are available to them. What are the clients' levels of understanding of the resources that exist to help them? Are they receiving services voluntarily or conditionally? How important is it for the clients to make positive changes with the help of the working alliance?

4. Gauge the clients' levels of personal control. What steps did they take to enroll in services? What are the clients' historical patterns of adjustment/coping? How motivated are they to participate in the working alliance?

5. Commit time and effort to meeting the clients' needs. How much time, effort, and expense will be involved in meeting the clients' needs? How

much time, effort, and expense are the clients able and/or willing to commit? How much time, effort, and expense is each team member able and/or willing to commit?

6. Gather relevant factual information. What resources exist within the working alliance to meet the clients' needs? What outside resources are needed? What constraints exist within the service delivery structure? How have people in similar situations as the clients fared within that structure?

7. Set a realistic goal. Specifically, what do clients see as the most desirable outcomes of the working alliance? How does each team member assess the appropriateness of those goals? Do the goals need to be modified to fit the parameters of the working alliance, or do the working alliance's parameters need to be expanded? How will the clients know when their goals have been attained? What are the clients' timelines for attainment? Are the goal attainment criteria and time lines compatible with the working alliance's ability to help? Do they need to be modified?

TASKS

As noted above, once the clients have assessed their needs for services, considered their expectations of the working alliance, and formulated specific goals, the case manager shifts to the *solution* phase of the rehabilitation/treatment process. Specifically, the focus is placed on what each member will do, when it will be done, and how it will be monitored for progress toward the clients' goals. Adopted from D'Zurilla's (1999) problem-solving model, task formation/goal-attainment activities can be operationalized as follows:

1. Re-appraise the goal's appropriateness. How will it be modified (if necessary) during the attainment process?

2. Generate solution-oriented tasks. What will each member do to assist the client in attaining the goal? Which tasks are interdependent, and with whom? How will task completion be monitored and reported? If additional service needs become evident, how will the line of referrals proceed? How will the client be involved with and apprised of other members' tasks?

3. Develop a contingency plan. What alternatives are available in the event that a task is not completed? If new members are added to the working alliance, how will their roles complement those of existing members? How will resigning team members select designees to represent their agencies? What if the client's motivation or ability to participate changes?

135

4. Anticipate positive outcomes. When will the client's goal be met? What needs exist for follow-along services? Do these needs coincide with the alliance's ability to help? Are other referrals necessary?

5. Reinforce task performance. Have team members been praised for completing the tasks to which they committed? How can the case manager highlight the client's role and involvement in the goal-attainment process? What is the best way to extend appreciation for team members' collaborative efforts?

6. Troubleshoot and recycle if necessary. What obstacles have impeded task performance? Who can assist in making needed adjustments? If the obstacle in question cannot be reduced or removed, how can the client circumvent the obstacle (or minimize its impact)? Considering pitfalls, what is the client's overall progress toward goal attainment?

7. Recognize goal attainment. Have the client's attainment criteria been met? Have additional goals become evident? Has a follow-up plan been established? Who will do what? When and how? How will the client's case be closed by each professional team member? What steps can the client take if the need for services recurs? What have all members of the working alliance learned that will help them with subsequent clients? What has the client learned that will help when future problems (opportunities for change) arise?

The preceding paragraphs describe (in behavioral terms) specific strategies that case managers can use to (a) establish bonds among members of the working alliance, (b) assist the client in setting informed and realistic goals, and (c) develop task-oriented plans through which the client's goals can be realized. As readers consider and implement these approaches, they are reminded that *the working alliance exists primarily to serve clients' needs,* and that *clients know best what is best for them.*

A NEGOTIATION/CONFLICT RESOLUTION MODEL
FOR MEMBERS OF THE WORKING ALLIANCE

As case managers progress through the stages of the working alliance, it is important to keep in mind that conflict is a natural and inevitable part of any group dynamic. Case managers' ultimate effectiveness will not be determined by their ability to avoid or suppress conflict, but, rather, by their ability to negotiate fair agreements and resolve conflicts in a proactive and forthright manner. Conflict occurs when an individual's actions or goals are perceived as incompatible with the actions or goals of another person (Fisher, Ury, & Patton, 1991; Fisher & Brown, 1988). In many conflict situations, it is not the actual goals and actions of the involved parties that are incompatible, but, rather, the greater problem arises from *misperceptions* of incompatibility. In the working alliance, conflicts may arise when members perceive discrepancies in expectations regarding each other's roles and responsibilities, the manner in which services are delivered, and/or the type and amount of services provided. Conflicts may surround issues of client eligibility, timeliness of services, case manager error, program policies, and/or case closure (Holmes, Hall, & Karst, 1989).

Directly addressing conflicts at the working alliance level is recommended because it demonstrates to clients that they are valued as members of the rehabilitation/treatment team, are to be treated fairly, and are to receive high quality services (Holmes et al., 1989). Communication is enhanced by clarifying the nature of differences before they escalate into formal disagreements. Furthermore, dealing with differences in the early stages of case management will strengthen the working alliance and result in higher client satisfaction and improved outcomes.

The same approaches to resolving conflicts at industrial and international levels can be applied at the working alliance level. In the following paragraphs, the steps involved in conflict resolution (Chan et al., 1997; Fisher et al., 1991; Fisher & Brown, 1988) are applied to the rehabilitation planning process. These steps include (a) dispel myths about "good" working alliances; (b) define and understand the conflict from the perspectives of each partner in the working alliance; (c) clarify misperceptions; (d) generate options for resolving differences; and (e) implement solutions.

DISPEL MYTHS ABOUT "GOOD" WORKING ALLIANCES
Perhaps the most common myth about relationships is the belief that the best partnership is one in which *no* discrepancies are present; in other words, partners in "good" working relationships *always* agree. Two other common myths are the beliefs that partners in effective working relationships have shared values and perceptions and that the goal of such relationships is to avoid disagreements and conflict.

As a prerequisite for resolving conflicts, it is necessary to accurately define effective working alliances and to dispute those myths that are treated as facts. A realistic understanding of the nature of "good" working relationships must be reached. Such relationships are best described as those in which (a) partners are able to deal effectively with conflicts, (b) partners seek to understand each other's values and perceptions, even if these differ, and (c) the goal of the working alliance is not to avoid conflict, but rather to work through disagreements in a manner that benefits all involved parties.

Step 1: Define the Conflict. The process of conflict resolution begins with an accurate understanding of the nature of the conflict from the perspectives of all involved parties. Open communication is required if partners are to begin working toward resolution. The aim of communication should be to develop an understanding and mutual acceptance of each other's interests, values, perceptions, and notions of fairness, even if these differ. Understanding and mutual acceptance are best facilitated when members of the working alliance have the opportunity to communicate their interests or goals, and then the other members restate those interests or goals as they understand them. This approach provides opportunities for clarification when communications are unclearly stated or inaccurately interpreted. Reversing roles and communicating from the other person's point of view also facilitates greater understanding and mutual acceptance. Partners who communicate in this fashion may even find that their viewpoints are not as discrepant as they originally believed.

Relationships often become entangled with problems and the tendency to think in adversarial terms and to treat people and problems as if a problem may be present. If this occurs, conflict must be reframed as a difference in interests and goals rather than a "contest of wills." Reframing the conflict as a problem that the rehabilitation/treatment team must confront together encourages the client's active participation and mutual responsibility in resolving the conflict. It also promotes a "we" attitude or an interdependency of partners who are striving toward the mutual goal of maximizing the effectiveness of the working alliance. In defining the nature of the conflict, it is crucial that the client be provided with the program or agency's point of view (Holmes et al., 1989). Guidelines and boundaries within which the rehabilitation/treatment team must work should also be clearly communicated and accurately understood by all (Curl & Sheldon, 1992).

Step 2: Clarify Misperceptions. After the nature of the conflict has been accurately defined and understood by all members of the working alliance, the next step is to clarify misperceptions, particularly when misperceptions, rather than true discrepancies, are the real problem. Careless communication is the source of many misperceptions. The case manager, for example, may make a statement that is interpreted by the client as a promise or commitment when the case manager does not in fact intend to make that commitment. Constantly striving to clarify, not only what is said, but also how one's statements are interpreted, can prevent miscommunications.

Trust is another key factor and has been described as "the single most important element of a good working relationship" (Fisher & Brown, 1988, p. 107). Keeping promises, following through with commitments, and behaving reliably help to establish a trusting relationship. Not only actual behavior, but also the interpretation of behavior, can either promote or impede a trusting relationship. Behaviors exhibited by members of the working alliance, such as arriving late for appointments, may be perceived by the busy professional as unavoidable. The client, on the other hand, may interpret these behaviors as evidence that the case manager or other team members are unreliable or lack respect for the client. As another example, a case manager may make a verbal agreement to contact an employer on behalf of a client but, after several phone calls, is still unable to reach the employer. From a case manager's perspective, the case manager has followed through with the agreement. From the client's perspective, however, the case manager may have broken the agreement. The case manager needs to provide clear and specific communication regarding the steps that will be taken to keep a promise (e.g., "I will make three attempts to contact your employer by telephone. If I do not speak with her by the end of this week, I will let you know") and then complete each step as stated to help ensure that communications and behaviors are interpreted in the way they are intended. Trust is also established by seeking out opportunities to act inconsistently with another's negative perceptions.

Step 3: Generate Options. The third step in conflict resolution involves the mutual sharing of ideas about how to move toward a single set of shared expectations. Brainstorming, without criticism, helps to produce a comprehensive list of potential strategies for resolving discrepancies. Each strategy can then be evaluated by all members of the working alliance, who, ideally, will reach consensus regarding which options are selected for implementation. Reconciling interests, as opposed to compromising between positions, should be the goal for any options chosen. The same principles of communication described in the previous steps apply to this step, and the guidelines and boundaries within which the rehabilitation/treatment team must work should, again, be clearly communicated and understood.

Step 4: Implement and Evaluate Resolutions. The final step involved in resolving differences comprises the actual implementation and evaluation of resolutions. At this point, all members of the working alliance should reach agreement on what each other's roles and responsibilities will comprise. Co-developing a written agreement outlining specific roles and responsibilities, revisiting the agreement at various points during the relationship, and revising the agreement as needed, will minimize the risk of future discrepancies. Ongoing communication about the effectiveness of resolutions and each member's degree of satisfaction with the working alliance also achieves this end. Furthermore, all members of the rehabilitation/treatment team must have "some bargaining power to provide impetus for negotiation" (Curl & Sheldon, 1992, p. 198) should new discrepancies arise. Above all, members of the working alliance must be prepared for some residual degree of discrepancy because it is unrealistic to assume that all differences can be resolved and a discrepancy-free alliance can be established (Chan et al., 1997).

SUMMARY

The case manager's interpersonal skills are among the most important determinants of the working alliance's success. In serving clients' needs, the paramount reason that the working alliance exists, case managers' most important product is people—and their best marketing strategy is communication.

Beginning with the intake interview and progressing through the stages of clarifying expectations, forming bonds, setting goals, and accomplishing tasks—case managers who can establish rapport and resolve conflicts among team members will facilitate working alliances characterized by responsive attention to client needs. By setting a tone of professionalism and respect for all members of the rehabilitation/treatment team, readers can direct an efficient interdisciplinary process whose cumulative benefit to the client far outweighs the individual additive impact of each team member.

REFERENCES

Al-Darmarki, F., & Kivlighan, D. M. (1993). Congruence in client-counselor expectations for relationship and the working alliance. *Journal of Counseling Psychology, 40*(4), 379-384.

Bergin, A. E., & Garfield, S. L. (1994). *Handbook of psychotherapy and behavior change* (4th ed.). New York: John Wiley & Sons, Inc.

Berven (2001). Assessment interviewing. In B. F. Bolton (Ed.), *Handbook of measurement and evaluation in rehabilitation* (pp.197-213). Gaithersburg, MD: Aspen.

Berzins (1971). *Revision of Psychotherapy Expectancy Inventory*. Unpublished manuscript, University of Kentucky, Lexington.

Bordin, E. S. (1979). The generalizability of the psychoanalytic concept of the working alliance. *Psychotherapy: Theory, Research, and Practice, 16*(3), 252-260.

Bordin, E. S. (1994). Theory and research on the therapeutic working alliance: New directions. In A. O. Horvath & L. S. Greenberg (Eds.), *The working alliance: Theory, research, and practice* (pp. 13-37). New York: John Wiley & Sons, Inc.

Carkhuff, R. R. (1969). *Helping and human relations*. New York: Holt, Rinehart, & Winston.

Chan, F., Shaw, L. R., McMahon, B. T., Koch, L., & Strauser, D. (1997). A model for enhancing rehabilitation counselor-consumer working relationships. *Rehabilitation Counseling Bulletin, 41*, 122-137.

Curl, R. M. & Sheldon, J. B. (1992). Achieving reasonable choices: Balancing the rights and responsibilities of consumers with those of rehabilitation counselors. *Rehabilitation Education, 6*(2), 195-205.

Duckro, P., Beal, D., & George, C. (1979). Research on the effects of disconfirmed client role expectations in psychotherapy: A critical review. *Psychological Bulletin, 86*, 260-275.

D'Zurilla, T. J. (1999). *Problem solving therapy: A social competence approach to clinical intervention* (2nd Ed.). New York: Springer.

Egan, G. (2001). *The skilled helper: A problem-management and opportunity-development approach to helping* (7th ed.). Belmont, CA: Brooks/Cole.

Fisher, R., & Brown, S. (1988). *Getting together: Building a relationship that gets to yes*. Boston, MA: Houghton Mifflin Company.

Fisher, R., Ury, W. & Patton, B. (1991*). Getting to yes: Negotiating agreement without giving in*. Boston, MA: Houghton Mifflin Company.

Galassi, J. P., Crace, R. K., Martin, G. A., James, & Wallace, R. L. (1992). Client preferences and anticipations in career counseling: A preliminary investigation. *Journal of Counseling Psychology, 39*(1), 46-55.

Gazda, G.M. (1973). *Human relations development*. Boston: Allyn & Bacon.

Gladstein, G. A. (1969). Client expectations, counseling experience, and satisfaction. *Journal of Counseling Psychology, 16*, 476-481.

Goldstein, A. P. (1981). Evaluating expectancy effects in cross-cultural counseling and psychotherapy. In A. J. Marsella, & P. B. Pederson (Eds.), *Cross-cultural counseling and psychotherapy* (pp. 85-101). Elmsford, NY: Pergamon.

Greenson, R. R. (1967). *The technique and practice of psychoanalysis* (Vol. 1). London: Hogarth.

Groth-Marnat, G. (1997). *Handbook of psychological assessment* (3rd ed.). New York: John Wiley & Sons.

Holmes, G. E., Hall, L., & Karst, R. H. (1989). Litigation avoidance through conflict resolution: Issues for state rehabilitation agencies. *American Rehabilitation, 15*(3), 12-15.

Horvath, A. O., & Greenberg, L. S. (1989). Development and validation of the Working Alliance Inventory. *Journal of Counseling Psychology, 36*, 223-233.

Ivey, A. E., & Ivey, (2003). *Intentional interviewing and counseling: Facilitating client development in a multicultural society* (5th ed.). Pacific Grove, CA: Brooks/Cole.

Koch, L. C. (2001). The preferences and anticipations of people referred to a vocational rehabilitation agency. *Rehabilitation Counseling Bulletin, 44*(2), 76-86.

Koch, L. C., Williams, C.L., & Rumrill, P. D., Jr. (1998). Increasing client involvement in vocational rehabilitation: An expectations-based approach to assessment and planning. *Work: A Journal of Prevention, Assessment, and Rehabilitation, 10*(3), 211-218.

McAlees, D., & Menz, F. (1992). *Consumerism and vocational evaluation. Rehabilitation Education, 6*(2), 213-220.

McKay, M., Davis, M., & Fanning, P. (1995). *Messages: The communication skills book.* Oakland, CA: New Harbinger.

Pietrofesa, J., Hoffman, A., Splete, H., & Pinto, D. (1978). *Counseling: Theory, research, and practice.* Chicago: Rand McNally.

Power, P. W. (2000). *A guide to vocational assessment* (3rd ed.). Austin, TX: Pro-Ed.

Raskin, N. J., & Rogers, C. R. (1989). Person-centered therapy. In R.J. Corsini, & D. Wedding (Eds.), *Current psychotherapies* (4th ed.) (pp. 155-194). Itasca, IL: F.E. Peacock Publishers, Inc.

Rogers, C. R. (1957). The necessary and sufficient conditions of therapeutic personality change. *Journal of Consulting Psychology, 21,* 95-103.

Roessler, R. T., & Rubin, S. E. (1998). *Case management and rehabilitation counseling: Procedures and techniques* (3rd ed). Austin, TX: Pro-Ed.

Roessler, R. T., & Rumrill, P. D., Jr. (1995). Promoting reasonable accommodations: An essential postemployment service. *Journal of Applied Rehabilitation Counseling, 26*(4), 3-7.

Rubenfeld (1988). The rehabilitation counselor and the disabled client: Is a partnership of equals possible? In S.E. Rubin & N.M. Rubin (Eds.), *Contemporary challenges to the rehabilitation counseling profession.* Boston: Allyn & Bacon, Inc.

Rumrill, P. D., Jr. (1996). *Multiple sclerosis and the world of work.* New York: Demos.

Rumrill, P. D., Jr., & Scheff, C. M. (1996). Enhance productivity and reduce turnover with worksite safety and disability management. *Journal of Long-Term Care Administration, 24* (3), 32-35.

Tinsley, H. E. A., Tokar, D. M, & Helwig, S. E. (1994). Client expectations about counseling and involvement during career counseling. *The Career Development Quarterly, 42,* 326-336.

Truax, C. B., & Carkhuff, R. R. (1967). *Toward effective counseling and psychotherapy*. Chicago: Aldine.

Tracey, T, J, & Dundon, M. (1988). Role anticipations and preferences over the course of counseling. *Journal of Counseling Psychology, 35*(1), 3-14.

Zetzel, E. R. (1956). Current concepts of transference. *International Journal of Psychoanalysis, 37*, 369-376.

6

ETHICAL ISSUES
IN CASE MANAGEMENT

Vilia M. Tarvydas
David B. Peterson
Susan Dominy Michaelson

Chapter Highlights

- Professionalism and case management

- Ethical decision making

- Case management as a profession

- Current status of case management

- Model of ethical standards

- Case management standards

- Ethical codes

- Comparison of codes

- Prominent ethical issues

- Summary

It is difficult to disagree with Mullahy (1995) when she noted that "case management is not for the faint at heart" (p. 3), especially when one considers the ethical implications of this work. Case management has offered its practitioners a unique and powerful role to play in the lives of their clients since the origins of this type of practice. Facilitation of clinical decision-making and service provision is often combined with direct or indirect control over the financial means to care for the client. This combination can be an effective, as well as a potentially dangerous, combination of roles in the client service delivery process. Gierman (1995) has described the mission of the case manager explicitly as involving "moral triangulation" through which the case manager assists the parties "to bring together their moral perspectives regarding quality of life, quality care, quality outcomes and balanced cost" (p. 53).

Banja (1991) has noted that one of the primary problems facing case managers is that they must deal with many other professionals who may make decisions that have ethical repercussions for the case. The case manager then must deal with these decisions and/or parties to the process who have competing interests. The case management process all too often leaves the case manager presiding over the key ethical decisions involved in the treatment of the client, without the benefit of that role being acknowledged. Case managers, therefore, must be prepared to exert extraordinary efforts to understand and comply with ethical standards that describe the moral obligations attendant to their work. The clients, payers, professional colleagues, and attorneys with whom they work are demanding no less. Case management is fraught with diverse, complex situations. Participants in the process may hold divergent and sometimes conflicting viewpoints about what action would constitute an appropriate solution for the situation.

Rinas and Clyne-Jackson (1988) detailed three types of situations that can set up major ethical concerns by creating conflicts of interests. Such conflicts often occur when mental health practitioners are involved in third-party situations, as are case managers. They noted that these problems could arise due to (a) conflicts in expectations or values; (b) conflicts in responsibilities; and (c) variability in roles.

The first type of conflict involves differing expectations regarding what services will be provided or what services a case manager is capable of competently providing. There may be conflicting values regarding what services, outcomes, or relationships are worthy. In rehabilitation, this conflict may be influenced by the values of the respective service providers, involving such matters as *maximization* of rehabilitation outcome or function, rather than restoration of the client to a *minimal* level of functional ability. The second type of conflict involves concurrently owing responsibilities to differing parties in

145

the case management process, most typically the client and the payer. As a result, differing allegiances may develop regarding goals that may conflict due to the disparate functions expected by each party to whom the case manager is obligated (i.e., advocate for the client versus compliance monitor for the payer). The final type of conflict results from role variability resulting from the case manager occupying differing roles vis-à-vis the same party at different times (i.e., client's claims adjuster, rehabilitation counselor, or evaluator). All three types of conflicts certainly can arise periodically for all professionals. The practice of case management includes all of these conflicts by definition, at least to some degree. Uniquely well-honed skills at discerning the ethically appropriate boundary between these forces are required of the case manager.

This chapter begins with a brief discussion of the nature of professionalism and development of appropriate ethical standards of practice in case management, as the skill area continues to evolve its core identity. The major codes of professional conduct relevant to practitioners of case management will then be overviewed in terms of their major commonalties and differences. Finally, several prominent ethical issues that emerge from this analysis will be summarized.

PROFESSIONALISM AND CASE MANAGEMENT

The explosive growth of the number of case managers practicing in the U.S. has been without precedent, and has occurred without accompanying clarity in the professional status and role of its practitioners. It is estimated that the field has grown from approximately five to ten thousand practitioners in 1985, to fifty to one hundred thousand by 1995 (Mullahy, 1998). Case management is practiced by an exceedingly divergent group of individuals who initially were prepared for practice in a number of professional disciplines. While becoming rarer, in some settings educational requirements for positions may begin with a high school diploma and some relevant experience. Some of the more prominent professional groups include social work, nursing, rehabilitation counseling, occupational therapy, and physical therapy. In recent years, even physicians increasingly have been placed in a case management role, in addition to exercising their clinical medical expertise, due to the demands of managed health care. It is estimated that over a half dozen organizations serve the various professional groups that identify themselves as case managers (Gambosh & Sager, 1995).

In all likelihood, these individual case managers have been prepared in differing professional training models, socialized to differing service models or cultures (e.g., medical, rehabilitation, or social welfare), and trained in ethical practice methods and traditions that are not similar. Their core professions have different codes of ethics; and they may differ in levels of awareness, training, and educational experiences concerning ethics (Tarvydas & Cottone, 1991; Wetle, 1992). Differing disciplines' codes of ethics may involve disparate instruction on similar issues (Patterson & Curl, 1990; Swenson, 1997), or be inadequate to provide guidance for the quickly evolving issues inherent in managed care (AMA Council on Ethical and Judicial Affairs, 1998; McClinton, 1995; Murphy, DeBernardo, & Shoemaker, 1998). It is not surprising, therefore, that when confronted with similar ethical issues, there is evidence that individuals exhibit significant differences across the allied health professions in how they view some of these issues (Tarvydas & Shaw, 1993).

ETHICAL DECISION MAKING IN PROFESSIONAL PRACTICE

Banja (1992b) has recognized that in settings where ethics issues are ubiquitous, rehabilitation teams and their members, in essence, assume the role of ethics remediator in addition to the more typical function in making patient care decisions. Practitioners' ethical knowledge bases and viewpoints differ, and any code of ethics cannot definitively provide the solutions to all ethical dilemmas. As a result, case managers should learn to use a comprehensive ethical decision-making model to insure appropriate processing of critical clinicoethical decisions (Cottone & Tarvydas, 2003). Groups or teams of professionals working together must become ethically aware of their collective role in ethics decision making, and:

a) learn and use a common language of ethics and ethical decision-making strategies;

b) determine some manner of gaining consensus when ethical problems have arisen that should be discussed; and

c) be clear in their awareness of how personal and professional ethical considerations differ, and the importance of utilizing professional standards.

Tarvydas and Cottone (1991) have developed a four level model of thinking about the contexts of ethical practice that is particularly relevant to the conflicts between individual care and systems-level interests. The model assists the practitioner in identifying the contextual forces at each of four hierarchical levels that may impact the ethical decisions made. The four levels are (a) the clinical counseling level; (b) the clinical multidisciplinary level; (c) the institutional/agency level; and (d) the societal resource/public policy level. These levels are interactive in that the activities or forces of one level will influence one or more of the others. Ethically relevant threats and opportunities at each level should be recognized and addressed in understanding and resolving the ethical concerns presented.

The Integrative Decision-Making Model of Ethical Behavior (Tarvydas, 2004) introduces consideration of these hierarchical factors into a four-stage model. The Integrative Model focuses on the actual production of ethical behavior within a specified context, rather than prematurely terminating the process when a decision is reached about the best course of ethical action. The Integrative Model emphasizes four underlying themes or attitudes of which practitioners must be mindful as they apply the specific operations detailed within the model itself. Specifically they must:

(a) maintain a stance of *reflection* concerning their personal issues, values, and decision-making skills, as well as extending efforts to understand those of the other parties involved in the situation;

(b) maintain *balance* among various issues, persons, and perspectives within the process;

(c) provide an appropriate level of attention to *context(s)* of the situation–specifically the hierarchical levels of counselor-client, treatment team, organizational/institutional, and societal implications and interests in the ethical situation; and

(d) seek to use a process of *collaboration* with all rightful parties to the decision, always being mindful of the client's ethical claim for primary consideration by the professional (Tarvydas, 2004).

The Integrative Model itself (for a complete discussion see Tarvydas, 2004) is composed of four main *stages* with several *components* that describe the particular steps to be taken within each step (the full model is displayed in Table 11.1).

Stage I requires the *interpretation of the situation through awareness and fact-finding*. At this point, the primary task of case managers is to be sensitive and aware of the needs and welfare of the people around them, and the ethical implications of these situations.

Within Stage II, the case manager actually *formulates an ethical decision*. In this stage, the ethical dilemma is defined; information is gained about how laws, codes of ethics, ethical principles and institutional policies and procedures may apply to it; possible ethical courses of action are determined; they are assessed for their positive and negative consequences; consultation is obtained; and an ethical course of action is selected. In the subsequent State III, *an action is selected by weighing competing, nonmoral values, personal blind spots, or prejudices,* and personal concerns. This stage recognizes that many concerns and personal considerations may sway the practitioner from actually discharging the ethical course of action. It explicitly requires that the case

148

manager recognize and address these factors. In Stage IV, the case manager *plans and executes the selected course of action*. Here there is recognition that it requires specific interpersonal, planning, and management skills and qualities to translate intention into effective action. On going monitoring, evaluation, and correction of the planned course of action is necessary as well.

Table I
THE INTEGRATIVE DECISION-MAKING MODEL OF ETHICAL BEHAVIOR

Stage 1. Interpreting the Situation through Awareness and Fact Finding

Component 1 Enhance **sensitivity** and **awareness**
Component 2 Determine the major **stakeholders** and their ethical claims in the situation
Component 3 Engage in the **fact finding** process

Stage 2. Formulating an Ethical Decision

Component 1 **Review** the problem or dilemma
Component 2 Determine what **ethical codes, laws, ethical principles, and institutional policies and procedures** exist that apply to the dilemma
Component 3 Generate possible and probable **courses of action**
Component 4 Consider potential positive and negative **consequences** for each course of action
Component 5 **Consult** with supervisors and other knowledgeable professionals
Component 6 Select the best **ethical course of action**

Stage 3. Selecting an Action by Weighing Competing, Nonmoral Values, Personal Blind Spots, or Prejudices

Component 1 Engage in reflective recognition and analysis of **personal competing values, personal blind spots, or prejudices**
Component 2 Consider **contextual influences** on values selection at the collegial, team, institutional, and societal levels
Component 3 Determine the **preferred course of action** to be taken

(table continues)

Table I (Continued)

Stage 4. Planning and Executing the Selected Course of Action

Component 1	Figure out a reasonable **sequence of concrete action** to be taken
Component 2	Anticipate and work out personal and contextual **barriers** to effective execution of the plan of action and effective **countermeasures** for them
Component 3	**Carry out, document, and evaluate** the course of action as planned

It should be noted that the influences of the other participants in the case management process and the payer/institutional requirements are well accommodated through consideration within the contextual influences in all four stages of the Integrative Model. This approach is richer in accommodating the real life forces operating in the practice of case management than many traditional models that emphasize only the practitioner-client relationship.

In addition to whether an appropriate ethical decision-making model is utilized, the particular code of ethics that directs the case manager's decisions is one of the most prominent influences on the quality of ethical practice. The diversity of professional backgrounds among case managers has splintered efforts to define and set ethical standards regarding ethical case management practice, as well as regulate this growing service group (Gambosh & Sager, 1995). There has been a recognition that continued development of more defined and stringent standards for practice must occur to accelerate the effectiveness and credibility of case management services that are provided by the disparate professions (Gambosh & Sager, 1995; Mullahy, 1998; Smith, 1995).

CASE MANAGEMENT AS A PROFESSION

Why is it so crucial to determine if case management is a profession? Issues of ethics in case management cannot be resolved until a core question is addressed. The question concerns whether or not case management is, in and of itself, a profession. It is essential to determine the professional standing of a group of practitioners and their core roles and functions in order to determine the nature of their ethical duties and obligations. While this task is intrinsic to the development of professional standards for all groups, for case managers there is no more important task. Their credibility, future professional standing, and exposure to ethical and legal liability depend on the outcome of this

150

question, which is far from settled at present. It would seem that currently, case management is best considered to be an advanced practice skill of professionals who have received their professional training in a core profession such as nursing, rehabilitation counseling, or social work. As such, case management would not be seen as a profession in itself. Case management would be practiced by professionals, if they are trained in a specific core profession and they learn the additional advanced knowledge and skills needed in the case management process.

Occupational sociologists have traditionally considered it an important hallmark of a profession to establish ethical standards to which its practitioners are held. It is important for the public welfare and to establish the profession's trustworthiness to clearly establish the rules and jurisdiction under which professional practitioners may be disciplined. (Cullen, 1978; Elliott, 1972; Emener & Cottone, 1989; Friedson, 1994).

While these concerns are pressing, the issue is deeper than these points. Some members of the professions that are now most active in case management (e.g., social work, nursing and rehabilitation counseling) claim that their professions have conducted case management activities for many years, and that the case management function is nothing new. It is also clear that the practice of case management is rapidly moving into new settings, and using new techniques and methods that are more and more divergent from traditional practices (Shaw, McMahon, Chan, Taylor, & Wood, 1997). The technology of case management increasingly includes a radical paradigmatic shift from an ethic of focusing solely on the well-being and needs of the client or patient, to an increased focus on cost containment, managed competition, and quality care, from a managed care environment (Owens, 1996). An upsurge in business perspectives has been requisite within many current health and rehabilitation care contexts. This change has led to the overwhelming dominance of two types of functions often opposed to one another; advocacy for the client with a disability and gate keeping on behalf of the institution or payer (Banja, 1991; Banja, 1992; Wetle, 1992). The explicit intrusion of the business or cost containment perspective in case management has increased the juxtaposition of these two competing functions. As a result, contemporary case management cannot be analyzed as merely an extension of the traditional professional practice of these professions (Kane, 1992). The contemporary practice of case management increasingly challenges the paradigm in which the client's needs are paramount.

The processes of coordinating services and facilitating team and systemic communication for the benefit of the client, historically, have not taken place in such a pervasive cost containment and business-oriented culture. The core case management professional groups have been socialized within a professional context that shares a helping, or client/patient-centered, philosophical basis as the defining milieu for professional decision-making. Scholars have found a key defining characteristic for professionalization is that the occupation is primarily a service-oriented enterprise in which the service provided is of great social value, and is not primarily profit-oriented (Emener & Cottone, 1989; Moore, 1970). The contemporary confusion regarding the status of professional case management can be heard in the statement of McClinton (1995). She noted the need to revisit ethics in light of the new roles of nurses as case managers: "Now, I have to look at it as a business—not as my business, but insurance is a business" (p. 13). She is not alone in this new puzzlement at how these new considerations of an "industry" into which professionals must fit themselves will be reconciled with their understanding of what it means to practice case management within a profession. Mullahy (1998) has taken a position that case management is not an interchangeable concept with managed care. She described it as a process that can be one component in a managed care strategy. In essence, she has invoked the conceptual distinction that has increasingly been made between managed dollars or services and managed care; the latter of which concerns itself with the ultimate well-being and benefit of the client.

The central concern about ethical practice does not involve the question of whether case management services can be profitable or whether business-based technical skills are utilized by the professional. Rather, the way in which the profit arises within the context of the professional-client relationship is at the crux of the matter. The issue involves whether making money in this case management process occurs through (a) abandonment of the primary ethical and professional obligation to serve the best interests of the individual client; and/or (b) creating, or allowing, the illusion of a trusting professional relationship that is service rather than business based to persist in the minds of the clients and/or their agents.

CURRENT STATUS OF CASE MANAGEMENT

There has been substantial development of the knowledge and credentialing base for practice in case management over the last decade, leading some to ponder whether case management itself is becoming a specific, differentiated profession. The completion of studies to empirically validate the knowledge dimensions of case management (Leahy, 1994; Leahy, Chan, Shaw & Lui, 1997), establishment and strong acceptance of a national certification process through the Commission on Case Manager Certification (CCMC), and promulgation of practice standards such as the (CCMC) Code of Professional Conduct and Standards of Practice for Case Managers by the Case Management

Society of America (CMSA) have been generated in response to the increased practice of case management.

The assumption held by some that these developments indicate the emergence of a new profession is misguided and flows counter to the explicit intent and design of the CCMC itself. This credential was designed and it is maintained as an additional *"advanced practice" credential* to be available to qualified individuals who have first achieved basic credentials in their profession of origin (e.g., social work, rehabilitation counseling, or nursing). This construction preserves the professionalism embedded in the professions of origin. Case management is thus grounded in professionalism; but originated in the practitioner's basic profession. *Professionalism* involves a special set of professional ideals regarding the authority of knowledge and service that sustain a profession (Friedson, 1994). If case management is based on the professional development of its practitioners within the professions of origin, then it is not left to rest solely on credentialism. *Credentialism* involves only politically establishing, exclusive credentials (e.g., certification) and creating a requirement for certain credentials needed to work in an occupation (Friedson). Just because a licensure or certification credentialing program can be structured around a sophisticated technical skill and its practitioners are in demand, this skilled occupation by definition does not, become a profession. A profession is broader than a particular set of circumscribed technical skills—if just one particular function drives a profession's identity, then testing could be considered a profession within psychology, and diagnosis could be a profession within medicine.

Authorities on ethics in the helping professions have cautioned practitioners concerning their obligations to refrain from unnecessarily engaging in "turf wars" based on unsubstantiated, unfair, or misleading statements concerning the qualifications and skills of other professionals (Corey, Corey, & Callanan, 1998; Cottone & Tarvydas, 2003). Powell (1996) has acknowledged that the question of who should be a case manager has been a contentious issue for the field: "[t]urf wars have ensued over it, articles have been written about it, and jobs have been lost over it" (p. 7). She considered the critical issues as revolving around the issue of assessing the type of population that needs case management services and determining what type of professional background is most suitable to meet the clients' needs. This viewpoint rejects a blatant exclusionary stance of one professional group against another. It invites the acknowledgement of the unique contributions of all valid professional preparations and their potential collaboration in a team approach to meeting clients' needs (Powell).

It is imperative that case management not define itself as a freestanding profession when this focus primarily would stem from a need to incorporate a management or business-skill base into its technology. For ethically sound practices to continue their evolution, the better course is that the *advanced practice model of case management* return to its closer linkage with the base professional client/patient-centered foci represented within the professions that provide its practitioners their core professional identities.

Banja (1992b) made several highly compelling points relevant to retaining this advanced practice model of case management when he considered the questions of whether case management should evolve as an industry or a profession, as he considered both legal liability and ethical issues. In defining the industry and professional worldviews or paradigms, he noted that a professional provides services from a beneficent or paternalistic framework focused on the uniqueness and individuality of the professional relationship with the client. Each professional encounter is seen as occurring within a unique person-to-person context. On the other hand, the industry perspective places emphasis on a product or services that are standardized or depersonalized, and based on economic or marketplace realties. Banja strongly advocated that case management "not compromise ... opportunity to forge a relationship based on trust and advocacy with the insured" (Banja, p. 20).

MODEL OF ETHICAL STANDARDS

The utilization of the advanced practice model of case management, if built upon the professional status of the underlying core professions, offers increased clarity in the application or governance of ethical standards of practice. This approach provides for ethical practice to be seated in the aspirational principles embodied in the profession's code of ethics to set the ethical paradigm and seat it in a beneficent, service-oriented, or patient/client centered context. It would then be important for setting-specific or advanced areas of practice, such as case management, to build upon this basic set of standards for ethical behavior or conduct within those more specific arenas. These supplemental, complementary codes of professional conduct extend and explicate the more general codes of ethics in the base professions. They provide guidance for ethical practice for particular special issues frequently encountered, or of particular concern to these professionals in this specialized area (Tarvydas, 2004). These latter codes of conduct may or may not be mandatory or enforceable on the professional, depending on whether the particular individual is a credential holder or member of the group that promulgated the code. However, these guidelines will offer guidance to all persons in that type of practice regardless of whether they are mandatory (Tarvydas).

If ordered in this way, for example, there would be greater clarity that the first ethical obligation of the case manager would be to the individual patient or client to whom they are providing services and not to the other professionals or business concerns that are a party to the process that is being case managed. Great assistance is provided through supplementary specialty guidelines in understanding what specific technical best practices should apply to serving the patient/client and these other parties in the specialized context. Professional psychologists have long utilized this model in applying specialized guidelines to their technical practices through such standards documents as the *Guidelines for Computer-based Tests and Their Interpretation* (APA, 2000); yet conforming to the American Psychological Association's (APA) *Ethical Principles of Psychologists and Code of Conduct* (APA, 2002) to set the broader ethical context of practice for the profession as a whole.

From this perspective, it becomes important to accord careful attention to the analysis of each of the core professions' codes of ethics for basic guidance in ethical matters, even within the advanced practice of case management. These dictates should then be supplemented by the guidance available through the specialty codes of conduct or standards of practice developed for the specific purpose of governing this specialty practice area. The importance of specific ethical standards was acknowledged by the 17 groups who gathered during the October 1997, Care and Case Management Summit through their discussion of ethical standards in case management as a shared area of concern for all groups with practitioners working in this area. It is incumbent upon the professionals to weigh carefully the guidance offered by both sources of ethical guidance; and not just the dictates that are directly enforceable upon them through direct, mandatory jurisdiction. It is for this reason that an overview of the major codes of professional conduct that are relevant to case management practice is provided next.

CASE MANAGEMENT STANDARDS

As case management service positions increased in response to managed care demands, various professional organizations generated ethical codes that specifically addressed case management practice within their respective disciplines. In view of this, the following codes will be reviewed in this section of the chapter: (1) Standards of Practice for Case Management, by the Case Management Society of America (CMSA, 2002); (2) Code of Professional Conduct of the CDMSC with Disciplinary Rules, Procedures, and Penalties, by the Certification of Disability Management Specialists Commission (CDMSC, 2001); (3) Code of Professional Ethics for Rehabilitation Counselors, by the Commission on Rehabilitation Counselor Certification (CRCC, 2001); (4) Standards of Practice for Professional Geriatric Care Managers, by the National Association of Professional Geriatric Case Managers (NAPGCM, 2003), and;

(5) NASW Standards for Social Work Case Management, by the National Association of Social Workers (NASW, 1992).

This section is organized according to the organization that authored the ethical document. First, the origins of the specific code are discussed, and then the essence of the code in terms of purpose and general philosophy are summarized. Finally, the impact of the code on the practice of case management, with specific focus on professionalization issues, is noted.

ETHICAL CODES

CASE MANAGEMENT SOCIETY OF AMERICA (CMSA)

The Case Management Society of America (CMSA) is a multidisciplinary organization that focuses on health care-based case management. CMSA committee members who authored the standards of practice were comprised predominately of nursing professionals.

The basic approach and structure of the standards were modeled after those of the American Nurses Association. The standards are voluntary practice guidelines. That is, they do not involve mandatory standards that, when violated, are enforced by a disciplinary process. The CMSA makes clear the notion that the practice of case management is in an evolutionary phase. This view means that the standards continue to reflect the foundational knowledge for case management practice, while monitoring evolving practice directions and emerging trends that may be included in future updates of the standards. The standards of practice were written with the intent of influencing case management practice by all professional orientations. When addressing standards of performance for quality care, the document directs case managers to adhere to the codes of ethics for their professional disciplines.

The CMSA provides a triangular model of case management, wherein the community is depicted at the top of the triangle, and the payer and the healthcare team is placed at the bottom corners of the triangle. The client and the case manager are pictorially conceptualized in the center of this triangle surrounded by a whirlwind of activities contained in a revolving circle. This circle, which appears to depict the client-centered activities, is comprised of assessment, planning, facilitation, and advocacy.

The Standards of Care for professional services within case management appear in a separate pictorial model, represented as a circle containing an inner circle of revolving functions. These include identification/selection of case management services, problem identification, planning, monitoring, evaluating, and outcomes.

Code overview. The code begins with an historical overview of case management in the nursing profession. Case management is defined as involving "the timely coordination of quality health care services to meet an individual's specific health care needs in a cost-effective manner" (CMSA, p. 5). The CMSA Board of Directors approved a more complete definition generated by a yearlong study of the National Case Management Task Force:

> Case management is a collaborative process which assesses, plans, implements, coordinates, monitors and evaluates options and services to meet an individual's health needs through communication and available resources to promote quality cost-effective outcomes (CMSA, p. 5).

Certain sections of the code utilize client-focused language in such situations as describing the collaborative professional relationships. It is important, however, to recognize the CMSA code makes special note that the case manager is advocate for both the client and the payer, in a manner that facilitates a positive outcome for the patient, the health care team, and the payer. While the intention of these standards is to provide case management services objectively, collaboratively, and without influence of self or special interests, one could interpret this philosophy as a paradigm shift away from exclusively client-centered health care. These standards might lead the practitioner into the conflicts of interests mentioned earlier in this chapter, through not fully addressing occasions were the conflicting interests of a situation cannot by resolved to the mutual benefit of both the client and the payer.

One of the purposes mentioned in the performance of case management services is the "timely coordination of quality healthcare services to meet an individual's specific healthcare needs in a cost-effective manner to promote positive outcomes" (CMSA, p. 5). The term "cost-effective" fails to distinguish whether cost-effectiveness is judged based on the client versus payer interests. This lack of clarity provides an environment that permits movement away from client advocacy to a payer advocate-philosophy, depending upon who employs the case manager, or whose interests are paramount.

Unique to this particular code, in comparison with the other codes reviewed herein, the CMSA code states the goal of enhancing employee productivity and tenure. If one considers the role of personnel management in the allied health care professions, such a human resource agenda is commensurate with prescribed activities. How these administrative tasks might compete for time and resources allocated for client care is unclear; but they certainly broaden the scope of practice of case management in nursing, if not the allied health profession.

THE CERTIFICATION OF DISABILITY MANAGEMENT SPECIALISTS
COMMISSION (CDMSC)
Disability management is an emerging area in rehabilitation counseling and other rehabilitation professions. The management activity is employer or payer-oriented, whereby the disability management specialist uses his or her expertise to minimize employer or payer loss that results from employee injury, which may occur on-the-job (e.g., typical Workers Compensation activities) or off (e.g., personal injury that results in loss of gainful activity). The Code of Professional Conduct authored by the CDMSC makes clear the point that the client is conceptualized exclusively as "the individual for whom a Certified Disability Management Specialist (CDMS) provides services," while the payer is referred to as the "CDMS certificant's customer" (Preamble).

The CDMSC acknowledges the fact that CDMSs are employed by entities that have a primary interest in controlling costs as opposed to providing services that achieve the maximum benefit for the client. This credential clearly is demarcated from the CRC credential, although an individual may hold both credentials. The CDMS's allegiance is, by definition, to the employer or payer, while the CRC's allegiance is primarily to the client. The potential conflict embedded in each of these respective ethical perspectives is clear.

As the preamble states, the CDMS recognizes that "their actions or inactions can either aid or hinder clients in achieving their objectives, and they accept this responsibility as part of their professional obligation." This statement begs the question of whether it is part of the CDMS's obligation to act or not act for the client based upon the payer's best interest. Are CDMSs then left in the position of engaging in client disservice, owing it to their professional obligations to the payer? How the CDMS should resolve such conflicting interests is not directly addressed in the code of professional conduct.

The basic objective of the CDMS Code is to "protect the public interest." The public interest is a sufficiently vague term that is vulnerable to sociopolitical interpretation. In a survival-of-the-fittest political reality, public interest may best be served by saving costs and increasing profit. In a more humanistic reality, the public interest may be served best by full participation of all citizens in society. Language is utilized that allows for a paradigm shift away from the primacy of the client's interest, toward an ambiguous public interest that may potentiate economic motivations over optimal client outcomes.

Code overview. The CDMSC Code begins with eight Principles. Principle 3 suggests that the CDMS use objectivity in relationship to "clients" (recipients of CDMS services); it is not clear if this objectivity is extended similarly toward the "customer" (the payer). The agenda of optimizing economy for the "customer," perhaps by definition, argues for pursuit of the payer's interest. In contrast, Principle 5 addresses the need for the CDMS to maintain adequate technical competency so that the "client" "will receive the benefit of the highest quality of service the profession can offer." The competing interests reviewed earlier are manifest once again in an ethical code that attempts to balance the interests of both the client and the "gatekeeper."

Following the eight Principles, 29 Rules of Professional Conduct are proposed, which are enforced by the CDMSC through the Guidelines and Procedures for Processing Complaints. The 29 Rules are consistent with standards established for many helping professionals in the allied health professions, with one notable exception. Rule 7 states that the client should be permitted to make informed choices based upon explanation of services "to the extent reasonably necessary." This language may not purposefully limit client access to service information. Given the potential conflicts of interest between optimal service provision and economy, what is "reasonable" begs the question: reasonable and necessary for whom, and to what end?

THE COMMISSION ON REHABILITATION COUNSELOR CERTIFICATION (CRCC)

The CRCC Code of Professional Ethics was established for Certified Rehabilitation Counselors (CRCs) by the Commission on Rehabilitation Counselor Certification (CRCC), and was adopted by the American Rehabilitation Counseling Association (ARCA), and the National Rehabilitation Counseling Association (NRCA).

The preamble of the code encourages the CRC's facilitation of the personal, social, and economic independence of persons with disabilities. The primary obligation of the rehabilitation counselor is to the client. The preamble acknowledges the multiple professional contacts made by rehabilitation counselors: people, programs, institutions, and service delivery systems. Certainly, the interdisciplinary nature of rehabilitation services creates situations with multiple stakeholders and subsequent disparate interests. Regardless, the CRCC code makes clear the primacy of client care over other special interests.

Services provided by rehabilitation counselors include counseling; vocational exploration; psychological and vocational assessments; evaluations of social, medical, vocational, and psychiatric information; job placement and job development activities: and "other" types of rehabilitation services. A major enhancement in the current code is the delineation of indirect services and the ethical obligations of those rehabilitation counselors who provide them. Indirect services include such activities as case consultation, forensic expert witness services, and case file review. All of the codes reviewed for this chapter require

CHAPTER 6CHAPTER 6

Ethical Issues in Case Management

that services only be provided with the appropriate educational and training experience.

Code overview. The code is comprised of eleven Sections that represent enforceable standards of ethical practice. The associated subsections under each of the eleven Sections are exacting standards to provide guidance in specific circumstances. Violators of the Code are subject to disciplinary action by the CRCC, such as revocation or suspension of the CRC credential, or other imposed penalties as warranted by the severity of the offense and its attendant circumstances. Procedures and penalties are established to ensure proper enforcement of The Code within a framework of due process and equal protection under the law (CRCC Guidelines and Procedures for Processing Ethical Complaints).

One unique aspect of the CRC code, in comparison with other helping professions, is the vocational focus. One finds within the first Section (A.1.c) the admonition to neither place nor participate in the placement of clients in positions that will result in damaging the interest and welfare of clients. The optimal outcome for many rehabilitation counselor interventions is gainful employment of persons with disabilities, so the employment practice focus stands to reason.

The CRCC Code also makes the distinction in Section A.3.b and A.3.c between services to the client (or consumer) and services to a "third party." The code does not support the concept of having as a primary client, an entity that is a third party to the counselor-client relationship. When services are provided at the request of a third party, the Code requires maintaining the primacy of the client's interests through the provision of unbiased, objective service. Where services are provided at the request of a third party, the RC is also required to clarify their relationship to all involved parties. If there is no pretense or intent of providing direct RC services to the client (e.g., as in a forensic evaluation), the RC is directed to define (orally or in writing) the limits of the relationship to all parties involved. This information regarding the limitations and conflicts in the relationship is especially important in regard to the limitations to informed consent, confidentiality, and/or legally privileged communication. Similar to the Standards of Practice for Professional Geriatric Managers developed by the National Association of Professional Geriatric Care Managers (NAPGCM) reviewed next, Section A.3.e encourages special consideration for those persons with disabilities who, due to cognitive limitations, are unable to make useful and healthy decisions independently. Section C is unique among ethical codes in that it thoroughly describes the need to evaluate accessibility issues as advocates for persons with disabilities. Not only are physical barriers addressed, but attitudinal barriers as well. This Section obligates the RC to advocate on behalf of their clients in terms of accessibility and effective service delivery. The CMSA Standards also direct the case manager to "advocate for the client and his/her family at the service-delivery and at the policy-making level" (CMSA, 1995, p. 20). In terms of working as an allied health care professional with clients with disabilities, the CRCC Code is unique in its attention to psychosocial and environmental issues related to disabilities.

The first mention of case management specific services occurs in Section D.7.c, which discourages the provision of ongoing counseling services or case management services to someone currently receiving services from other related service providers, without informing the associated providers (excluding file reviews and second opinions). This particular rule is sensitive to the interdisciplinary nature of case management, specifically rehabilitation counseling case management. Without effective communication among service providers in a case management situation, services may become redundant, counterproductive, and perhaps even harmful to the client. In this Section, rehabilitation counselors are discouraged from discussing with their clients the competency of associated providers, in a disparaging way.

In summary, the CRCC's Code of Professional Ethics for Rehabilitation Counselors represents exemplary case management as being a service that is client-centered; encourages a collaborative, multidisciplinary focus; is disability sensitive; is defined within the context of an established profession, and is vocationally inclusive.

THE NATIONAL ASSOCIATION OF GERIATRIC CARE MANAGERS (NAPGCM)

Given the "graying of America" that has occurred as baby-boomers approach their fifth decade of life, the need for qualified health care professionals skilled in working with older persons will continue to increase. Working with an older population creates situations unique in comparison to working with children, adolescents, or young and middle-aged adults. The goal of the National Association of Geriatric Care Managers (NAPGCM) Code is to address these specific needs in a manner that will enhance the health care of older persons across America.

The NAPGCM code highlights in its preamble that no one profession can "claim exclusive domain over the knowledge and skills required to provide geriatric case management services" (Preamble). This supports the argument that case management in general is, in fact, a service that is provided by many professions, none of which "hold all of the cards." The purpose of the NAPGCM code at its outset is to "supplement already existing standards of other professions and organizations and to provide guidance to the members of the National Association of Professional Geriatric Care Managers" (Preamble).

161

Code overview. The code is comprised of standards that are supported by associated rationale and guidelines. As with the Standards of Practice for Case Management authored by the CMSA, these standards of practice are aspirational, and are not enforced by disciplinary procedures of a credentialing body.

The GCM Code places the client center stage. While the primary client is the older person, Standard One states that geriatric care is often concerned with family member's lives as well. Family members must be treated as part of the "client system" (p. 1). The emphasis upon the family system is unique to, and necessary for, working with older persons. To a lesser degree, this issue is also highlighted for work with persons with disabilities in the CRCC Code of Professional Ethics.

Standard Two contains a guiding principle that likely is difficult to adhere to by impatient or over-worked allied health professionals. It encourages the fostering of client self-determination, regardless of competency. Rather than labor over important decisions with someone whose cognitive capacity has been compromised, many care providers may be tempted to rush to judgment on behalf of their client. This temptation argues for a thorough presentation of situational factors associated with decision making to the older person, particularly in a case management context with multiple stakeholders/service providers. On a related point, Standard Seven requests the development of a flexible care plan that offers self-determination balanced with the person's need for safety. For extreme cases, Standard Nine provides guidelines for assuming fiduciary responsibilities for clients, another potential responsibility unique to an older population.

Given the nascent stage of development in professional geriatric care management, Standard Six encourages clear communication with other professionals regarding roles and scope of practice of GCMs. In an important directive, Standard Four obliges the professional to ensure the integrity of client system's treatment through GCM self-examination of values, beliefs, and standards, before accepting or referring a case.

The CRCC and the CMSA codes were not alone in addressing vocationally related issues. The NAPGCM Code addresses the use of private duty caregivers, professionals, and service providers in Standard Eight, suggesting that they should be coordinated consistent with laws related to employment practices. In this instance, the vocational aspect is related to the service providers hired for client care, as opposed to an outcome of client interventions as in rehabilitation counseling, or the administrative focus of the CMSA code.

THE NATIONAL ASSOCIATION OF SOCIAL WORKERS (NASW)

Written for professional social workers who perform the role of case manager, the NASW code was developed in order to help clarify the nature of case management and the role of case manager in the social work profession. The document begins with a contextual overview, followed by an explanation of each of ten standards, and their interpretations. It is important to note that this set of standards is one of a number of NASW Professional Standards, all of which are subsumed and accountable to the more general Code of Ethics (revised in 1999). This Professional Standard was constructed by the Case Management Standards Work Group, and was approved by the NASW Board of Directors in June of 1992.

The NASW Standards for Social Work Case Management states that case management has its origin and earliest history in social work. Case management in a social work context is described as "establish(ing) helping relationships, assess(ing) complex problems, select(ing) problem-solving interventions, and help(ing) the client to function effectively and, thus, is a therapeutic process" (p. 4).

These standards follow the basic social work ethical tenets of the NASW Code of Ethics: Primacy of client's interests, recognition of the inherent worth and capacity of the individual, and the individual's right to self-determination and confidentiality. In terms of definition, the code acknowledges, "full recognition that there is no universally accepted definition of case management, nor is there one definitive model of case management as practiced within the social work profession" (p. 4). By definition, social work case management distinguishes itself from other forms of case management:

Social work case management is a method of providing services whereby a professional social worker assesses the needs of the client and client's family, when appropriate, and arranges, coordinates, monitors, evaluates, and advocates for a package of multiple services to meet the specific client's complex needs....addresses both the individual client's biopsychosocial status as well as the state of the social system in which case management operates (p. 5).

By definition, social work case management focuses upon the individual, and the individual's context (system or environment), which is similar, but not identical, to the family-system perspective of the NAPGCM code. The client-level intervention requires direct one-to-one contact with the client to develop an individualized service plan. The system-level intervention involves knowing "how the agency and environmental systems can both positively and negatively affect clients, and to intervene at the system level to optimize these conditions" (p. 7).

Code overview. The Code consists of 10 standards and associated "Interpretations." Standard 1 emphasizes respect for diversity in its broadest sense, clearly interpreting the need to attend to socioeconomic status, cultural, gender, racial, and sexual orientation issues. Nowhere in the other four codes reviewed herein is such an exhaustive list of diversity issues addressed.

A unique admonition is made in Standard 9 that focuses on keeping caseload size appropriate to the scope and complexity of the case management system, and the nature of the population served. In a managed care environment that seeks to do more with less, attention to case manager/client ratio is unique to the NASW code. Standard 10 discusses the need for clear policies when more than one person functions as case manager for a client. It is suggested that one individual will serve as primary case manager, to be chosen by the client when possible. This recommendation is indicative of the rise in the number of professions involved in case management activities, so much so that the anticipation of multiple case management involvement is worthy of ethical consideration.

In terms of the client-focus in the NASW's client-system paradigm, Standard 2 underscores the primacy of the client's concerns in case management clearly stated for social work practice. Given the history and well-evolved concept of professionalism in this particular helping profession, it is not surprising to find the adherence to the client-first paradigm. Standard 3 further ensures client self-determination and involvement in the case management process.

Concluding the client-focus is Standard 5, which addresses the types of services provided directly to the client: (1) Outreach, referral, identification; (2) biopsychosocial assessment (client self assessment, other professional assessment); (3) development of a service plan (collaboratively with client); (4) implementation of the plan; (5) coordination and monitoring of service delivery; (6) advocacy on behalf of the client (creating, obtaining, or brokering needed client resources); (7) reassessment of client status, and; (8) termination of the case when services are no longer needed.

The Standards that address the systems-focus of the client-system paradigm include Standard 6, which addresses intervening at the system level to assure existing services are available, and to work toward expanding and increasing access to them. In comparison to codes that define the payer or employer as "customer," this Standard describes a proactive advocacy for the client, which could bode less favorably for the payer/employer, depending upon the agendas present.

While the client-focus clearly dominates, social work case management is not without its commitment to strive for effective gate keeping services for payers and employers. Standard 7 states the responsibility of the case manager to be knowledgeable about resource availability, and to be fiscally responsible in carrying out all case management functions, serving as "gate keeper and resource allocator." The need to develop fiscal management skills is regarded as particularly important, given the ethical dilemmas that may arise regarding client need and available resources. To conclude, Standard 8 suggests social work case managers participate in the evaluation of their service delivery system, as well as their own case management services.

COMPARISON OF CODES

All of the codes address ethical issues of clinical competency in their requirement that case managers should possess at least an undergraduate degree, and often a Master's degree in an allied health profession, as well as substantial clinical experience with the service population (e.g., 2 years for the CMSA code). They also encourage the practice of research-based case management standards of care, and encourage active participation in research projects.

The need for continuing education to remain competent is also consistently noted among the case management-related ethical codes. Confidentiality, and conditions under which it may be breached, is reliably addressed across originating professions. Special attention is given to communication between providers of only the most essential information, and under the strictest of confidence possible. These cautions regarding the protection of client information are particularly critical in the contemporary behavioral and medical healthcare environment.

The degree to which the case management-based ethical codes offer consistent guidance to the field is questionable. It is also true that knowledge of any code of ethics must be supplemented by study and application of a comprehensive model of ethical decision-making to resolve inconsistencies and to supplement its considerations with other authoritative ethics resources. In terms of advocacy for the client, it should be noted that certain codes are more client-centered than others are. A good number of "mixed messages" are embedded in some codes, and other codes clearly describe payer/employer as "customer" obligations.

From a business perspective, it is not wrong for gatekeepers with case management training to assist with cost containment for employers and. The issue becomes ethically tenuous when one realizes that the payer/employer controls access to a finite pool of resources, and for clients need these resources in order to live within their range of potential functioning. In such a situation, if the case manager does not place primacy on the client's interests, the risks of receiving substandard health care escalate dramatically.

PROMINENT ETHICAL ISSUES

Several particularly prominent ethical obligations of concern to case managers emerged in the analysis of both the ethical standards and the literature for this field. These areas and commentary related to them are summarized below. Generally case managers are obligated to (a) engage in individual or systemic advocacy on behalf of their clients; (b) function as gatekeepers to contain costs for an employer or payer, and control access of clients to a finite pool of resources; and (c) maintain client confidentiality in the face of insurer and employer reporting requirements, and the client provides appropriate informed consent to the service process.

ADVOCACY ON BEHALF OF CLIENTS
One of the most meaningful and troublesome ethical responsibilities allocated to case managers is to advocate for their clients. This task involves providing the clients information and conditions necessary to decision-making, supporting clients' needs and informed choices, actively attempting to bring them to the attention of the appropriate parties, and making all reasonable attempts to achieve the needs of the client.

This obligation stems from the very powerful ethical principle of autonomy, whereby clients are seen as having a right to self-determination of choice and freedom from the control of others (Beauchamp & Childress, 1983). Helping professionals have historically considered upholding the principle of autonomy to be a primary requirement of their ethical practice. Patients have been socialized to expect that persons who hold themselves out to be professionals and who enter into a professional relationship with them will assist them in advocating for their needs and decisions with other parties. This ethical requirement of advocacy is detailed in case managers' ethical codes reviewed earlier. In a competitive business environment, the time-honored concept predominates that "let the buyer beware," where clients are seen purely as consumers or customers. A related idea in managed care is that services are provided to equally matched parties to a business contract, may seem to capture the new climate of case management services. These views, however, have been actively challenged. Goldman (1990), for example, has stated the concern that health care consumers often lack the knowledge and information to make truly educated choices. Patients are particularly vulnerable, and therefore are different from other customers in their ability to exercise freedom of choice and advocate for their needs (Nelson, Clark, Goldman, & Schore, 1989). The question becomes, what are the ethically appropriate limitations on advocacy? As with any ethical rule or obligation, this requirement must be balanced with other obligations that have appropriate ethical standing in the situation, such as justice or fairness to other clients' interests. As discussed earlier, the combination of the advocacy and gate keeping functions in the work of the case manager interjects the potential of ethically troublesome conflicting interests in many situations with which the case manager deals. While discussing the role of entrepeneurism in medicine, Braithwaite (1994) offered the opinion that entrepeneurism "may oppose the principle of justice and underlie the virtue and trustworthiness of the profession" (p. 297). In addressing the question of whether ethical considerations require the professional to renounce marketplace practices, she noted that while there should be a "balance between charity and self-preservation, self-preservation does not require self-aggrandizement" (p.300).

Kane (1992) discussed advocacy and gate keeping tensions within long-term care and offered some measures to be considered and adapted to ease these concerns by maximizing separation of these two functions. First, private practice of case management could be available where clients directly hire case managers who will clearly be obligated to advocate for their needs. Second, a model could be utilized in which case managers who pay for services are separately funded from those who do the direct client services of assessing, ordering, or providing direct care. This concept would clearly separate the interests involved in the case. Even where case managers are not able to avoid mixing direct case management services with functions such as claims adjustment, they should still seek not to provide both functions on the same case. Third, she called for the use of individual advocates to be available to clients within the services system. Some managed care companies, such a Merit Behavioral Care Corporation, have been utilizing in-house advocates to enhance their services. Lastly, Kane recommended the use of clearly defined benefits, entitlements, and eligibility criteria. The presence of fair, clear, and consistently applied rules would limit the intrusion of conflicted interests into case management decisions. If this clearly articulated information were freely provided to the clients and their agents, it would facilitate self-advocacy where fair due process and appeals are available.

While each of these concepts has its drawbacks, they present opportunities to think creatively about how to discharge very important responsibilities to the client. If the expectation that clients will benefit from a case manager's advocacy is not realistic, the client should be clearly informed of this situation at the outset of the case management relationship, and informed of other means through which this function might be fulfilled (e.g., a client advocacy or assistance office). The ability to advocate for clients' needs is so important ethically that such ideas as the gatekeeper's ethical *duty to appeal* (or assist the client in appealing) a negative decision made by a managed care organization, is being actively discussed as a reasonable professional obligation.

GATEKEEPER FUNCTION

The tension between the roles of the case manager as advocate for the client and gatekeeper for societal or institutional resources and funds already has been discussed at length. In this section are presented the broader issues involving a lack of consensus on the social policies that ultimately result in the specific mandates to which case managers are subject as gatekeepers. This pivotal position of the case manager can be summarized by the statement that "in the broadest sense, a case manager is the person who makes the health care system work, influencing both the quality of the outcome and the cost" (Mullahy, 1998, p. 9).

The obligation of determining access to services and resources involves the ethical principle of justice. The concept of justice can be seen as the idea of fairness and equality in terms of access to resources and treatment by others (Beauchamp & Childress, 1983). The specific concerns raised by how to allocate or limit access to resources involve the concept of distributive justice or "the comparative treatment of individuals in allotment of benefits and burdens" (Purtillo, 1993, p. 23).

There can be several models which might be utilized to determine how resources might be distributed, including (a) equal shares; (b) distribution by need; (c) distribution by motivation or effort; (d) distribution by contribution of person; (e) free market exchange or purchase; and (f) fair opportunity, or equalizing unequal opportunity (Howie, Gatens-Robinson, & Rubin, 1992). Health and rehabilitation care is theoretically an available resource in this society, but millions of people cannot access these services since they cannot pay for them, whether directly or through some public or private insurance plan. Obviously, there are "serious ethical questions about values and 'justice': how our society views the cherished resource of health care and who should have priority when trying to gain access to it" (Purtillo, 1993). Banja (1991) summarized the core issue for our society in straightforward terms:

> we're ethically confused in our country over whether health care should be a right or a commodity...our society has not been able to summon the political will to identify and reserve enough money to adequately pay for everyone's health needs (pp. 78-79)

As a result of the failure to resolve this critical access issue through a just and fair social policy, the responsibility for controlling health care and rehabilitation costs has been shifted. Both public and private care are increasingly being managed by entrepreneurial interests as the American public refuses to shoulder the tax burden of a more just system of care (Banja, 1993). The case manager may be faced with managing the increasingly limited funding resources that are available to the individual client. The concern becomes whether there is a point at which excessive concern for cost containment makes is impossible for the case manager to construct a plan of care that advances the client's welfare (Banja, 1994).

The case manager is cautioned not to interpret benefits; but rather to establish a plan to stretch those dollars and insure that funds are spent in the most efficacious manner possible. Additionally, the case manager is advised to tap into alternate resources such as non-profit and state funded programs. They are urged to uncover creatively other community support resources, such as churches and charitable associations, to provide for the client's needs. It is also clear that limited funding most likely shifts the financial and care burden to the family or significant others (McClinton, 1995). Shifting of the care burden to the family may be unavoidable as a short-term social solution. This pressure on the family to accept the social burden of disability through heroic self-sacrifice without broader social support is morally suspect as a long-term societal policy (Callanan, 1988).

Case managers are adept at accessing services and communicating across service systems for individual clients. Ethical concerns may arise when the discrepancy between professional practice standards and public or payer policy requires them to take on yet another role. Wetle (1992) stated that: "Expanding on their duties as client advocates, case managers also may need to become advocates for policy change and system reform as yet another strategy for addressing value conflicts and ethical dilemmas" (p. 74).

CONFIDENTIALITY AND INFORMED CONSENT

The case manager's ethical responsibility to protect the client's confidentiality is among the oldest, most sacred, and jealously guarded in the professions. Confidentiality involves the ethical and legal responsibility of the professional to safeguard clients from unauthorized disclosures. Confidentiality is based on clients' right to privacy. Privacy involves clients' freedom to choose for themselves the time and circumstances under which and the extent to which their beliefs, behavior, and opinions are to be shared with or withheld from others. It stems from the ethical principles of autonomy, fidelity (being loyal, honest, and keeping promises), and non-maleficence (refraining from any action that might do harm) (Cottone & Tarvydas, 2004).

In reality, the concept of professional confidentiality has suffered progressive inroads on its unlimited exercise by helping professionals for some time. The primary force, until more recent years, has been as a result of the legal system's need to have access to evidence of socially harmful acts (Swenson, 1997). The *Tarasoff v. Regents of the University of California* (1976) ruling and the subsequent series of related cases regarding how clients who are dangerous to themselves and/or others have substantially impacted and limited the ethical obligations of helping professions to keep client information in confidence. As a result, the ethical duties to warn and/or protect potential victims of violence, as well as the duty to predict and prevent suicide, have been well established in both ethical and legal arenas.

The clarification of the limitations to confidentiality has not eliminated the exercise of professional judgment; but sharpened how and when it must be exercised. The additional ethical duty to inform the client at the outset of the professional relationship regarding the *limitations to confidentiality* is now an accepted standard of practice.

Some of the standard legal exceptions to confidentiality of which the client should be informed include instances when (a) there is a medical emergency; (b) the client is considered to be incompetent or incapacitated (e.g., minor children or adults who have dementia); (c) the client is a danger to self or others; (d) when required by law (e.g., mandatory reporting of child abuse, court order requiring release of information); and (e) attempting to commit, or hospitalize, a person with a psychiatric illness who is a danger to self or others (Purtillo, 1993). Other exceptions include when the client requests release of information or when there is a need for clinical consultation within the treatment team providing services to the client.

Office and paraprofessional staffs who are involved in handling confidential materials must be carefully trained and monitored in their responsibilities to protect the confidentiality of client communications and records. Special procedures for using facsimile (FAX) transmission of confidential materials should be instituted. Recommendations include locating the FAX machine in a limited access location; calling ahead to the appropriate persons to whom the release of information is directed to ensure that the proper individual is available to physically receive the FAX; and using a top sheet that includes a confidentiality warning statement noting that the information should be viewed only by the person to whom it is directed.

Perhaps the more substantial threats to confidentiality have been the more recent concerns with the widespread use of computerized data systems and transmission of health and financial information. The increased use of these data management systems within the context of managed care has compounded the level of concern about potential threats to the client. Concern has risen to such a level that Bernard Aarons of the U.S. Department of Health and Human Services Center for Mental Health recently stated, "It would be misleading for us to lead people to believe that confidentiality exists."

The traditional ethical concern has been to structure the transmission of information in such a way that maximized benefit to the individual client while minimizing risk. Increasingly, the decision of who has access to what data has been structured to benefit organizations and society, rather than to minimize risk to the individual (Donaldson & Lohr, 1994). One estimate is that at least 17 people have some degree of access to information about a client's treatment in a managed case system (Zuckerman & Guyett, 1992). Many caregivers are becoming convinced that it has become impossible to provide a confidential environment for client disclosure, regardless of what assurances are given (Davidson & Davidson, 1995).

With increased access comes increased possibility of compromising the client's confidentiality. Potentially stigmatizing information may reach persons who have no entitlement to view the information. This information may be utilized in some way that harms the client without the client's knowledge of how the information would be sent and consent for that use. Many diagnoses (that are not necessarily carefully or appropriately assigned), such as major depression, panic disorder, or borderline personality disorder, are stigmatizing. If the data bank is tapped into by a life or health insurance company or an employer, the information may result in either denial for insurance coverage, loss of job, or loss of opportunities for advancement for the client. A recent survey of psychologists' perceptions of the effects of managed care on practice and ethics revealed how deep these concerns have cut. The majority of the respondents believed that not only did managed care companies not safeguard the confidentiality of client information; but that there was a high potential that information forwarded to these companies would be used to harm their clients (Murphy, DeBernardo & Shoemaker, 1998).

As a result of these concerns, several recommendations are relevant to case management practice. First, information that "may be harmful to the patient's ability to function freely and confidently in society must be carefully weighed before it is recorded in the medical record" (Purtillo, 1993, p. 102). This is especially true of extremely sensitive information regarding psychiatric diagnoses or hospitalizations (Larkin, 1991). Particular concern exists when it cannot be ascertained that the diagnosis was provided by a qualified professional, or when the information is not directly relevant to the client's current health care concern. A variety of measures has been proposed to better protect the privacy of medical information and improve date storage and security. A detailed review of these issues is provided in a document produced by the U.S. Department of Health and Human Services (Ziglin, 1995).

Second, if confidential information will be released to a managed care organization, insurance company, or employee assistance organization, the full knowledge and consent of the client must be obtained before disclosure. The ethical obligations of the case manager still require this step, despite whatever contracts or policies may exist within the case management-payer service system. The information regarding these types of limitations to confidentiality should be fully discussed with the client at the outset of the service relationship together with the more traditional limitations to confidentiality.

SUMMARY

The challenges of practice in case management are many and diverse. Case management services have taken on greater importance in the provision of health and rehabilitation care for millions of Americans in recent years. As case managers grow more powerful, so do their ethical obligations to conduct their practices in such a manner that justifies the trust their clients or professionals of other disciplines, place in them. Within this chapter, the nature of professionalism and evolution of case management and its standards of practice were reviewed. Attention was given to the importance of utilizing an appropriate ethical decision-making process and having a clear understanding of applicable codes of ethical conduct. Several major codes relevant specifically to case management were discussed. Emerging from this analysis were several prominent ethical issues for case managers. These three areas of ethical concern were explored in greater depth in the concluding section of the chapter. The controversies, challenges, and intricacies facing case managers are great. It is hoped that this chapter will also highlight for the reader the clarity and wisdom that firm grounding within the ethical traditions, standards, and decision-making practices of the professions that infuse case management offer in the pursuit of a just and caring practice.

REFERENCES

American Medical Association Council on Ethical and Judicial Affairs. (1998). Ethical issues in   managed care. *Journal of the American Medical Association, 273*, 330-335.

American Psychological Association. (2002). *Ethical principles of psychologists and code of conduct.* Washington, DC: Author.

American Psychological Association. (2000). *Guidelines for computer-based tests and their interpretation.* Washington, DC: Author.

Banja, J. (1994). Ethical challenges of managed care. *The Case Manager, 5*(3), 37-40.

Banja, J. (1993). Who ruined health care? *The Case Manager, 4*(2), 30-32.

Banja, J. (1992a). Conflicts of interest (Part II). *The Case Manager, 3*(1), 20-21.

Banja, J. (1992b). Patient rights, ethics committees, and the 1992 Joint Commission standards: Implications for traumatic brain injury programs. *Journal of Head Trauma Rehabilitation, 7*(4), 46-56.

Banja, J. (1991). Profile. *The Case Manager, 2*(3), 76-81.

Beauchamp, T. L., & Childress, J. F. (1983). *Principles of biomedical ethics.* Oxford: Oxford University Press.

Braithwaite, S. S. (1994). Distributive justice: Must we way yes when society says no? In J. F. Monagle & D. C. Thomasma (Eds.), *Health care ethics: Critical issues* (pp. 295-301). Gaithersburg, MD: Aspen.

Callanan, D. (1988). Families as caregivers: The limits of morality. *Archives of Physical Medicine and Rehabilitation, 69,* 323-328.

Case Management Society of America. (2002). *Standards of practice for case management.* Little Rock, AK: Author.

Certification of Disability Management Specialists Commission. (2001). *Code of professional conduct of the CDMSC with disciplinary rules, procedures, and penalties.* Rolling Meadows, IL: Author.

Commission on Rehabilitation Counselor Certification. (2001). *Code of professional ethics for rehabilitation counselors.* Rolling Meadows, IL: Author.

Corey, G., Corey, M. S., & Callanan, P. (1998). *Issues and ethics in the helping professions* (5th ed.). Pacific Grove, CA: Brooks/Cole.

Cottone, R. R., & Tarvydas, V. M. (2003). *Ethical and professional issues in counseling* (2nd ed.). Upper Saddle River, NJ: Merrill/Prentice-Hall.

Cullen, J. B. (1978). *The structure of professionalism: A quantitative examination.* New York: Petrocelli Books.

Davidson, T., & Davidson, J. (1995). Cost-containment, computers, and confidentiality. *Clinical Social Work Journal, 23*(4), 453-464.

Donaldson, M. S., & Lohr, K. N. (1994). *Health data in the information age: Use, disclosure and privacy.* Washington, D.C.: National Academy Press.

Elliott, P. (1972). *The sociology of the professions.* New York: Macmillan.

Emener, W. G., & Cottone, R. R. (1989). Professionalization, deprofessionalization, and reprofessionalization of rehabilitation counseling according to criteria of professions. *Journal of Counseling and Development, 67,* 576-581.

Friedson, E. (1994). *Professionalism reborn: Theory, prophecy and policy.* Chicago, IL: University of Chicago Press.

Gambosh, M., & Sager, D. (1995, January/February). Case management challenges, present and future. *Continuing Care*, 25-31.

Gierman, L. (1995). The case manager's role in maintaining corporate morality. *The Case Manager, 6*(5), 50, 53.

Goldman, R. (1993). Practical applications of healthcare marketing ethics. *Healthcare Financial Management, 47*, 46-48.

Howie, J., Gatens-Robinson, E., & Rubin, S. E. (1992). Applying ethical principles in rehabilitation counseling. *Rehabilitation Education, 6*, 41-55.

Kane, R. A. (1992). Case management in long-term care: It can be ethical and efficacious. *Journal of Case Management, 1*, 76-81.

Larkin, H. (1991). Network of computerized patient records seen ahead. *American Medical News, 34*, 9-10.

Leahy, M. J. (1994). *Validation of essential knowledge dimensions in case management* (Technical report). Rolling Meadows, IL: Foundation for Rehabilitation Certification, Education, and Research.

Leahy, M., Chan, F., Shaw, L., & Lui, J. (1997). *Preparation of rehabilitation counselors for case management practice in health care settings* (Technical report). Rolling Meadows, IL: Foundation for Rehabilitation Certification, Education, and Research.

McClinton, M. (1995). Balancing the issue of ethics in case management. *Continuing Care, 14*(5), 13-16.

Moore, W. (1970). *The professions: Roles and rules.* New York: Russell Sage Foundation.

Mullahy, C. M. (1998). *The case manager's handbook* (2nd ed.). Gaithersburg, MD: Aspen Publishers.

Mullahy, C. M. (1995). *The case manager's handbook.* Gaithersburg, MD: Aspen Publishers.

Murphy, M. J., DeBernardo, C. R., & Shoemaker, W. E. (1998). Impact of managed care on independent practice and professional ethics: A survey of independent practitioners. *Professional Psychology: Research and Practice, 29*, 43-51.

National Association of Professional Geriatric Case Managers. (March, 1997). *Standards of practice for professional geriatric care managers.*

National Association of Social Workers (June, 1992). *NASW standards for social work case management.* Washington, DC: Author.

Nelson, L., Clark, H., Goldman, R., & Schore, J. (1989). Taking the train to a world of strangers: Health care marketing and ethics. *Hastings Center Report, 19*, 36-43.

Owens, C. (1996). The glue of managed health care. *The Case Manager, 7,* 75-80.

Patterson, J. B., & Curl, R. M. (1990). Ethics education in supported employment preparation. *Rehabilitation Education, 4,* 247-260.

Powell, S. K. (1996). *Nursing case management: A practical guide to success in managed care.* Philadelphia: J. B. Lippincott Co.

Purtillo, R. (1993). *Ethical dimensions in the health professions.* Philadelphia: W. B. Saunders.

Rinas, J., & Clyne-Jackson, S. (1988). *Professional conduct and legal concerns in mental health practice.* Norwalk, CT: Appleton & Lange.

Shaw, L. R., McMahon, B. T., Chan, F., Taylor, D., & Wood, C. (1997). *Survey of CORE-accredited programs in rehabilitation counseling regarding private sector case management* (Technical Report). Rolling Meadows, IL: Foundation for Rehabilitation, Education, and Research.

Smith, D. S. (1995). Standards of practice for case management: The importance of practice standards. *The Journal of Case Management, 1*(3), 6-16.

Swenson, L. C. (1997). *Psychology and law for the helping professions.* Pacific Grove, CA: Brooks/Cole.

Tarvydas, V. M. (2004). Ethics. In T. F. Riggar & D. R. Maki (Eds.), *Handbook of rehabilitation counseling* (pp.108-141). New York: Springer Publishing.

Tarvydas, V. M., & Shaw, L. (1993). Interdisciplinary team member perceptions of ethical issues in traumatic brain injury rehabilitation. *NeuroRehabilitation, 6*(1), 97-111.

Tarvydas, V. S., & Cottone, R. R. (1991). Ethical responses to legislative, organizational, and economic dynamics: A four level model of ethical practice. *Journal of Applied Rehabilitation Counseling, 22,* 11-18.

Wetle, T. (1992). A taxonomy of ethical issues in case management of the frail older person. *Journal of Case Management, 1,* 71-75.

Ziglin, A. L. (May, 1995). *Confidentiality and the appropriate uses of data.* (Technical Report #MC-95-55). Washington, D.C.: U.S. Department of Health and Human Services, Center for Mental Health Services.

Zuckerman, E. I., & Guyett, I. P. R. (1992). *The paper office I.* Pittsburgh, PA: The Clinician's Toolbox.

7

Community Resources

Martha H. Chapin

Chapter Highlights

- Community resource development

- Medical resources for case management

- Vocational resources for case management

- Conclusion

Case management involves coordinating the various services needed by a person with a chronic illness or disability in order to help the person reach maximum medical improvement and return to work. Coordination of these services often requires referral to community resources. Vandergoot and Jacobsen (1978), who developed a model for resource utilization, suggest that using community resources requires knowledge of available resources and an understanding of how to use the resources. Learning the resources frequently required by clients of the agency develops knowledge. Reviews of agency procedure manuals, discussions with colleagues, and reviews of client files can also provide insight into client resource needs. After identifying potential client needs the case manager can visit prospective referral sites. During these visits or through telephone calls with community resources, the case manager can gain further understanding of agency requirements for client referrals.

Community resource utilization requires interactive services focusing on the client's needs and providing effective communication, planning, and problem solving skills (McCollum, Swenson, & Hooge, 1979). An assessment of client needs is typically performed to identify the services that will assist the client to achieve medical stability and/or return to work. Contact with the community resource allows the case manger to see if the chosen resource can meet client needs. In addition, teaching clients how to assess community resources will help them after their case files are closed (Vandergoot & Jacobsen, 1978).

Referral to a community resource follows a careful review of the client's case file and an initial assessment of the client's medical and vocational needs. This assessment provides a thorough understanding of all the issues influencing medical improvement and return to work of a person with a chronic illness or disability. To support the client's assessment of his or her status, medical information should be requested from all physicians, therapists, health care providers, and hospitals that have treated the client for the present or other medical conditions.

Upon receipt of all medical and vocational information, the case manager decides what additional information is required to understand the client's medical and vocational needs and provide appropriate services (McCollum et al.; Vandergoot & Jacobsen, 1978) to move the client toward maximum medical improvement and return to work. Clients should always be consulted about referrals before information is released to referral sources.

This chapter provides an overview of community resources used by nurses and rehabilitation counselors to serve their clients effectively. Medical, psychotherapy and counseling services, and vocational resources are reviewed.

Return-to-work issues are discussed under vocational resources, even though nurses and rehabilitation counselors also deal with these issues.

COMMUNITY RESOURCE DEVELOPMENT

Quality and cost efficiency are the goals of managed care and case management (Powell, 2000). To achieve these goals, nurses and rehabilitation counselors must know what resources are available, and how these resources can help to meet their case management needs.

To identify community resources and develop a community resource list, it is helpful to contact other case management professionals. They may be employed at your company or may be colleagues you have met through professional associations. Additionally, many communities have community service directories or referral agencies, and local and national disability organizations can provide information about services and professionals available for particular disabling conditions. Physicians or physician referral services can recommend medical specialists. Other resources include local hospitals, nursing homes, rehabilitation centers, and the Internet. Internet resource guides available at the library include the *Internet Resource Guide for Nurses and Health Care Professionals (2001)* and *Internet Resources for Nurses* (2000). The *Internet Resource Guide for Nurses and Health Care Professionals* provides information on accessing the Internet and using electronic mail (e-mail) and lists references such as nursing and health care organizations, drug information, and government agencies. *Internet Resources for Nurses* lists general health care, pharmaceutical, consumer health, disability specific and professional web sites and provides a description of these sites.

Ideally, the case manager should compile multiple positive recommendations about a community resource prior to making a referral and thoroughly assess the quality of services provided, the referral source's ability to meet the client's needs, and the cost of the needed service. A visit to the facility by the case manager may be required to assess the resource.

Once a resource is determined appropriate, contact with the agency is made. The purpose of the referral is stated and a date for service completion obtained. A letter of referral should be sent to confirm the appointment date and time and to provide background information on the client including name, address, telephone number, age, disability, reason for referral, and expected date of completion, if known. Appropriate supporting medical or vocational information should be enclosed. Once a referral has been made, close contact should be maintained with the client to ensure satisfaction with the services provided and with the referral source to ensure that they provide timely, complete services and a progress report.

MEDICAL RESOURCES FOR CASE MANAGEMENT

Following an injury or illness, clients usually receive treatment from a physician at the hospital or at his or her office. For hospitalized clients, the case manager may assist in discharge planning. The client may be discharged to a nursing home, extended care facility, or discharged home, with or without assistance. Therapy may be needed to restore, maintain, or enhance an individual's abilities (Holland, 2003). Transportation services may be needed to transfer the client at discharge, or to transport the client for follow-up care. In addition, the client may need modifications to his or her home or adaptive equipment to assist with everyday functioning. Throughout the client's treatment, the case manager maintains contact with the physician.

PHYSICIAN REFERRALS
A referral is made to a new physician to obtain treatment, a second opinion, or a functional capacity report and release to return to work. A physician referral may be needed because the client's initial contact is with the company or family physician, who may not specialize in the medical condition of the client. Additionally, the client's physician may recommend surgery and a second opinion regarding this may be needed.

Nurses and rehabilitation counselors often make referrals for treatment to a medical specialist who has successfully treated former clients. Referrals for a second opinion are made to specialists who have knowledge about the specific disabling condition. Medical specialists are likely to know more about current treatments in their area of expertise than general practitioners. Referral to a medical specialist is essential as early as possible to make sure that the client receives the most appropriate care. The medical specialist may help reduce medical complications and delays in recovery.

Second opinions are useful when the client is not progressing according to standard medical guidelines, or when costly medical procedures, such as surgery, are recommended. The purpose of the second opinion is to suggest an alternative treatment or confirm the recommended medical procedure. Some treating physicians are uncomfortable completing functional capacity reports and releases to return to work. Referral to a specialist may facilitate the process. If a referral is necessary, the release to return to work from the second physician should be forwarded to the treating physician.

SKILLED NURSING FACILITIES
If clients are unable to return home, they may be discharged to a long-term care or skilled nursing facility. A level of care below acute hospitalization is offered by skilled nursing facilities, which are designed for clients who require ongoing

care from licensed personnel. Nursing homes, intermediate care facilities, and extended care facilities are all skilled nursing facilities (Powell, 2000). Books listing skilled nursing facilities are available in many communities, often with names, addresses, telephone numbers, ratings, level of care offered, and Medicare certification. Since facilities provide differing levels and quality of care, a visit to the facility is warranted to assess its ability to meet the client's needs (Powell). According to Powell, issues that need to be considered before placing a client at the facility include (a) location, (b) client and family agreement on the facility, (c) staff skills and capabilities to meet client needs, (d) primary physician approval, and (e) a decision on whether the primary or facility physician will provide follow-up care. Some insurance benefits require that the facility must be contracted with the payer. The case manager needs to determine if the payer will cover the care needed by the client at the facility (Powell).

INPATIENT REHABILITATION
Inpatient rehabilitation facilities generally require that clients tolerate three hours of combined rehabilitation services daily, five times per week. The services include physical therapy, occupational therapy, and speech-language pathology. In addition, the client must be able to follow one- to two-step commands (Powell, 2000). Usually a client is admitted to inpatient rehabilitation because the client experienced a recent functional loss in an area where independent functioning was present prior to the injury or illness. Many major insurance plans cover inpatient rehabilitation, but strict criteria often must be met because of the cost-intensive nature of these settings (Powell).

HOME HEALTH CARE
Many clients can leave the hospital early if they have support at home for their health care needs. Home health care provides such support, helps to reduce a disability's effect on the individual, and enhances the individual's quality of life (Holland, 2003). When a client does not need intensive, full-time institutional care or supervision, but would have difficulty using outpatient services due to ambulation problems, home care services are appropriate (Lundberg, 1984)., Having home health care providers often reduces medical care costs by allowing the client an earlier release from the hospital or nursing home.

Skilled nurses are frequently used in home health care services. Nurses can help with dressing changes and monitor the client for medical complications or serious health changes. Nurses can also teach the family how to care for the client. The Visiting Nurses Association is a volunteer home health care agency that the case manager may wish to consider (Holland, 2003).

Home health care also can provide paraprofessional support to help the client handle personal care needs and to provide housekeeping assistance and companionship (Holland, 2003). Personal care includes activities of daily living such as feeding, bathing, and toileting needs. Services that are more technical are occasionally required, such as taking blood samples, x-rays and cardiographic (EKG) readings, and providing chemotherapy and intravenous therapy. Therapeutic interventions such as physical and occupational therapy also may be needed (Holland, 2003).

Prior to initiating home health care services, Holland (2003) suggests that case managers answer the following questions: (a) Can the agency provide the services needed? (b) Are these standard services of the agency? (c) Are staff properly trained and supervised? (d) Can special personnel requests be accommodated? (e) Are assessments completed by the home health care agency before a care plan is initiated? The agency should contact the physician or other appropriate professionals when developing the care plan. Care plans should outline the problem, services needed, and client goals (Holland).

THERAPY REFERRALS

Therapy provides symptom control or allows the client to maintain basic functioning in activities of daily living (Powell, 1996). Therapy services include physical therapy, occupational therapy, work hardening, speech-language pathology, audiology, and recreational therapy. The services are provided at hospitals, inpatient rehabilitation facilities, and extended care facilities, in the home, or on an outpatient basis. The quality of the service is a key consideration for a therapy referral, in addition to cost.

Physical therapy can assist persons with disabilities to restore physical functioning and prevent disability following disease, injury, or loss of a body part (Austin, 2001). The focus of physical therapy is to increase physical movement (Holland, 2003) such as balance, mobility, muscle strength, and joint mobility (Maczka, 1990). Physical therapists are oriented toward an individual's symptoms and dysfunctions. They assess pain, limitations of the range of motion of joints, weakness of muscles, and poor coordination of movement (Parry, 1980). Treating physicians prescribe physical therapy, and therapy facilities may be affiliated with physician clinics. Case managers may also be able to make therapy recommendations.

Occupational therapy helps people learn to function in the daily activities that are important to their lives (Blesedell Crepeau, Cohn, & Boyt Schell, 2003). Upon referral, an occupational therapist should evaluate the client and develop a plan of action that includes developing, improving, reestablishing, or maintaining functions and performance. Reevaluations should occur as clients progress through therapy to assess goal attainment (Reed & Sanderson, 1983).

Occupational therapists can also provide driver evaluations. Clients who have a medical condition that impairs brain functioning and upper or lower extremity movement may require such driver evaluations. For example, persons who have epileptic seizures, brain injuries, and/or spinal cord injuries require an evaluation. Frequently the evaluations are provided by hospitals or rehabilitation centers.

Work tolerance screening is used to determine whether further medical intervention is needed before proceeding with work hardening treatment. It can also serve as a preliminary evaluation for measuring progress during therapeutic treatment. Physicians use work tolerance screening for completion of a functional capacity evaluation (FCE) (May, 2003). The FCE is a comprehensive assessment that provides objective measures of clients' functioning and their abilities to perform work related tasks (Fenton & Gagnon, 2003). Rehabilitation professionals can use this information to determine if the client has the physical capabilities to meet the demands of the desired job, or whether job modifications or work hardening is needed.

Occupational therapists, rehabilitation counselors, and vocational evaluators provide work hardening, which often includes graded work activity as a conditioning tool to gradually build a client's physical tolerance and stamina (May, 2003). The client participates in a simulated work environment for 4-8 hours per day, with breaks and lunch. The goal is for the client to accomplish the job's essential functions, meeting physical exertional demands, environmental demands, and productivity requirements (May). Since work hardening is done in preparation for return to work, it functions best when a job is available for the client upon completion of the program. The program is less effective without an immediate return to work, unless the client continues to use the knowledge gained to maintain physical stamina. Work hardening at the job site helps to ease a person with a chronic illness or disability back into the workplace.

Speech-language pathologists "evaluate and provide remedial services to children and adults with speech, language, voice, and swallowing problems" (American Speech-Language-Hearing Association, 1994c as cited in Spahr & Malone, 2002, p. 11). They help clients with aphasia, cerebral palsy, voice disorders, articulation disorders, or stuttering, children whose language develops slower than their mental age, and people who need speech patterns modified (Spahr & Malone).

When clients have a disability or impairment that hampers their spoken or written communication, they may be prescribed augmentative and alternative communication (AAC) strategies. AAC techniques include manual signing, paper and pen, picture boards, and computer-synthesized speech. People who may benefit from AAC strategies include those with sensory, motor, and cognitive impairments including autism, mental retardation, traumatic brain injury or progressive diseases such as Parkinson's disease (Kangas & Lloyd, 2002).

Audiologists "specialize in prevention, identification, and assessment of hearing disorders and...provide treatment and rehabilitative services" (American Speech-Language-Hearing Association, 1994a; 1994b as cited in Spahr & Malone, 2002, p. 7). Prevention involves educating consumers and professionals about the causes of hearing loss, including medical problems, drugs, loud noises, and aging. Early identification of hearing loss is essential to facilitate normal development of language in the young and to prevent permanent hearing loss. The audiologist develops a rehabilitation plan once the extent of hearing loss is determined. This may involve referral to a specialist (otologist, otolaryngologist, or otorhinolaryngologist) for medical or surgical intervention, or recommendation of a hearing aid, speechreading, or an accommodation such as sitting close to presenters (Spahr & Malone).

Therapeutic recreation specialists use leisure activities to restore health and foster growth for persons with physical and mental disabilities, or substance abuse problems, and for the aged. These services are offered in a variety of agencies, including general and psychiatric hospitals, rehabilitation centers, nursing homes, correctional facilities, and parks-and-recreation departments. The activities used by the therapist are based on the client's rehabilitation needs and goals (Austin, 2001). Persons with a spinal cord injury, for example, may consult with a therapeutic recreation specialist to assist them in returning to their pre-injury leisure activities.

PROSTHETICS AND ORTHOTICS

Prosthetic referrals are generally made when a client has had a limb amputated. Functional independence and psychological adjustment may be a major challenge for some amputees (Wikoff, 1994). Clients need to be prepared, as much as possible, for these challenges. For example, clients should be aware that they might experience postoperative pain and phantom sensations. They also need to know about the treatment and exercise that will help in their recovery (Wikoff).

According to Meier (1994), prosthetic prescription and fabrication should begin 3-4 weeks following the amputation. Initially, clients receive information about the type of prosthesis needed and the prosthetic fabrication process. The client may also require emotional support in dealing with the limitations of the prosthesis. Based on the client's physical capabilities, occupational goals, and recreational needs, the decision must be made whether the client will function best with a body-powered or an electric prosthesis. Training on how to use the prosthesis is also needed. The case manager needs to be aware of the client's emotional response to the amputation and his or her adjustment to using the prosthesis (Meier).

Orthotics, which are prescribed by physicians, are external appliances such as braces, splints, and other appliances used to assist, allow for, or restrict the motion of specific parts of the body (Redford, 1987). Orthotics restores function after both temporary and permanent losses. Occupational and physical therapists provide training on how to use these devices (Redford).

An agency or company may manufacture both prosthetics and orthotics. Referral to a prosthetist or orthotist requires the case manager to have knowledge about the quality of the work produced. The prosthetist or orthotist should work closely with the client to resolve any problems with the prosthetic or orthotic. If the prosthetic or orthotic does not fit or function properly, the client may not wear it, increasing functional loss, causing recovery delays, and wasting financial resources.

PAIN MANAGEMENT

Pain prevents many people with disabilities from achieving maximum medical improvement and return to work. A person who continues to experience pain so severe that it precludes effective functioning at home and prevents return to work may require a pain clinic evaluation. Kuhlman and Maki (2003) suggested that pain clinics should be considered whenever a unidimensional approach to medical treatment does not appear effective. Pain clinics are multidisciplinary agencies that provide clients with many modalities to help them understand and more effectively manage their pain. Services often include medical assessments and management, individual and group counseling, a structured exercise program, physical therapy, work hardening, family counseling, biofeedback, relaxation training, education on pain, and vocational rehabilitation. Individualized services are provided based on the client's chronic pain issues.

Admission to a pain clinic generally requires a physician referral. Referrals can come from physicians outside the pain clinic; however, the program physician evaluates the client before admission and decides on the appropriateness of the referral and the client's willingness to commit to the pain clinic program. The advantages of pain clinics include continuity of care, constant observation and supervision, and medical specialist access for consultation and treatment (Kuhlman & Maki, 2003). Since pain clinics are very expensive, the case manager and pain clinic personnel should determine prospective clients' level of commitment before admission to this extensive treatment program.

184

TRANSPORTATION

Clients may require transportation to access services. Private vehicles are the most common mode of transportation, and the case manager needs to consider two issues: the client's ability to sit for the length of the trip, and the vehicle's ability to transport necessary equipment such as an oxygen tank or wheelchair (Powell, 2000). For clients without access to a private vehicle, taxicabs or private transportation services can be considered. The case manager needs to assess whether the taxicab company or private transportation service can provide both pickup and delivery services at designated times. The client's ability to pay for this service or the taxicab company's willingness to accommodate billing for services must also be considered.

Wheelchair vans are recommended if a client is unable to complete a wheelchair to vehicle transfer. Individuals with quadriplegia or cerebral palsy might require wheelchair vans. Van companies need notification if clients require restraints or become easily confused or disoriented (Powell, 2000).

According to Powell (2000), ambulances generally carry paramedics trained in Basic Life Support or Advanced Life Support. Basic Life Support ambulances are needed for clients who require a basic life support paramedic and limited cardiac monitoring. Psychiatric or suicidal clients are also possible candidates for this service. For involuntary transfers during which the client may become combative, additional help should be requested and restraints may be required. Advanced Life Support ambulances are for clients with intravenous lines who require cardiac monitoring or medication administration.

Powell (2000) suggests an air ambulance for transporting an unstable client from one facility to another when speed is essential. This transfer is generally to an acute care facility. The air ambulance has advanced cardiac life support personnel on board, including a registered nurse, cardiac monitoring equipment, and medications. This is the most costly mode of transportation available; however, it may be the safest for medically unstable clients.

HOME MODIFICATIONS

Home modifications are needed when clients' conditions precludes access into or within their homes. Modifications can include installing a ramp to help the client gain access to the home, widening doorways, installing railings, or providing a roll-in shower. Practitioners familiar with state and local ordinances and correct installation techniques should complete home modifications. The modifications need to be completed in time to avoid extending the client's stay at a facility.

DURABLE MEDICAL EQUIPMENT

Durable medical equipment (DME) is designed to withstand repeated use (Holland, 2003) and may include hospital beds for clients who are not mobile or require traction. Clients with mobility impairments may need wheelchairs, walkers, canes, or shower chairs. Individuals with hearing or visual impairments may require devices for visual input and tactile stimulation including flashing lights for a doorbell or an amplifier for the telephone (Powell, 1996). Occupational therapists often perform assessments for adaptive or assistive devices. These devices can be purchased from occupational therapist and DME suppliers (Puckett, 2003). Issues to consider include the availability of items, timeliness of delivery, and cost. These issues can be significant if they delay the client's release from the hospital or nursing home.

Commercially available adaptive equipment may enhance the lives of people with disabilities. ABLEDATA, an electronic database listing available aids and devices for people with disabilities (Weisman, 1990), can be accessed at http://www.abledata.com. The National Institute of Disability and Rehabilitation Research (NIDRR) provide funding for maintenance and updating of this resource. Since the cost of adaptive equipment can vary by manufacturer and commercial source, case managers may want to investigate multiple resources to provide the most cost effective equipment.

PSYCHOTHERAPY AND COUNSELING SERVICES

Some clients may have mental disorders that require treatment or need counseling to resolve problems experienced as a result of a disability or job loss. This treatment may be provided by a psychiatrist, psychologist, counselor, or social worker. Olkin (1999) suggests that therapists who treat people with disabilities should be aware of the minority or social model of disability, family systems theory, systemic theory, and use a biopsychosocial model that includes legal, political, and cross-cultural elements. Clients who have a chronic illness or disability may need assistance in learning to live with a progressive disorder, pain, fatigue, and discrimination. For clients with a spinal cord injury, a referral to a sex therapist may be needed to address issues related to dating and romance, sexuality, and pregnancy (Olkin).

Issues of substance abuse may also need to be addressed. Persons with disabilities often have substantially higher rates of substance abuse than the general population. Substance abuse can lead to disability and it can be used as a mechanism to cope with disability (Olkin, 1999). Alcohol and drug use can complicate and lengthen recovery (Sparadeo & Gill, 1989 as cited in Olkin, 1999).

One of the greatest obstacles to treatment is cost (Olkin, 1999). Payers may not want to cover treatment due to the cost and the fear that therapy may go on forever. To address this concern, the case manager will want to clearly specify the reason for referral (e.g., to address issues related to the client's adjustment to the disability) and suggest a time-limited authorization that is evaluated and reauthorized at appropriate intervals.

VOCATIONAL RESOURCES FOR CASE MANAGEMENT

The goal of vocational case management is to assist the client to return to work. The services needed by the client will vary depending on whether the client will return to work with the former employer or a new employer. The case manager should attempt to assist clients with prior work experience to return to work with their former employer in the job held before the onset of the illness or disabling condition, or a new job. When return to work with the former employer is not possible, return to work with a new employer in the same job or a new job should be considered. Clients who have never worked or cannot return to work with their former employer may need assistance in exploring vocational alternatives, given their physical capabilities. Some of these clients will require training to develop the skills needed to return to work. Others may consider self-employment as an option. A vocational or psychological assessment may be needed to determine appropriate goals for job placement or training. Community and vocational resources are available to help clients in developing alternate job goals and returning to work.

VOCATIONAL ASSESSMENT AND EVALUATION
Vocational assessment and evaluation helps clients clarify their aptitudes, interests, abilities, and behaviors. This information can then be used to identify employment goals and services and help clients understand their current functional capabilities (Roessler & Baker, 1998). Vocational evaluation generally is considered when clients are unable to return to work with their former employer and must consider alternate job placement or short-term retraining. When making a referral for a vocational evaluation, the case manager should state the reason for referral (e.g., to assess interest and abilities, to develop vocational alternatives, or to assess the viability of a vocational option) (O'Brien, 2003). Two issues of concern in referring a client for a vocational evaluation are the characteristics of the person referred and the characteristics of the rehabilitation facility. The case manager must be knowledgeable about the facility and the type of clients usually served. Rehabilitation facilities designed for clients with severe intellectual and/or psychiatric disabilities may not be effective for persons with physical disabilities and higher intellectual functioning (Roessler & Baker).

Vocational evaluation facilities generally use standardized assessments to obtain information on aptitudes and achievement. A facility may also use work samples to observe a client's skill in completing job tasks. Work samples also can provide clients with hands-on experience performing unfamiliar work tasks (O'Brien, 2003) and assist clients to broaden their vocational options.

SITUATIONAL ASSESSMENT

Situational assessment allows the case manager to clarify a client's vocational potential by placing the client in a situation that allows for observation and documentation of behaviors (O'Brien, 2003). In a situational assessment, the client is placed on a job task in either a facility or the community. According to O'Brien, situational assessments evaluate the client's ability to learn tasks, adjust to changes, interact with others, make decisions, and seek help when necessary. This assessment is helpful in deciding what interventions will assist the client to become successful in the job task. Interventions may include teaching the client about modifications, job aids, or instructions at work that will assist the client to become successful. Skills can then be developed in identified need areas. Vocational evaluation facilities frequently complete situational assessments.

PSYCHOLOGICAL EVALUATION

Psychological evaluations usually involve psychometric tests to provide information on abilities, aptitudes, interests, and personality/behavior patterns. Psychological evaluations are suggested when (a) expensive training is required by a client who has no work history in the area; (b) there is no apparent vocational alternative from the client's prior work history; (c) several vocational alternatives are apparent from the client's work history; (d) the case manager has concern about the feasibility of the client's vocational alternative and needs to assess its appropriateness; (e) the client's educational and/or vocational history has gaps or conflicting information of concern to the case manager; (f) the case manager is concerned that the client has unidentified limitations or talents that need to be assessed; or (g) specialized evaluations are required for the client based on disabilities or chronic illnesses such as head injury, blindness, or deafness (McGowan & Porter, 1967 and Patterson, 1960 as cited in Roessler & Rubin, 1998). Psychological evaluations also determine the person's ability to cope with life's demands. Upon completion of a psychological evaluation, the case manager should receive predictive statements about the client's behavior (Roessler & Rubin).

Prior to referral, clients must be informed about the nature of the psychological evaluation and the information expected from it. Case managers should use a psychologist who has experience in working with persons with chronic illnesses and disabilities and understands the effects of disability on psychological adjustment and personal functioning. The psychologist should also understand that the behavioral effects of a disability can be psychogenic and/or organic (Roessler & Rubin, 1998).

VOCATIONAL RESOURCES
A number of standard vocational references are used by case managers to assist in describing jobs, assessing transferable skills, developing resumes, and in expert witness testimony. These include the *Dictionary of Occupational Titles* (DOT), Occupational Information Network (O*NET), and the *Occupational Outlook Handbook* (OOH).

The DOT (U. S. Department of Labor, 1991) provides descriptions of over 12,000 jobs, including the physical demands of the job; the *Guide to Occupational Exploration* (GOE) code; reasoning, mathematics, and language requirements; and the amount of time required to learn the techniques and requirements of the occupation. This resource provides the DOT code numbers used by many computerized search systems. The DOT is used by the Social Security Administration for information about the requirements of work in vocational experts' and vocational specialists' opinions (Social Security Administration, 2000). The DOT can be accessed on-line at http://www.oalj.dol.gov/libdot.htm or http://www.immigration-usa.com/dot_index.html.

O*NET, the newest occupational resource, was designed to replace the DOT. It provides continually updated occupational and labor market information in both English and Spanish and is sponsored by the U. S. Department of Labor (U.S. Department of Labor, Employment and Training Administration, 2003). Information on skills, abilities, knowledge, work activities, and interest are available on 950 occupations based on the 2000 *Standard Occupational Classification* system. The DOT database was used to develop O*NET; however, new data continues to be collected and that will eventually replace the existing data (Occupational Information Network, O*NET OnLine, 2003). Information on the O*NET is available at http://www.doleta.gov/programs/onet/. The O*NET online address is http://online.onetcenter.org/.

The *Occupational Outlook Handbook* (OOH) (U. S. Department of Labor, 1996) describes specific occupations, including (a) the DOT code; (b) general information about the job; (c) working conditions; (d) training, qualifications and advancement needs; (e) job outlook; and (f) earnings. The OOH is located at http://www.bls.gov/oco/home.htm. O*NET codes are included. The Bureau of Labor Statistics (BLS) Occupational Employment survey (http://www.bls.gov) also provides estimates of the number of people employed and their hourly and annual wages for specific occupations. These resources provide information useful for vocational exploration, the completion of job analyses, and resume development.

COMPUTER RESOURCES

Using computers, clients, and case managers can explore vocational alternatives, identify transferable skills, and search for jobs. Additionally, these resources can help case managers complete job analyses and help clients develop job-seeking skills.

Computer guidance systems for vocational exploration consider a client's interest, abilities, values, and work experience in exploring vocational alternatives. Many computer guidance systems are geared toward academic training, and they allow the user to indicate the maximum education desired.

Computer information systems for education and career planning have access to large occupational databases including (a) lists of occupations; (b) work tasks, required abilities, work settings, and salary; (c) educational institutions; (d) military information; (e) financial aid; (f) job search strategies; (g) national employment outlook (Zunker, 1998); (h) employers for specific jobs by geographic area; and (i) sometimes the physical demands of a job. Examples of these systems include DISCOVER® (ACT, Inc., 2003) and SIGI PLUS® (ETS, 2003). Information about these resources can be found on-line at http://www.act.org/discover/ and http://www.ets.org/sigi/ respectively.

Case managers using computer-assisted career-guidance systems need to know the computer system and the client's comfort with computers. The manner in which a client responds to questions influences the occupations suggested by the system. Some responses, such as restrictions in physical capabilities and educational requirements, can decrease the number of occupations suggested. Other responses can provide so many occupations that it is difficult for the client to narrow down a career choice.

OASYS (Vertek, 2003) is an example of vocational software that can be used for career exploration, transferable skills analysis, and labor market employability assessments. To use systems such as this, the case manager must know the client's previous job titles or know the corresponding DOT and/or O*NET code for each job. A computer search of related occupations can then be completed. To expand or decrease transferable skills, information can be entered on changes in client aptitudes, temperaments, and physical capabilities. Some of these programs allow the user to input employer data and can provide a list of jobs in a geographic area that relate to the transferable skills or a specific job title of interest. Labor market and employment information generally includes the employer's name, address, telephone number, and company size. Information may also be available on salary ranges for some occupations. If the cost of the software is prohibitive, some of these resources can be accessed on-line and for a flat fee per client.

TRAINING PROGRAMS

Clients may need various types of training to return to work, including adult education, career and technical education (formerly vocational education), community college or university training. The Department of Education may have information available on state-approved training programs including types of training provided by the facility, the location, cost, and whether financial aid is available. This information may be accessible on the web or found on the computerized software systems mentioned earlier or on state-specific occupational software. The appropriate credentialing body should certify the training program.

Adult education can include adult basic education (e.g., English and math), GED (General Education Development), high school completion, English as a second language, literacy, and skill building such as computer knowledge or specific training to obtain a builder's license. Clients who have not completed high school may need to obtain their GED for employment or for access to other training programs. Training in English as a second language may also be required to facilitate employment. Adult education may be offered at the local high school or community college.

Career and technical education can help a client gain the skills needed to obtain employment. Career and technical education usually focuses on developing specific job skills, such as auto body repair, without requiring completion of a two-or four-year degree program. These programs should be considered for clients who are interested in obtaining training only in their area of interest.

Some clients require more extensive training than adult education or career and technical education provides. These clients may pursue training through a community college or university. Community colleges offer both certificate and associate degree programs. A certificate program is a one-year program that focuses on the client's primary area of interest. These certificate programs can also lead to an associate degree. Further, colleges and universities are now providing distance learning and shortened times to degree completion. Clients with strong academic skills may be able to complete a bachelor's degree in three years or a combined bachelor and maser's degree in five.

The case manager needs to assess employment potential upon completion of a training program to decide the best option for the client. Additionally, the case manager must be aware of limitations placed on the length of training by either the payer or the benefits the client is receiving. Outlining a schedule for training completion and maintaining close contact with the client's training program advisor can facilitate timely completion of the program. The advisor can also help locate resources such as tutors, note-takers, and special accommodations should the client need these to complete the training.

JOB SEEKING SKILLS

The case manager or facility personnel can provide job-seeking skills. Job seeking skills training helps the client learn how to search for a job, complete employment applications, interview, and follow-up on job leads. Job seeking skills training should be considered when the case manager's time is limited or the client would benefit from group support.

JOB ANALYSIS AND JOB ACCOMMODATIONS

Before a client returns to work in a specific job, a job analysis is often recommended. This analysis describes the job task, physical demands, and essential functions of the job. The analysis is reviewed with the client's treating physician. The goal is to obtain a written release for the client to return to work and to determine whether job accommodations are needed for the client's return to work. The case manager can complete the job analysis and use resources to identify and access accommodations. If the client has worked with an occupational therapist, the case manager can contact the therapist, who can then evaluate the job and recommend accommodations. The case manager can also contact the Job Accommodation Network (JAN) at 1-800-526-7234 or 1-800-ADA-WORK. Their web address is http://www.jan.wvu.edu/. Searchable Online Accommodation Resources (SOAR) can also be accessed at http://www.jan.wvu.edu/soar/ to gain information on accommodations in work and educational settings.

Rehabilitation engineering and technology firms are also available (Kohn, Proctor, & Barker, 1990). Many states have accommodation agencies to assist with accommodations. Contact with the Rehabilitation Engineering and Assistive Technology Society of America (RESNA) at www.resna.org/reshome.htm or the state federal rehabilitation program can help locate these resources. The International Center for Disability Resources on the Internet (ICDRI) located at http://www.icdri.org/index.html also has accessibility information.

JOB PLACEMENT

The client, the case manager, or both working together can complete job placement. Clients can also be referred to employment agencies for assistance. Employment agencies relieve employers of the cost of advertising a job opening and screening applicants (Matkin, 1985). They charge a fee for clients placed in a job. Ideally, a case manager should consider an employer fee-paid agency rather than employee fee-paid agency. With an employer fee-paid agency, the employer pays the fee for hiring the applicant. Employee fee-paid agencies require the applicant to pay a portion of his or her annual income following placement.

Temporary employment agencies are useful to assist a client in trying out a job or gaining temporary employment until full-time employment is obtained. The case manager, however, must be aware of the effects of temporary employment on the clients' benefits. Their benefits may be reduced while they are temporarily working or clients may experience difficulty or delays in getting benefits reinstated once the temporary employment position ends. Clients may also be without income for a few weeks from the day they start work until the first paycheck is received. The case manager may need to negotiate with the payer to help the client successfully transition into the work force.

Case managers can also have their clients contact the state employment security commission. Some employers only advertise for positions where screening is done by this agency. This state agency does not charge a fee for service. Job openings may also be posted on the agency's website.

CONCLUSION

Community resources should be consolidated in a database or notebook, the information updated regularly with new resources added, and ineffective resources deleted. An up-to-date file in a central location can be used by all staff when a particular service is needed for persons with chronic illness and/or disability. The availability of such a database is essential since clients have individualized needs and medical conditions.

REFERENCES

ACT, Inc. (2003). DISCOVER career guidance and information system. Retrieved on September 17, 2003 from http://www.act.org/discover.
American Speech-Language-Hearing Association. (1994a). *The audiologist*. Rockville, MD: Author.
American Speech-Language-Hearing Association. (1994b). *Helping your patients with speech, language, or swallowing disorders*. Rockville, MD: Author.
American Speech-Language-Hearing Association. (1994c). *The speech-language pathologist*. Rockville, MD: Author.

Austin, D. R. (2001). Introduction and overview. In D. R. Austin & M. E. Crawford, *Therapeutic recreation* (3rd ed., pp. 1–21). Boston: Allyn and Bacon.

Blesedell Crepeau, E., Cohn, E. S., & Boyt Schell, B. A. (2003). Occupational therapy practice today. In E. Blesedell Crepeau, E. S. Cohn, & B. A. Boyt Schell (Eds.) *Willard & Spackman's occupational therapy* (10th ed., pp. 27-29). Philadelphia, PA: Lippincott Williams & Wilkins.

Commerce Department. (2000). *Standard occupational classification manual.* Lanham, MD: Bernan Associates.

ETS. [Computer Software]. (2003). SIGI Plus educational and career planning software: Power up to a brighter future! Retrieved on September 19, 2003 from http://www.ets.org/sigi/.

Farr, J. M. (1991). The *enhanced guide for occupational exploration.* Indianapolis, IN: JIST Works, Inc.

Fenton, S., & Gagnon, P. (2003). Work activities. In E. Blesedell Crepeau, E. S. Cohn, & B. A. Boyt Schell (Eds.) *Willard & Spackman's occupational therapy* (10th ed., 342-346). Philadelphia, PA: Lippincott Williams & Wilkins.

Fitzpatrick, J. J., & Montgomery, K. S. (Eds.). (2000). *Internet resources for nurses.* New York: Springer Publishing Co.

Holland, B. E. (2003). Home health services. In W. Crimando & T. F. Riggar, *Utilizing community resources* (pp. 21-28). Prospect Heights, IL: Waveland Press, Inc.

Kangas, K. A., & Lloyd, L. L. (2002). Augmentative and alternative communication. In G. H. Shames & N. B. Anderson (Eds.) *Human communication disorders: An introduction* (6th ed., pp. 545-593.). Boston: Allyn and Bacon.

Kohn, J. G., Proctor, S., & Barker, M. (1990). Rehabilitation engineering clinic. In R. V. Smith & J. H. Leslie, Jr. (Eds.), *Rehabilitation engineering* (pp. 465-493). Boca Raton, FL: CRC Press.

Kuhlman, B. W., & Maki, D. R. (2003). Pain clinics. In W. Crimando & T. F. Riggar (Eds.), *Utilizing community resources* (pp. 37-45). Prospect Heights, IL: Waveland Press, Inc.

Lundberg, C. J. (1984). Home health care: A logical extension of hospital services. *Topics in health care financing, 10*(3), 22-33.

May, V. R., III. (2003). Work hardening programs. In W. Crimando & T. F. Riggar (Eds.), *Utilizing community resources* (pp. 3-6). Prospect Heights, IL: Waveland Press, Inc.

Maczka, K. (1990). *Assessing physically disabled people at home.* London: Chapman and Hall.

Mascara. C., Czar, P., & Hebda, T. (2001). *Internet resource guide for nurses and health care professionals* (2nd ed.). Upper Saddle River, New Jersey: Prentice Hall, Inc.

Matkin, R. E. (1985). *Insurance rehabilitation*. Austin, TX: Pro-ed, Inc.

McCollum, P. S., Swenson, E., & Hooge, N. C. (1979). Community resources revisited: Sources of support in the rehabilitation process. *Journal of Applied Rehabilitation Counseling, 10*(3), 72-77.

McGowan, J. F., & Porter, T. L. (1967). *An introduction to the vocational rehabilitation process*. Washington, D.C.: Department of Health, Education and Welfare, Vocational Rehabilitation Administration.

Meier, R. H., III. (1994). Upper limb amputee rehabilitation. *Physical Medicine and Rehabilitation: State of the Art Reviews, 8*(1), 165-185.

O'Brien, J. K. (2003). Rehabilitation facilities. In W. Crimando & T. F. Riggar (Eds.), *Utilizing community resources* (pp. 131-142). Prospect Heights, IL: Waveland Press, Inc.

Occupational Information Network, O*NET OnLine. (2003). Welcome to O*NET online. Retrieved June 26, 2003 from http://online.onetcenter.org/help/welcome/.

Olkin, R. (1999). *What psychotherapist should know about disability?* New York: The Guilford Press.

Parry, A. (1980). *Physiotherapy assessment* (2nd ed.). London: Croom Helm.

Patterson, C. H. (1960). Psychological testing and the counseling process. In C. H. Patterson (Ed.), *Readings in rehabilitation counseling*. Champaign, IL: Stipes.

Powell, S. K. (with Wekell, P. M.). (1996). *Nursing case management: A practical guide to success in managed care*. Philadelphia: Lippincott-Raven Publishers.

Powell, S. K. (2000). *Case management: A practical guide to success in managed care*. Baltimore: Lippincott Williams & Wilkins.

Puckett, F. D. (2003). Rehabilitation engineering/technology services. In W. Crimando & T. F. Riggar (Eds.), *Utilizing community resources* (pp. 167-176). Prospect Heights, IL: Waveland Press, Inc.

Redford, J. B. (1987). Orthotics: General principles. *Physical Medicine and Rehabilitation: State of the Art Reviews, 1*(1), 1-10.

Reed, K. L., & Sanderson, S. R. (1983). *Concepts of occupational therapy*. Baltimore: Williams & Wilkins.

Roessler, R. T., & Rubin, S. E. (1998). Psychological evaluation. In R. T. Roessler & S. E. Rubin, *Case management and rehabilitation counseling* (3rd ed., pp. 69-81). Austin, TX: Pro-ed.

Roessler, R. T., & Baker, R. J. (1998). Vocational evaluation. In R. T. Roessler & S. E. Rubin, *Case management and rehabilitation counseling* (3rd ed., pp. 83-98). Austin, TX: Pro-ed.

Spahr, F. T., & Malone, R. L. (2002). Human communication disorders: An introduction. In G. H. Shames & N. B. Anderson, (Eds.) *Human communication disorders: An introduction* (6th ed., pp. 1-27.). Boston: Allyn and Bacon.

Sparadeo, F., & Gill, D. (1989). Effects of prior alcohol use on head injury recovery. *Journal of Head Trauma Rehabilitation, 4,* 75-82.

U.S. Department of Labor. (1991). *Dictionary of occupational titles* (4th ed. revised). Indianapolis, IN: JIST Works, Inc.

U.S. Department of Labor. (1996). *Occupational outlook handbook* (1996-1997 edition). Washington, D. C.: U. S. Government Printing Office.

U.S. Department of Labor, Employment and Training Administration. (2003). O*NET–beyond information–intelligence. Retrieved September 17, 2003 from http://ww.doleta.gov/programs/onet/.

Vandergoot, D., & Jacobsen, R. J. (1978). Identifying, developing and using community resources in rehabilitation counseling. *Journal of Applied Rehabilitation Counseling, 9*(4), 159-163.

Vertek, Inc. [Computer Software]. (2003). OASYS. Retrieved on September 19, 2003 from http://www.vertekinc.com/VERTEKWEB/NewFiles/oasys.html.

Weisman, G. (1990). Rehabilitation engineering in the workplace. In R. V. Smith & J. H. Leslie, Jr. (Eds.), *Rehabilitation engineering* (pp. 253-297). Boca Raton, FL: CRC Press, Inc.

Wikoff, E. K. (1994). Preprosthetic management. *Physical Medicine and Rehabilitation: State of the Art Reviews, 8*(1), 61-72.

Zunker, V. G. (1998). Using computers for career counseling. In V. G. Zunker, *Career counseling* (5th ed., pp. 131-147). Pacific Grove, CA: Brooks/Cole Publishing Co.

8

Assistive Technology for the Rehabilitation Case Manager

Charles Merbitz
Nancy Hansen Merbitz
Marcia J. Scherer

Chapter Highlights

◧ The context of rehabilitation and assistive technology

◧ An overview of major applications of assistive technology

◧ Conclusion

THE CONTEXT OF REHABILITATION
AND ASSISTIVE TECHNOLOGY

Assistive Technology (AT) has the potential, as yet only partially actualized, to help people with disabilities live in the least restrictive environments and attain their maximum achievements, just as persons temporarily without disability use a myriad of other technologies to live and get things done (Verbrugge, Rennert, & Madans, 1997). Eyeglasses, autos, carpets, refrigerators, telephones…all of these devices play roles in supporting full and productive lives for people, as AT supports the activities of people with disabilities. Like "regular tech," AT is a huge area, involving many different things, functions, and people with varying levels of skill, credentials, training, and experience. A challenge for the case manager is to uncover and sort out the options so as to acquire the appropriate AT for a given client at a reasonable price. In this chapter, we will survey AT, beginning with some basic issues, organizing principles, and AT service issues, then reviewing different specific AT areas. Our goal is to help the case manager more intelligently invest resources to help empower the consumer/client with a disability (Scherer, 2000).

What is AT? AT is defined rather broadly in law as any kind of device or product system that assists persons with disabilities in the performance of daily tasks and activities. The Assistive Technology Act of 1998 (AT Act) has built on its legislative predecessors, especially the Technology-Related Assistance for Individuals with Disabilities Act of 1988 (Tech Act), and reaffirms the Federal role of promoting access to AT devices and services for individuals with disabilities of all ages. More formally, the "Tech Act" defined AT as: "any item, piece of equipment, or product system, whether acquired commercially off the shelf, modified, or customized that is used to increase or improve the functional capabilities of individuals with disabilities" (Cook & Hussey, 2002, p.5). This includes technology that allows people with disabilities to improve their "capacity to carry out activities of daily living and employment" including "the systematic application of technologies, engineering methodologies, and scientific principles to meet the needs of, and address the barriers confronted by individuals with handicaps in areas which include education, rehabilitation, employment, transportation, independent living, and recreation" (Federal Register, Feb.18, 1994, p.8346).

GROWTH IN TECHNOLOGY SERVICES, SITES, AND PROFESSIONALS
Assistive technology use and need in the United States today is difficult to estimate precisely. Data from surveys, such as the Disability Followback Survey (DFS), administered between 1994 and 1997 (National Center for

Health Statistics, 1999a, 1999b), show that, based on a weighted sample of 41.8 million American adults with disabilities:

- 8.3 million Americans with disabilities needed special equipment or aids (AT) to perform basic activities of daily living (ADLs).
- 15.4 million Americans with disabilities reported using assistive devices or technologies such as hearing aids, crutches, canes, walkers, wheelchairs, scooters, catheterization equipment, glucose monitors, diabetic equipment and supplies, inhalers, nebulizers, and feeding tubes.
- 14 million Americans with disabilities lived in homes modified to meet their special needs. Among these, over 1.5 million persons reported needing further home modifications. An additional 1 million persons with disabilities who did not have any home modifications indicated that they needed such accommodations.
- 511 thousand Americans with disabilities reported using modified cars or vans. 369 thousand persons with disabilities reported needing modifications to their cars or vans.
- 15.1 million Americans with disabilities worked at the time of the interview. In this group, 4.2 million persons reported being limited in the kind or amount of work they could do.
- 714 thousand Americans with disabilities reported having an accessible work environment, with hand rails or ramps, elevators, including elevators designed for persons with special needs, specially adapted work stations, restrooms designed for persons with special needs, automatic doors, voice synthesizers, TDDs, infrared systems or other technical devices, Braille, enlarged print, special lighting or audio tape devices, and special pens or pencils, chairs, or other office supplies. 1.3 million Americans with disabilities working at the time of the interview reported needing (but not having) one or more of the above-mentioned work place designs and accessories.

Over the past three decades, legal changes in the US, including the 1973 Rehabilitation Act, the 1986 Tech Act, the 1992 Americans with Disabilities Act, and the AT Act of 1998 have fostered great expansion of AT services (Cook & Hussey, 2002). As a result of the 1986 Rehabilitation Act Amendments, Federal regulations require that rehabilitation engineers be included in teams that provide federally funded services to people with disabilities. The Tech Act Amendments of 1992 required state plans to describe how a range of rehabilitation technology services are to be provided at each stage of vocational rehabilitation, and how AT devices, services and worksite assessments are to be included in assessing eligibility and rehabilitation needs (Segdy, 1992). This legislation and growth has meant that technologically skilled staff have been sought for positions in a variety of organizations, including rehabilitation hospitals and facilities, state VR agencies, schools, business, industry, and in commercial enterprises that support rehabilitation. Staff members in these organizations have always needed the traditional "people-oriented" clinical skills; now technological skills also are needed.

AT still does not reach all consumers. In a recent national survey (Carlson, Ehrlich, Berland, & Bailey, 2002), conducted by the Rehabilitation Engineering Society of North America (RESNA), consumers with disabilities voiced awareness of the benefits of AT for increasing independence in daily activities and vocational pursuits, but reported difficulty in getting information about available AT and funding for acquiring it. They also reported a very low frequency of obtaining AT-related information from any state Tech Act agency; thus, RESNA concluded that greater dissemination of AT information is needed for rehabilitation professionals.

Now, efforts to implement Ticket to Work programs and federal and state responses to Olmstead have sparked further awareness of AT. President Bush's "New Freedom Initiative" and subsequent Executive Order 13217 on Community-Based Alternative for People with Disabilities have emphasized the importance of AT for vocational and residential independence. In the 2001 report "Delivering on the Promise," federal agencies described AT efforts. These include a focus on AT to decrease numbers of people with disabilities living in institutional settings, to increase their employment, and to decrease the "digital divide" which differentially limits the access of people with disabilities to information and skills needed in the modern work-place. "The New Freedom Initiative promises to level the playing field by ensuring that Americans with disabilities have affordable access to the best technologies of today and that even better technologies are available in the future. In order for people with disabilities to maximize the opportunities that technology presents, it is imperative that adequate training and skills development be provided" (hhs.gov/newfreedom/prelim/fullrpt.html#tech).

How can case managers, who themselves may be unfamiliar with technology, provide this increased tech access and support for the persons that they serve? Merbitz, Lam, Chan, and Thomas (1999) discussed the assistive technology information needs of professionals such as rehabilitation counselors acting in case management roles with people with disabilities. They pointed out that while appropriate technology is critical, poor technology choices can be harmful or even fatal, and that a tremendous breadth of knowledge can be required to serve persons with tech needs. Because so many professionals are not trained in AT, there may be an extended impact when resources are devoted to training, since trained personnel are frequently sources of information for their peers. Justesen and Menlove (1994) suggest that the lack of AT content in human services curricula has led to a neglect of basic tech information for consumers, since human services providers can scarcely communicate about (or refer others to be evaluated for) technology that they themselves know little about.

Professionals in AT. As noted by Enders and Hall (1989, p. 222) "No one professional discipline can be identified as the sole or even primary source [of employment-related technology services]." They proceed to list engineers, Occupational Therapists (OTs), Physical Therapists (PTs), Rehabilitation Counselors, Nurses, and others who now provide AT services. Mann and Lane (1991) have identified ten professions as "especially involved" in AT. In an effort to assure quality of services among these diverse providers, RESNA (the Rehabilitation Engineering and Assistive Technology Society of North America) established a voluntary credentialing program for people providing AT. RESNA developed criteria and an examination for the Assistive Technology Provider (ATP), a service provider (usually now a health care professional) who specializes in the analysis of consumer needs and training, and the Assistive Technology Supplier, who is primarily concerned with providing commercial equipment. RESNA also continues to credential the RE, or Rehabilitation Engineer, who is a Professional Engineer working in AT. These actions were taken in consultation with the National Association of Medical Equipment Suppliers and the National Registry of Rehabilitation Technology Suppliers. Persons with these credentials have passed the RESNA examinations and are committed to practicing in an ethical way. This includes limiting their practice to their areas of competence, avoiding conflicts of interest, and holding paramount the interest of the client. Even though these services sometimes may be more costly in the short term, we recommend that case managers call upon ATPs (Assistive Technology Providers) when possible to help their clients achieve satisfying outcomes.

Case managers and AT. Rehabilitation case managers may judge the effectiveness of AT solutions, recommend AT, and coordinate AT and other services. They often search out AT resources, allocate resources to AT, or may present cases to payers or supervisors in an effort to have resources devoted to AT. They help clients to problem-solve, make decisions, become comfortable with new technology and learn to use it. Finally, experienced case managers can serve as technology resources for other professionals. AT is, however, an area that is rapidly changing, exceptionally diverse, and shared among many professionals and disciplines. The rapid change from technological innovation, economic pressure, and legal developments means that today's knowledge of what AT offers for a specific person with a disability (and even which services are provided by a given vendor) may be obsolete tomorrow and should almost certainly be revised within a few years.

AT now covers so many areas that it is not feasible for one person to have state-of-the-art skills in all areas. Both engineers and clinicians in health professions generally specialize in one or two areas and of necessity are not current in other areas. Healthcare clinicians also tend to specialize by discipline (e.g. Occupational Therapy, Speech and Language Pathology), and bring the unique perspectives and contributions of their disciplines to bear on functional problems. Usually, however, it is the rehabilitation case manager who must see to it that a client's budget is wisely invested, and hence may be responsible for very broad knowledge of AT, since any client may require AT in any area. This *breadth* of knowledge is not required of AT specialists within healthcare professions, but conversely and fortunately the rehabilitation case manager does not need the same *depth* of specialized knowledge within any one area of AT.

Like other professionals, it is appropriate for managers to recognize their own limitations and refer clients to the proper specialized professionals depending on their specific needs. This could be a Seating and Mobility professional for seating issues or a Speech-language Pathologist for communication issues. As managers gain experience, they will learn when it is safe and cost-effective to order directly some of the many off-the-shelf items that have clear-cut applications for particular consumers.

Finally, we must remember that a consumer is the person who will actually use the technology, and a device is successful only when it meets the personal, idiosyncratic situation, and needs of the one individual who is to use it. Experienced, articulate, thoughtful consumers, therefore, offer an unmatched perspective. They have years of deep experience with AT, and if one can listen closely and work with the consumer to make the best possible match between the consumer and technology, the promise of AT can be fulfilled and failure avoided.

Strategies to keep current. With the rapid change in the AT market, and the virtual impossibility of keeping current across all AT areas, the case manager can use several strategies to keep up. First, a foundation of basic knowledge and vocabulary will be helpful. Cook and Hussey (1995, 2002) have provided an excellent but inexpensive text for AT. It is highly recommended both as an overview and as a reference.

Short courses and in-service education are one means of providing reviews of different areas, such as home and worksite modification and accessibility, and updates or deeper treatment of topics of particular interest. Second, instead of trying to keep up in each area of technology, the case manager can form relationships with ATPs in various specialties, asking questions and sending referrals. Third, conferences allow one to meet vendors and other professionals, and maintain the personal relationships. Fourth, computerized searches (see the section on Internet and Abledata) can provide current information when it is needed; these leads then can be followed as appropriate. Finally, since an experienced consumer is an outstanding resource, the case manager can build relationships with clients, Centers for Independent

Living, State Assistive Technology Projects, and similar consumer sources that will allow them to share their expertise to help others. Of course, these latter strategies are based on working with other players, not against them, in long term "win-win" relationships.

OUTCOME MEASURES IN AT AND REHABILITATION
An area of great concern in AT is the assessment of rehabilitation outcomes, to improve efficiency and effectiveness of AT services, to justify their cost, and to validate their utility. For the case manager who may have to assess the capabilities of unfamiliar providers, outcome data contributed by those providers may be critical sources of information in making choices among them. Similarly, data reflecting the outcomes of cases handled by an individual or institution may be seen as the index of overall success or failure of rehabilitation. Case managers, therefore, need to develop familiarity with the kinds of data used in outcomes measurement, and become savvy about their limitations as well.

In an ideal situation, outcome measures would reflect effectiveness and efficiency, and rehabilitation efforts achieving better outcomes would be eligible for larger reimbursements, as compared to those leading to poorer outcomes. In the absence of good effectiveness information, resource allocation decisions may be made on the basis of cost alone. Unfortunately, there is no satisfactory general rehabilitation outcome measurement system available. The FIM (Functional Independence Measure) is arguably the most widely used outcomes assessment in rehabilitation. On the FIM, a lower (less independent) score is given for tasks performed with AT. This scoring system means that with the FIM, any AT usage means that the person is dependent, even though on a practical level, the AT device user may be seen as fully independent (Smith, 1996). It has also been criticized on other grounds (Merbitz, Morris, & Grip, 1989). Alternative approaches (Merbitz, 1996; Smith, 1996; Whiteneck, Charlifue, Gerhart, Overholster, & Richardson, 1992) and considerations (Cushman & Scherer, 1996; Jutai, Ladak, Schuller, Naumann, & Wright, 1996; Oldridge, 1996a, 1996b) eventually may yield more satisfactory ways to address outcomes.

EMPOWERMENT AND LEARNING PERSPECTIVE
Sometimes AT is viewed as mysterious and overpriced. Dictionary definitions reveal "technology" to involve the application of knowledge to solve some problem or reach some outcome. Technology becomes assistive when used by a person with a disability. It can be helpful to relate AT to the everyday world and other technology with which clients are familiar. Newly injured clients and families, for example, sometimes seem surprised, confused, and both submissive and resistant to professionals' advice. Such emotional responses are

understandable when one considers the situation from an empowerment point of view: the client is making an important purchase, and may have been told how critical it is to avoid making a mistake. An empowerment model holds that we can learn from experience, so as to be able to do better in the future. Consider the purchase of a large consumer product by an inexperienced consumer as a cycle with several stages:

	Stage description	**Typical Statement**
1)	Unawareness or denial	"I don't need a {new house, car, wheelchair}" "I can't afford it."
2)	Information	"Well, maybe I need a {house, car, wheelchair}" "I'll look around"
3)	Action and concrete steps	"Tell me about the features of this one..."
4)	Purchase	"I'll buy this one"
5)	Buyer's remorse	"Maybe that other one was better, I should have waited, acted earlier, etc."
6)	Maintenance	"I can do OK with what I have"/ get it repaired
7)	Holding on - and return to unawareness/denial #1	"I don't need a {new house, car, wheelchair}"

Many people seem to experience distressing emotional states when trying to decide about major purchases. Persons buying their first car or house often make several visits, take along experienced relatives, or otherwise access emotional support. Another factor is that when persons feel like novices with some purchase, they are often suspicious and wary of vendors, and may even expect the vendor to lie, misrepresent, or otherwise swindle them in order to make the sale. A case manager may be similarly uncertain and wary when dealing with a new vendor, or one whose performance in the past was less then stellar, but who a client prefers. The client's stress can be exacerbated when the purchase decision is part of a one-time settlement or on a lengthy (five-year) schedule before a replacement will be available, and few complex purchases are entirely satisfactory if one feels forced to act with insufficient information. What seems to occur as the person cycles through several buying experiences is that the emotional states associated with the different parts of a purchase cycle become much less distressing. One's second or third house, car, or wheelchair may be a much less stressful purchase when one builds on what was learned from the previous experiences, and the knowledge base is so much greater. In contrast to the client, professionals in rehabilitation and health care have internships, practica, orientations, and similar training experiences that help them adjust their emotional responses. In addition, they may have been through a wheelchair purchase literally hundreds of times, and they are not the ones who may have to "make do" with mistaken purchases for years to come. A challenge for the experienced professional is to retain empathy for the understandable hesitancy and distress of the newly rehabilitated client and family. This vision of the process also shows the value of peer-advisors to help the newly disabled person. Peers are experienced (unlike the family) and not financially bound to any particular vendor (unlike sales representatives.) Centers for Independent Living (when sufficiently staffed and resourced) and other community agencies can be of great benefit in AT purchases, home modifications, adapting vehicles, and similar major investments.

Within an empowerment perspective, the critical task is to learn. First, learn about the person and the specific technology proposed for that person, environment, and goals. The knowledge will ultimately be put to use when technology is deployed, but the learning does not stop there. Devices break, wear out, become inappropriate due to changes in the client's capabilities or environment, or become obsolete when more functional or capable devices are invented. If the client and case manager have continued to learn, a replacement or improved device can be acquired. Even if a mistake is made, and a wrong or useless device is purchased, learning from the error can prevent that mistake from happening again. When it comes time to replace the first device, or when a similar client is assigned, that knowledge will be invaluable to prevent another error.

Empowerment also involves another advantage. Recall that all AT is deployed in the context of someone's life, within some physical and social environment. It is critical for the technologists and case manager to learn enough about the client for an accurate view of the environment in which the device will be deployed. For example, an expensive computerized device does not help a client if it is stolen, and integrating a home security system with a medical call system may be cost-effective when done as part of the AT. Clients may have difficulty in telling professionals enough about their lives for accurate decision-making. With the client's permission, it is helpful to have the AT specialist communicate with all members of the team, especially including the client, but also OT, PT, physician, family, nurses, peer-advisors, employers, and others who can discuss the client's capabilities and the environment within which the tech will be deployed. (See also the discussion of Scherer [2002], below.)

MODELS OF ASSISTIVE TECHNOLOGY

The development and use of AT takes place in the context of changing views of function and disability. The World Health Organization's model of function and disability continues to be refined and revised (WHO International Classification of Function (ICF), 2003). The work of AT specialists can benefit from the distinctions it makes between function or impairment at the level of the Body (its systems and parts), and function or limitations at the levels of Activity and Participation (carrying out activities such as reading or walking, and taking part in major life roles such as parenting or employment). AT interventions can be applied at any of these levels. Brandt and Pope (1997), in their influential *Enabling America*, also discussed AT in terms of support for action and accomplishment by people with disabilities.

Smith (1996) offers five different areas of intervention that expand on this structure. According to Smith, a rehabilitation intervention may be used to (1) reduce the impairment through rehabilitative treatment; (2) train compensatory functions or skills to achieve the desired ends; (3) use assistive technology; (4) change the environmental demands or supports so that the task can be done; and (5) use an attendant. Smith gives the example of a person with cerebral palsy, severe athetosis, and severely limited verbalizations ordering food in a restaurant. Following Smith's distinctions, one may (1) try speech therapy to gain functional vocalization; (2) point or use gestures; (3) use a speech synthesizer; (4) go to a cafeteria-style restaurant; or (5) have a companion order. Smith also notes that often we pursue several of these options simultaneously, as when training with new AT, or when existing AT is out for repair.

The Technology Pyramid. Hedman (1991) presented a "technology pyramid" (Figure. 1) with four levels, and as will be seen, it is almost always better to deploy AT at the lowest level possible. Level 1 is "no technology" – simply changing the environment, workflow, or similar factors can often solve the problem. A good Level 1 solution has no batteries to replace; nothing to break, get lost, misplaced, stolen, or otherwise fail; and is always available.

Level 2 includes "off the shelf" commercially available items and Level 3 includes commercial items that require modification or skilled fitting.

Figure 1. The Technology Pyramid

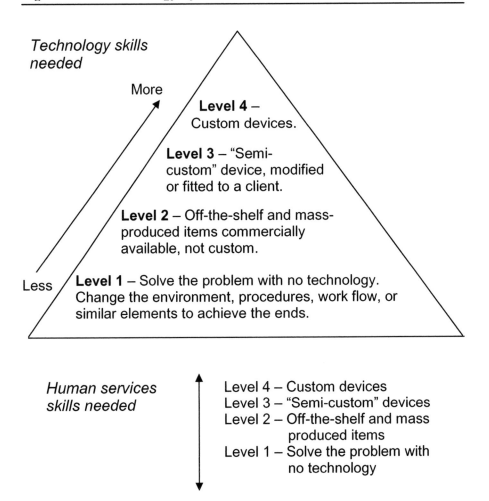

Adapted from Hedman. 1991.

Level 4 includes custom items designed and built specifically for one consumer (although successful ones may become commercial items eventually). Since Level 2 and 3 are commercially made, they usually enjoy far more design, test, and manufacturing reliability than Level 4 items, and also better warranties, service, reliability, replacement parts, and so forth. Hence, tech interventions should usually be kept as low on the Pyramid as possible.

When the cost of skilled workers to design, fabricate, fit, and maintain unique items is considered, there is much greater cost for any item at Level 4 as compared to similar items at 3 or 2. This economy of technology also roughly parallels the professional engineering skills needed at each Level.

The picture is very different for the *non-engineering*, "people" skills. Advanced skills in assessment and knowledge of psychosocial issues, functional implications of disabling conditions and the like are needed to match AT and human needs at *all* levels of the pyramid. Whether deployed by an engineer or by a clinician, these "people" skills make the difference between useless junk and meeting the personal needs of an individual. Tech that does not meet a personal need gets abandoned, representing a waste of dollar resources, professional time, and perhaps client opportunity, since resources expended uselessly are not available to meet the next need. Successfully fitting the technology into a life requires spending the time to collect information about the environment in which the person will deploy the tech. To this end, Scherer (2002) has developed the Technology Match System to assess and raise the likelihood of successful technology adoption. The system provides an organized way to assess both the client and the environment in which the AT is to be deployed to help avoid "technology abandonment" and to better utilize tech resources (Brown and Merbitz, 1995).

Hedman's Pyramid also illustrates other points. People often complain about the costs of AT without considering the market issues that drive costs. AT items have a smaller market than most consumer goods. Small market size means that tooling, advertising, and so forth must be recouped over a smaller production run. The skills and training needed for a successful assistive technology implementation, including knowledge of a host of disabling conditions, is applied over relatively few cases, also raising the cost of AT.

One basic question seems to express many key challenges of working with Assistive Technology. "At what price can we get something to solve this problem and for how long?" This question illustrates the *life cycle* of a tech intervention, and a way of characterizing phases of the technology intervention process. A generalized view of steps in a tech purchase is shown in Figure 2. Note that even one cycle involves a number of participants, since various clinicians, gatekeepers, vendors, and others may be involved in transactions with one client.

Since some steps depend upon approvals from other participants, it also shows how a tech purchase can seem to take forever while a step waits for completion of a previous one. This lengthy process also may heighten clients' stress. as they wait for AT, desiring something that will play a positive role in increased independence and perhaps simultaneously fearing that it may prove to be unworkable or unsuitable and hence a costly error.

In the remainder of the chapter, we review the major areas of AT, with examples of equipment and providers. Because of rapid changes in development of all kinds of technology, including AT, we do not attempt to recommend particular brands, types, et cetera, but seek to inform rehabilitation case managers about many of the key considerations as they help clients evaluate and choose AT.

AN OVERVIEW OF MAJOR APPLICATIONS OF ASSISTIVE TECHNOLOGY

INTERNET SITES WITH REHABILITATION AND AT INFORMATION

Access to the Internet has become indispensable in AT work, and the Internet often is the first source of information about disability resources including AT. The Abledata database (originally developed at the Trace Center at the University of Wisconsin at Madison) at www.abledata.com has tens of thousands of AT devices and applications arranged in an easy to use database. Devices can be accessed by category and manufacturer' phone numbers and contact information are included. Similar databases are offered elsewhere, such as www.assistivetech.net at Georgia Tech. The Internet also offers many other tech resources; any Web browser will rapidly locate a wider array of tech sites then we can list here. As more people accessed the Web, manufacturers scrambled to have a Web presence, and it is a perfect medium with which to reach the geographically diverse population that requires specialized equipment to accommodate their disabilities. Both government and private organizations devoted to various disabilities also offer great resources on the Web. The Job Accommodations Network, for example, at http://janweb.icdi.wvu.edu/ offers specific information about AT and job accommodations addressing many disabilities.

The Web also offers other benefits to both professionals and clients. First, it is a fast and convenient way to provide cost-effective follow-up contacts to clients. Second, professionals can use it for efficient communication with each other. Clients also can use the Web to contact other persons with similar disabilities. This contact may be especially important for persons with low-incidence disabilities, and may allow clients to discuss issues with distant, but experienced, peers when contemplating tech decisions. In short, using the web is a most critical technological skill for any professional in AT. When arranging internet access for clients, budget for the fastest possible connection to enhance productivity.

PERSONAL COMPUTERS

While personal computers have substantially benefited people with disabilities, access remains difficult for many. In addition to mobility, automotive, point-of-sale, communication, and other specialized devices, people with disabilities use computers for the same purposes as the "temporarily able-bodied," and they face many of the same choices in selecting useful PC systems. As with other AT, an experienced client may be able to select, order, and put in service an operational system virtually unaided. Conversely, a client inexperienced in computers will do well to consult an experienced ATP; if there are issues with seating and positioning, or having a single switch access, or similar issues, an ATP is strongly recommended. In either case, after setting a budget, the next task is deciding what the computer will do, and finding software that does those things. Next, one can select an operating system, then hardware for input and output. The whole system must be assembled, the software installed, and the user must learn the system. Upgrades, troubleshooting, maintenance, and system replacement complete the cycle. Computers are intimidating to many people and, in those cases, a friendly teacher or mentor may be essential to getting the system running. These issues are briefly explicated below.

Software. Personal computers are used by consumers with and without disabilities for work, word processing, spreadsheets, graphics, email, games, databases, and Web (Internet) access. The computer's easy text editing capability makes it an ideal tool for persons whose impairments involve poor handwriting but who want to correspond or produce neatly written material. It has become an essential tool at college and even at lower levels of education. Email and Internet access allow rapid communication for more efficient, more productive work. Less well known are the programs for assisting in personal and

family management, specifically in personal banking and grocery shopping, but these functions may be even more useful to persons with mobility impairments. Each requires specialized software, a connection such as a modem and a telephone line, cable modem, or DSL (digital subscriber line) and a cooperating institution (bank or grocery store). Personal banking programs (like Quicken) keep checkbook balances and allow one to pay bills by electronic funds transfer, thus eliminating check writing and stamps. They will also print checks if desired. Grocery shopping systems (like Jewel Tea Company's "Peapod") allow one to select desired grocery items from a list and transmit the order to a store.

Figure 2. Life Cycle of a Technological Intervention

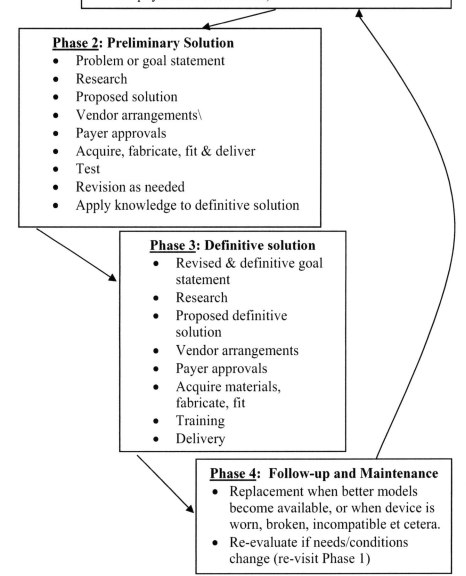

Phase 1: Assessment
- Client's needs, current skills, and preferences
- Environmental resources and barriers (social and physical environments)

Phase 2: **Preliminary Solution**
- Problem or goal statement
- Research
- Proposed solution
- Vendor arrangements\
- Payer approvals
- Acquire, fabricate, fit & deliver
- Test
- Revision as needed
- Apply knowledge to definitive solution

Phase 3: **Definitive solution**
- Revised & definitive goal statement
- Research
- Proposed definitive solution
- Vendor arrangements
- Payer approvals
- Acquire materials, fabricate, fit
- Training
- Delivery

Phase 4: **Follow-up and Maintenance**
- Replacement when better models become available, or when device is worn, broken, incompatible et cetera.
- Re-evaluate if needs/conditions change (re-visit Phase 1)

Store personnel then select the items and they are delivered at a preplanned time. A small service charge is added to the bill; however, for a person with MS or other movement impairment, and/or a demanding job, the system saves an enormous amount of time and energy. The Internet has many useful sources of information, and talking to several experienced users about a particular software package can save hours of frustration.

Operating systems. Computers use specialized software called the operating system (OS). At this point, two OS systems are popular. While only a brief review of advantages and disadvantages of each can be listed here, if at all possible, a prospective user should spend some time with each type of OS before making a choice. Of the two systems, the Macintosh system generally has the reputation as a more reliable, user-friendly system that is faster to set up and run, experiences fewer configuration problems and crashes, and has far fewer "computer viruses." The Mac also has fewer users, vendors, and software options. The other major OS is the "Windows" OS, which accounts for over 80% of the personal computer market. The larger market share for this operating system means that hardware components are available in a wide range of prices and quality. While mixing and matching components can save money initially, one also risks compatibility issues, more system crashes, and a greater investment in skilled time to get and keep the system running. For workers, a primary issue is often making the new system compatible with computers at their place of employment.

Hardware. For the user with disabilities who needs some specialized software or hardware, a critical point will be to select the hardware that is compatible with the user's computer and operating system. Apple (Mac), IBM, Microsoft (Windows), and other vendors maintain offices to help users with disabilities select appropriate equipment. An ATP who specializes in this area will also be helpful. Users with mobility impairments who have trouble using standard keyboards can provide inputs to the computer in several ways. Among the least expensive are key guards, which allow one to rest a hand over the keyboard and select a key with a finger. Expanded keyboards are larger, and mini keyboards require less movement; either may be appropriate for users with upper extremity movement and control issues.

A more expensive option is to use voice input, in which the user "trains" the software to interpret his or her voice, and then speaks all commands and inputs. Head pointers, mouth sticks, and simple hand held pointers are effective "low-tech" alternatives for some. Output from the computer may be to a screen, a printer (or Brailler) or some electronic communication to another computer, a telephone, or some other device. Voice output also is possible. In any case, as the system becomes more complex or specialized, configuring the computer to the user and maintaining it in operation requires greater and greater skill, time, and maintenance. An AT Professional may be indispensable if the user has a severe disability, requires single switch inputs, specialized hardware, a connection to other adapted devices, or similar services, such as mounting a laptop computer on the wheelchair. Budgeting for routine maintenance of the system must be a part of the plan.

SEATING AND POSITIONING

If the disability is such that the client lacks mobility, cannot maintain an upright posture, or has reduced sensation in the lower body, then specialized seating and positioning assistance is usually needed. We separate seating and positioning (S&P) considerations from the choice of a mobility base (i.e. the equipment that enables the client to get around from one place to another), since many modern S&P systems allow one to "mix and match" the S&P to different bases. Clients with intact sensation and posture may require only the mobility base and a standard chair. Many other clients, however, may do better replacing the sling wheelchair seat with a solid but properly padded support surface. If both S&P and mobility are required, the use of one professional source is usually preferable to integrating two systems and making sure the integration is functional across the client's different operating environments.

When needed, seating and positioning are usually one of the first and most critical areas addressed in a comprehensive AT intervention. An appropriate seating surface positions and stabilizes the client for vocational, social, and communicative activity, and these functions can be difficult or impossible to sustain without adequate positioning. A person exerting constant effort to remain upright has less energy to work and fatigues more rapidly. Someone who incurs a pressure ulcer due to an inadequate seat cushion experiences an expensive and dangerous preventable complication. In some cases, appropriate positioning can mitigate skeletal or neuromuscular deformity, or prevent its progression. An upright posture and stable support may also allow enhanced respiratory, digestive, urinary tract, and oral-motor function.

It is especially important to refer clients to qualified professionals with adequate specialized training and a track record for good S&P, since an inappropriate or poorly implemented seating system can have disastrous or even ultimately fatal effects (e.g. pressure ulcer with sepsis is one common cause of death for people with mobility impairment). RESNA's ATP certification and membership in a professional discipline (such as RPT or OTR), are good beginnings for selecting an S&P consultant. Seating and positioning interventions range from simple cushions usable on any chair to complex, custom-built suspension systems. Some S&P professionals do measurement, order hardware and cushions from durable medical equipment vendors or direct from manufacturers, and then do final fitting and modifications in their clinic or hospital. Others work directly for durable medical equipment vendors; clients are then fitted to the lines of cushions and wheelchairs that the vendor carries. Some areas of the US and Canada have excellent coverage and numerous skilled professionals from which to choose, while other areas require hours of travel and overnight stays to access services. Another complication is that the client's home or worksite may be inaccessible, and the persons performing accessibility modifications need to be aware of any constraints imposed by the S&P and mobility base, such as its width or the approach used for transfers.

Appropriate S&P intervention is a team effort (including the client) that requires good communication among members and a substantial amount of information about the environment and circumstances within which the client is expected to live. Inexperienced clients (or inexperienced case managers) may not understand the reasons for investing in seemingly expensive professional help to make what appear to be simple choices about a seat cushion. Clients who themselves have experience in seating systems can be the best sources of information about what will work and not work in their particular circumstances.

A stable posture and extended sitting tolerance is generally required for evaluation and fitting of other AT, such as specialized switches, environmental controls, worksite modifications, home modification, and similar interventions. Frequently the S&P system is the primary element, and other technology is built around it. Seating intervention is commonly used for individuals with cerebral palsy, muscular dystrophy, multiple sclerosis, and similar disabilities. It is also used in the early stages of rehabilitation after traumatic brain injury. Individuals with spinal cord injury generally need S&P intervention, as do individuals with reduced sensation or movement. For these individuals, it is critical to provide an appropriate cushion, and to follow-up with replacement cushions as needed. For example, the service life of a standard foam cushion is about six months; after that, its protection deteriorates and it should be replaced.

Pressure ulcer prevention. Clients with impaired or absent sensation, orthopedic or neuromuscular deformity, and poor or compromised cognition and communication are especially at risk for a pressure ulcer (PU), which was previously referred to as pressure sore or decubitus ulcer. For many hours each day, some system, adequate or not, totally supports the client's body weight and maintains the body's orientation. Skilled and careful measurement and fitting are needed to make sure that the weight is appropriately distributed, and the client should receive or perform weight shifting or pressure relief movements on some schedule. If pressure is unrelieved on some body area long enough, the client will develop a PU at that point. Since any more pressure will exacerbate the ulcer, a totally different posture must be used while the PU heals—often taking several months. A person sitting for long periods in one position at work when busy with job tasks may develop a pressure ulcer and miss work for several months. During this time, the person may have limited or no sitting time while the PU heals, and there will be a spot that is forever after more vulnerable to another PU. These ulcers may not heal without treatment, and may require plastic surgery or extended hospital stays, incurring treatment costs in the $50,000 to over $100,000 range. If ignored and untreated, PUs can progress through the fascia and to the bone, and necessitate amputation of all body parts below the sore in an attempt to preserve life. An ATP and skilled S&P intervention is far less costly in both financial and human terms.

Persons who stay in bed all day are also at risk for PUs, and various specialized flotation beds have been developed for PU prevention. PUs are among the great killers of the elderly, whose skin seems especially vulnerable. Other risk factors for pressure ulcer include incontinence (associated with prolonged moisture on the skin), heat, postural deformities (that exert shearing pressure), impaired cognition (poor self-care and limited reporting of discomfort), poor transfer technique (dragging the client across a rough surface), poor nutrition, and a thin, bony body type.

Flotation systems. Aggressive prevention and skilled, professional application of a modern seating/flotation system is required to prevent PUs and position the client with a severe disability. In the last three decades, substantial progress has been made in S&P systems, and many new materials and designs have been developed. Professionals may fit seating systems filled with air, water, different viscous fluids, elastomeric gel, open-or closed cell foams, or combinations of these materials. System elements may be planar (flat) or contoured; the latter may be custom fitted to an individual or made in various standard sizes. The cover must be chosen so that it does not compromise the pressure, heat, and moisture handling properties of the cushion material, and all choices must meet the client's life circumstances (such as climate, job, and transportation). In general, each type and brand of S&P system will present its own characteristics and trade-offs. Large-sized air-filled cells, for example, have excellent reputations for pressure relief, but require careful maintenance to avoid over filling and will not provide enough stability for some clients. The height of the support system is also a consideration in selecting and fitting the mobility base for armrests, footrests, controls, and similar features.

Advances in seating for persons with severe disability also promise to benefit the less severe populations, such as persons of short stature, the elderly, and persons with low back pain. Individuals in these categories can have independence, comfort, and productivity enhanced by S&P systems that address their unique circumstances and needs. It is important for work sites to provide ergonomic seating, since the demands of the job often require extended periods in one position. Frequent brief breaks, position changes, and exercises can be helpful for virtually any seated worker, even if some repetitive stress disorder has not yet surfaced.

MOBILITY BASES

While the traditional X-frame folding wheelchair, designed by H. A. Everest and H. C. Jennings in the 1930s, is still available, many improvements in design and materials have been made in recent decades. Basic categories include the manual wheelchair, powered chair, recliners, and scooters. International standards for wheelchairs have been developed, making objective information about chair functions available beyond what is reported in a manufacturer's literature. Clients with sensory and mobility impairments also may require a specialized seating surface, as discussed above.

Rehabilitation engineers, technicians, OTs, PTs, and physicians often are involved in the mobility base selection process. Many families, unfortunately, do not obtain professional consultation, and simply buy a wheelchair from a previous user. That may be acceptable for short-term usage by a cognitively intact client with good sensation and motor skills, but in most cases, consulting an ATP is appropriate. Some vendors maintain skilled staff that fit bases for some clients, while referring clients with complex issues to other providers; other vending companies employ salespeople whose main consideration seems be to move certain product lines, regardless of the appropriateness for a given user. The consumer skills of a sophisticated user who is upgrading a mobility base may be very different from those of a newly injured first-time user. In any case, the mobility base must physically fit the client and the environment(s) in which it will be used. Brakes, controls, and accessories must be positioned for the user, and the height, depth, width, footrests, armrests, and cushioning must be sized and matched to the user's requirements and the environments in which it will be used.

Manual wheelchairs. Modern lightweight and ultra lightweight (25 lb.) manual designs usually require less energy to push than older 40 lb. "hospital-style" wheelchairs. Some users can tolerate the sling seat and back of the older designs; others do better with solid seats or custom designed seat or back supports fitted by an ATP. Modern wheelchairs often offer the option of moving the chairs' center of gravity to enhance performance or stability, or cambering the wheels or changing push rims for greater propelling efficiency. Chairs with these designs often are easier to transport by car, and come in a variety of colors and designs to match the client's living environment and lifestyle. Certain designs are more robust; others are suitable for lighter clients. One-handed drives are available. Solid tires require less maintenance, but pneumatic tires give better performance. Quick-release hubs allow fast disassembly for dexterous clients or caregivers. Some wheelchairs are designed for sports and outside use while others are limited to the indoors. Narrower models and a slender client may require less home and worksite modification for full accessibility as compared to a wider or powered model. Electric units that add to the wheels can give a "power assist" when needed has and have been reported to be quite helpful to many clients. Such units can help preserve arm and shoulder function. Well-resourced users may have several chairs to use in different environments.

Powered mobility. Powered mobility bases include power wheelchairs and scooters, and add-on power units for manual wheelchairs. All powered units use electric power from heavy lead-acid batteries that resemble auto batteries, so battery maintenance and periodic replacement must be budgeted. Sealed gel-type batteries are supposed to allow air travel without the disassembly and special crating required by liquid-filled lead-acid batteries, but calling the airline in advance is prudent. Batteries generally charge each night so they are ready for use the next day.

Power wheelchairs are generally prescribed for those users having little or no upper extremity function. They are expensive enough that consulting an ATP's is typical. Various drive/wheel options are available; for example, mid-wheel drive chairs offer a tight turning radius. Power wheelchairs may be operated by a joystick if the user has hand function, or by a mouth switch, head switch, or a switch operated by any other muscle movement the user can reliably produce. The ATP can adjust the chair's control characteristics so that it can be controlled by the user, does not pose undue risks, and, in general, it is safe and appropriate. The ATP can also train the user in care and upkeep of the chair. Power mobility bases also offer "tilt-in-space" or "reclining" options that tilt the back of the chair toward the ground, allowing at least partial pressure relief. The latter (recliner) options change the angle between the back and the seat; the former tilts the seat as well, so that the seat to back angle remains constant, and reduces the risk of shear.

Scooters. For people with marginal ambulation but good balance, trunk control, and upper extremity function, a scooter may be a useful option. Most are fitted with a standard office-type seat, but some allow replacement with custom seating. Scooters come in three and four-wheeled versions. Generally, the former are lighter, better suited to indoor use, easier to transport in an auto, and easier to maneuver in a small space. The latter are better suited to the larger, heavier client, provide more power and utility for outdoors or longer distances, and have larger turning radii. Some clients leave a scooter at work overnight to charge, and use a manual wheelchair, crutches, or other powered device at home.

Vehicle modifications. Wheelchair users and other people with disabilities may need modifications to standard motor vehicles in order to drive safely. Modifications can include controls to allow operation of the vehicle with just one hand, or to accommodate missing or nonfunctional limbs. Major domestic auto manufacturers readily provide information about converting vehicles. Specialized professionals assist in planning vehicle modifications and training the user to drive a modified vehicle. In some states, a physician may be required to approve driving. Clients with good upper body function may be able to transfer to a standard auto and lift the wheelchair into the back seat. Lift systems are available for light scooters or wheelchairs to be carried in roof racks or the car's trunk. Other clients may use a minivan or full-sized van with a lift for the wheelchair. Some clients drive from the wheelchair; others transfer to a seat to drive. Wheelchair tie-downs and occupant restraint systems are needed to minimize injuries in case of an accident. Some commercially available systems have been crash-tested; some have not. The ATP can discuss the merits of each type of crash-tested restraint system, vehicle access method, driving control interface, and other option.

COMMUNICATIONS

Communication is a central human function. Persons living independently need communications to summon emergency help as well as to meet the needs of daily living. Effective communications are required for work, social interaction, self-care, living, and family relationships—the ability to communicate with caregivers and health professionals can be critical to the preservation of life itself. Perhaps more commonly, poor communications with health care providers can exacerbate problems, complicate care, and contribute to a more costly, less satisfactory, and less functional lifestyle. For these reasons, if clients are non-vocal or have communication impairments, it may be a medical necessity to arrange for an effective communication system and also a backup for times when the primary system is out of service. An evaluation by a competent professional can reveal areas of concern and strategies or technologies that may help improve function or prevent further impairment.

Alternative and augmentative communication. Devices and methods for *alternative and augmentative communication* ("AAC") require something other than the person's own body. Clients who may benefit from AAC include those with neuromuscular conditions that cause dysarthria or apraxia, those with low vocal volume or larynx damage (perhaps due to cancer or trauma), and those with traumatic brain injuries, cerebral palsy, amyotrophic lateral sclerosis, multiple sclerosis, or stroke. Sometimes a client can communicate adequately when well rested, but needs an AAC system during periods of fatigue and as an emergency backup.

AAC selection often is a team effort. Since clients must have some way to control AAC devices, AAC intervention may require consultation with OTs or specialists in control systems. It may require PTs or specialists in seating and positioning, so that the definitive positioning system also has the controls for AAC placed and configured in a useful way. AAC specialists (often Speech-Language Pathologists with the Certificate of Clinical Competence, or SLP-CCC) do a comprehensive evaluation of the client's current and probable future communication capabilities, needs, and environment. Then they work with the technology team to deliver appropriate AAC device(s), integrate them into the client's environment, and train the client and caregiver. The specialists also provide follow-up and follow-along services, including advanced training, repair, maintenance, and upgrades when systems that are more functional become available.

In general, AAC systems can be classified as electronic or manual. To command the system, clients either use a code (such as Morse code) or select the message or a component thereof. AAC systems must have some output: vocal, printed, visual, or tactile display; or electronic output to another device. Many AAC systems support conversation with vocal or visual outputs. Others provide electronic communication, writing, mathematics, or drawing as outputs. Primary considerations for AAC systems are the speed of input and output. In conversation, since the listener can repeat the message, speed is generally more important than accuracy. Spoken conversation occurs at about 150-175 words per minute, while common AAC systems provide three to twenty-five words per minute. Conversations with an AAC user, therefore, may be characterized as slow, awkward, and uncomfortable, and may be dominated by the person using vocal speech. AAC developers are work hard to increase the speed of their systems. Caregivers, if present, often must be trained to adapt their speed to the client's.

Manual AAC systems. The manual systems often consist of communication boards or books. These systems have words, letters, numerals, symbols, phrases, or sentences written out, and the user selects them one at a time to spell out or indicate the message to the communication partner. Since communication boards are cheap and quick to implement, they are usually the first AAC device used after TBI or other sudden-onset communication impairment. Some letter boards or word boards are made of clear plastic, so both parties can face each other. The client may select a letter by looking at it, pointing with an arm, head stick, or light pointer (a laser pointer or mini light source on a headband).

Electronic AAC systems. These are typically computer-based. They are also often heavier, require a constant supply of electricity, and may be more complex to prepare, use, and maintain while offering more flexibility, utility, speed, and function. Electronic AAC systems allow message quantities, selection methods, strategies to increase the communication speed, and output options that are impossible for a manual system. Systems that are more expensive will have more memory and hence more messages; as the price of RAM has dropped, the capability of AAC systems has improved. A more expensive system may support several different selection methods. Almost always, a direct selection system is preferable if the client can point to or otherwise indicate a choice. If the client cannot directly select, but can move any body part to reliably open or close a switch, then a scanning system can be implemented. (See also IADLs, below). When activated, the AAC device will step an indicator across each communication element; the client triggers the switch to indicate his selection. In this way, the message is spelled out. An alternative strategy for clients with good memory and learning abilities is the use of a Morse code system instead of scanning. Another alternative is the use of linguistic symbols (such as Blissymbols or Minspeak) representing concepts to speed communication. Computerized AAC devices also often support abbreviation expansion, macros, and word prediction. These "speed up" features use the computer's memory to minimize the keystrokes or selections required for each word.

AAC systems also vary widely in the outputs that they provide. Some electronic AAC systems provide a variety of synthesized voices in both genders and a range of ages, from which the client can select. Other systems allow caregivers to record short messages and play them back whenever needed. Some systems "listen" to the client's vocalization, electronically filter and manipulate it, and immediately "say" each spoken word more loudly and clearly. Other systems display the message on a portable screen for the communication partner or send it to a small portable printer. Some computerized systems provide a display like a communication board. The selected item may be spoken or be displayed in a special area of the device, so that it can be vocalized or read when complete.

Whatever the AAC system, training is critical component in a functional system. A system that a client can use immediately is often not the most functional for the long-term. Often the most capable systems also require the most skill to program and set up; they may or may not require more user skills. Clearly, evaluation, definition, fitting, training, and support for AAC systems can be complex and time consuming. When considered against the dimensions of the problems to be solved, the potential consequences of poor communication, and the benefits to be derived, the professional time for a good AAC implementation is well invested.

ELECTRONIC AIDS TO DAILY LIVING (EADLS)

Also called Environmental Control Units or ECUs, EADLs allow persons with limited mobility and dexterity to control a large array of household and worksite appliances. IADLs generally include a base unit, an operating control, and remote units that attach to electrical appliances. The control unit transmits to the base unit, which in turn transmits to the selected appliance. Transmission is usually either by infrared light beam, FM radio signals, or electrical signals through the house wiring. Infrared (as is used in TV and VCR remote controllers) is inexpensive and easy to implement, but is limited to line-of-sight and easily blocked. FM transmissions penetrate walls and do not require line of sight, but are more expensive. The BRS or X-10 system, also inexpensive, uses modules that simply plug into existing electrical sockets. The base unit communicates to remote BRS units through the house's electrical wiring. The control unit must be configured to accept whatever switch input or movement is possible for the user. For persons with voice but limited movement, units that respond to spoken commands are useful. For a person with tongue movement, a mouthpiece resembling a dental retainer can be ordered. The mouthpiece has up to nine tiny switches, which the user can trigger with specific tongue movements. The switches trigger radio transmissions to the base unit, which in turn transmits to the selected appliance. A similar arrangement can be set up to control computer, IADL, or AAC systems; however, an ATP and team usually are required to integrate these diverse elements and make them all work. Some ATPs are specialists in finding control sites and training users to reliably control their movement; for a client with few reliable movements, difficulty in reliably controlling any movement, or similar severe impairments, an experienced ATP offers the best hope of finding and utilizing an effective control site.

Most electric appliances can be controlled by an IADL. The choice of IADL will depend on the user's needs, preferences, environment, and available ongoing support. IADLs often include integrated control and communications (such as telephone dialers) that are critical in emergencies and may be called upon in life-threatening situations, thus the ATP will often propose both a main system and backup methods for communication and control for when the main system is incapacitated, under repair, et cetera.

SERVICE ANIMALS FOR PEOPLE WITH DISABILITIES
The use of animals (usually dogs) to assist people with mobility impairments has grown dramatically in recent years (Sachs-Ericsson, Hansen & Fitzgerald, 2002). These animals join the more widely known Seeing Eye and Hearing Ear dogs. For a person with a disability who has the emotional and cognitive resources to work with an animal, the service dog can offer a welcome companion and partner. Service dogs provide increased independence and are ready and eager to help. At work, service dogs usually curl up under a desk or table and sleep, but wake up to retrieve dropped objects as needed. Larger dogs often pull the wheelchair whenever the client needs additional help with propulsion. In stores, the dogs can lift credit cards and money up to counters, and return change to the user. They also usually retrieve dropped items, bring shoes, turn on wall switches, and in general help the user do small everyday tasks that otherwise sap energy. Users are generally trained to teach the dogs new behaviors as needed. Users who experience seizures often report that the dogs will warn them of imminent seizures in time to take appropriate

precautions, and some service dog training programs are now capitalizing on this unique ability.

While service dogs are far more numerous, small monkeys are trained as personal assistants for some persons with high quadriplegia. Providers of trained monkeys remove their teeth, sometimes use shock collars, and do not claim they will be housebroken, so the relationship with these monkeys tends not to be as happy and collaborative as is often seen between service dogs and their owners.

PROSTHETICS AND ORTHOTICS
Prosthetics (replacements for missing body parts) are AT components developed and fitted by highly specialized professionals. In cases of amputation, surgeons seek to preserve functional joints, and the prosthesis generally is fitted below the last remaining functional joint. A definitive device can be fitted once the stump is stable, but consultation with the prosthetist should not be delayed. Upper extremity (UE) prostheses are generally fitted with a fixture that can accept various terminal devices depending on the activity the user anticipates next, usually including a hook (more functional) or an artificial hand (more cosmetic). Myoelectric UE prostheses have battery-powered electric motors that open and close the terminal device when a sensor detects contraction of a specific muscle. The client is trained to tense and relax the muscle to operate the device. Body powered prostheses have a harness and cable arrangement that operates the terminal device when the opposite shoulder is flexed or moved. All prostheses require skilled practitioners to fit and train the client, and periodic follow-ups to maintain functionality.

Orthotics (external supports), like prosthetics, have become increasingly functional as new, lighter, stronger materials have become available. Orthotics are often described by the joints that they support, such as a KAFO (knee ankle foot orthosis). An exception is the BFO (balanced forearm orthosis) used to neutralize gravity so an arm can be used for self-feeding or oral facial hygiene. Some OTs or PTs supply commonly used or less complex orthotics while orthotists fabricate and fit custom devices for more demanding applications.

AT FOR FARMERS
Farming is a dangerous occupation, and rehabilitation of injured farm workers presents unique challenges. Rural areas often are poorly served by AT professionals, financial resources may be limited, and people socialized within the self-reliant farm culture may be not accept outside help. Farmers are also frequently technologically adept, creative, and used to a problem-solving approach. The "Breaking New Ground" program at Purdue University is dedicated to helping farmers with disabilities (800-825-4624 or http//abe.www.ecn.purdue.edu/ABE/Extension/BNG/Bnginfo.html). The BNG

program provides a clearinghouse for farmer's rehabilitation issues and in particular disseminates information about adapting farm equipment for farmers with disabilities. There is also a national AgrAbility Project (www.agrabilityproject.org) that can refer to projects in other states.

SENSORY ACCOMMODATIONS: AT FOR HEARING, VISION, TACTILE IMPAIRMENTS

Persons with sensory impairments now have a variety of AT solutions for their particular issues. Major cities also have centers dedicated to disseminating AT designed for those with hearing or visual impairments. AT professionals who specialize in working with these populations can recommend proven technologies that are adapted to the needs of each individual.

Tactile impairments. AT for persons with these impairments are generally "low-tech" innovations or modifications of techniques used by most people. For example, persons with peripheral neuropathies may be at risk for burns due to handling items when cooking without realizing how hot they are. Always using a potholder will prevent many of these burns. Similarly, food thermometers can be positioned for handy access by the stove and microwave when temperatures must be judged while cooking. For a parent with tactile impairment, feeling a child's head to detect fever can be replaced by an electronic thermometer. Consultation with an experienced OT or ATP can help find other simple solutions to these and similar problems.

Hearing. Persons with hearing impairments should be referred to audiologists to determine the sound frequencies over which there is hearing loss and the prospects for compensating for the loss. These professionals can recommend hearing aids that provide amplification in the exact frequency ranges needed by the client. Clients with profound losses or deafness can also be helped by a variety of AT innovations. TDD (Telecommunications Device for the Deaf" also known as TTY, or teletype) systems allow telephonic communication, and a telephone relay service is available all over the US to allow communication with non-TDD telephones. With this system, a person with a TDD phones the relay center, which in turn calls the non-TDD participant. The relay service operator listens and talks to the non-TDD participant, and "relays" the communication to the TDD user. ADL aids, such as vibrating or extra loud alarm clocks, strobe light smoke alarms, doorbells, and similar innovations are also available through catalogs and specialized centers. Some persons use "Hearing Ear" dogs, which are trained to listen for and alert their owners to auditory cues.

Vision. Many AT resources are available for people with visual impairments through blindness/low vision professionals. A variety of visual displays can maximize the utility of residual vision, and screen-reading software translates computer screen displays to spoken words. Devices to assist

223

Activities of Daily Living (ADLs) include sensors that give an audible cue when a cup is filled, talking clocks, templates for writing checks, and a variety of optical and electronic magnifiers for limited vision. Mobility aids include canes and electronic sensors to detect a clear path. Following the military's development of the global positioning system (GPS), such units are now available as orientation aids. A GPS unit can locate one's position on the earth's surface to within a few meters, and indicate direction and distance to one's destination. Seeing Eye dogs also vastly improve access to work and quality of life for people able to use them.

HOME AND WORKSITE MODIFICATIONS/LOW TECH AND ADL AIDS

These innovations range from free to thousands of dollars, and from user-invented and implemented to professionally designed and custom manufactured. The variety of these solutions and their sources defies description. Perhaps the best key is to help the client attain and maintain an empowered, "problem-solving" attitude and search both professional and personal sources for solutions. Discuss prospective solutions with experienced ATPs and clients with similar disabilities, and use the same criteria for judging these providers as a careful person would use for any major purchase.

Home and worksite modification. The complexity and size of the job will range widely. Many worksite modifications are trivial, such as moving desks to provide an accessible path, using non-slip safety appliqués on stairs, rearranging the storage of heavy materials to avoid back strain, or providing more light to a work area. Some are more complex and can involve redesign of a whole industrial process. When these sorts of interventions are made to accommodate a worker with a repetitive stress disorder, they may benefit all workers, and actually lower the incidence of claims from that worksite. Often an experienced ATP will be able to assess the site and rapidly design a solution. Some contractors carry out both design and accessibility construction work. Since the quality of the solution may vary widely; attention to the qualifications, reputation, and references of the vendor is, again, strongly suggested.

ADLs and low tech solutions. Devices to aid "activities of daily living" (ADLs) are available from hardware stores, specialized catalogs, OT departments, and many other sources. A person with marginal impairments in some area can often function perfectly with just a small assist, such as non-slip pads to open jars, a more convenient "lazy susan" turntable to bring work materials or cabinet contents closer, or a footrest for use at the computer. Aids to mobility range from canes to quad canes to walkers; accessories include various pouches, storage systems, and special non-slip tips for use on icy sidewalks. Simply attaching a short dowel to a light switch can allow its operation by a person in a wheelchair. The range of these items defies description; an inquiring and empowering attitude, frequent discussions of the problem, and a willingness to try will increase the likelihood of satisfactory solutions.

CONCLUSION

Tech innovations range from free to thousands of dollars and from user-invented to team designed. AT can make it possible to work, carry out daily activities, and, in general, plays the same roles for people with disabilities as does "regular tech" for all citizens. But the key to a successful, economical tech intervention is to think *personal*. Any given tech innovation can be a lifesaver to me and junk to you, if it meets my personal need and situation, and does not meet yours. The user, therefore, is the center of a good tech team, and meeting the short term and long term personal needs of clients with disabilities is the team's goal.

REFERENCES

Author: Delivering on the Promise: Preliminary Report of Federal Agencies' Actions to Eliminate Barriers and Promote Community Integration. Presented to the President of the United States, December 21, 2001. http://www.hhs.gov/newfreedom/prelim/fullrpt.html#tech

Brandt, E. N. and A. M. Pope, Eds. (1997). *Enabling America*. Washington, DC, National Academy Press.

Brown, D., & Merbitz, C. T. (1995). Comparison of technology match between two types of functional electrical stimulation hand grasp systems. In A. Langton (Ed.), *Proceedings of the RESNA '95 Annual Conference, RECREAbility*, (pp. 381-383). Vancouver, BC: RESNA Press, Washington, D.C.

Carlson, D., Ehrlich, N., Berland, B. J., Bailey, N. (2002). Highlights from the NIDRR/RESNA/University of Michigan Survey of Assistive Technology and Information Technology Use and Need by Persons with Disabilities in the United States. Technology Assistance Project, http://www.resna.org/taproject/library/highlights.html

Cook, A. & Hussey, S. (1995). *Assistive Technologies: Principles and Practice*. St. Louis, MO: Mosby.

Cook, A. & Hussey, S. (2002). *Assistive Technologies: Principles and Practice*. St. Louis, MO: Mosby. Second Ed.

Cushman, L. A., & Scherer, M. J. (1996). Measuring the Relationship of Assistive Technology Use, Functional Status Over Time, and Consumer-Therapist Perceptions of ATs. *Assistive Technology*, *8*(2), 103-109.

Enders, A. & Hall, M. (Eds.). (1990). *Assistive Technology Sourcebook.* Washington, DC: RESNA Press.

Hedman, G. (1991). Rehabilitation Engineering. Lecture, Illinois Institute of Technology, Chicago, IL., see also Hedman, G. (Ed.). (1990). *Rehabilitation Technology.* Binghamton, NY: Haworth Press.

Justesen, T., and Menlove, M. (1994). Assistive technology education in rehabilitation counselor programs. *Rehabilitation Education* , *7* (4), 253-260.

Jutai, J., Ladak, N., Schuller, R., Naumann, S., & Wright, V. (1996). Outcomes Measurement of Assistive Technologies: An Institutional Case Study. *Assistive Technology*, *8*(2), 110-120.

Mann, W. C. & Lane, J.P. (1991). *Assistive Technology for Persons with Disabilities.* Rockville, MD: The American Occupational Therapy Association.

Merbitz, C. T. (1996). Frequency Measures of Behavior for Assistive Technology and Rehabilitation. *Assistive Technology*, *8*(2), 121-130.

Merbitz, C. T., Morris, J., & Grip, J. C. (1989). Ordinal scales and foundations of misinference. *Archives of Physical Medicine and Rehabilitation*, *70*, 308 - 312.

Merbitz, C. T., Lam, C. S., Chan, F. & Thomas, K. R. (1999). Assistive Technology for Case Managers. Chapter 13 in F. Chan & M. J. Leahy, (Eds.) *Health care and disability case management* (pp. 379-413). Lake Zurich, IL: Vocational Consultants Press.

National Center for Health Statistics. (1999a). National health interview survey on disability, Phase 1 and Phase 2, 1994 (machine readable data file and documentation, CD-ROM Series 10, No. 8). Hyattsville, MD: National Center for Health Statistics.

National Center for Health Statistics. (1999b). National health interview survey on disability, Phase 1 and Phase 2, 1995 (machine readable data file and documentation, CD-ROM Series 10, No. 10B). Hyattsville, MD: National Center for Health Statistics.

Oldridge, N. B. (1996a). Outcomes Measurement: Health Related Quality of Life. *Assistive Technology*, *8*(2), 82-93.

Oldridge, N. B. (1996b). Outcomes Measurement: Health State Preferences and Economic Evaluation. *Assistive Technology*, *8*(2), 94-102.

Sachs-Ericsson, N., Hansen, N. K., Fitzgerald, S. (2002). Benefits of assistance dogs. *Rehabilitation Psychology, 47,* 3-35.

Scherer, M. J. (2002). *Assistive Technology: Matching Device and consumer for Successful Rehabilitation.* Washington, DC: APA Books.

Scherer, M. J. (2000). *Living in the State of Stuck: How Technology Impacts the Lives of People with Disabilities, Third Edition*. Cambridge, MA: Brookline Books.

Segdy, A. (1992). Congress puts technology on top. *Team Rehab Report, 3* (8), 6.

Smith, R. O. (1996). Measuring the Outcomes of Assistive Technology: Challenge and Innovation. *Assistive Technology, 8*(2), 71-82.

Verbrugge, L. M., Rennert, C., & Madans, J. H. (1997). The great efficacy of personal and equipment assistance in reducing disability. *American Journal of Public Health, 87*, 384-92.

Whiteneck, G. G., Charlifue, S. W., Gerhart, K. A., Overholster, J. D., & Richardson, G. N. (1992). Quantifying handicap: A new measure of long-term rehabilitation outcome. *Archives of Physical Medicine and Rehabilitation, 73*, 519-526.

9

Life Care Planning

Chris Reid
Paul M. Deutsch
Julie Kitchen

Chapter Highlights

- History and development

- Methodology

- Research and resource support

- Knowledge, skill, and expertise required

- Future applications

- Summary

Life care planning (LCP) is a systematic methodology for identifying and quantifying the multidimensional, disability-related needs of an individual. A Life Care Plan is a document that summarizes those needs and provides a "roadmap" for case managers to follow, providing services to meet the needs identified in a comprehensive, yet cost-effective manner. Through use of LCP methodology, case managers can maximize beneficial outcomes for individuals with disabilities while minimizing costs. Costs are kept down through both a proactive approach to preventing complications and a systematic approach to curtailing duplication of services. At the same time, service effectiveness is enhanced by careful consideration of a multitude of factors interacting to affect rehabilitation and quality of life outcomes.

Officially, the professionally agreed-upon definition of a Life Care Plan is "a dynamic document based on published standards of practice, comprehensive assessment, data analysis, and research, which provides an organized concise plan for current and future needs with associated costs, for individuals who have experienced catastrophic injury or have chronic health care needs (Weed & Berens, 2001, p. 1)." Careful choice of the term "dynamic" in this definition emphasizes the importance of updating and revising the Life Care Plan over time, as case managers become aware of new information relevant to an individual's disability-related needs.

Case managers can view Life Care Plan implementation as a problem-solving approach that promotes continuity and consistency of care. The Life Care Plan outlines the short-term and long-term needs of the individual with a disability, and essentially provides a standard of care for that individual that is both needs driven and outcome-oriented. In terms of the overall expected outcome, the Life Care Plan should (a) maximize independence; (b) enable the client/patient to live or function in the least restrictive environment; (c) minimize medical complications; and (d) plan for productive work activity.

If new information about effective techniques for prevention of anticipated problems becomes available after the Life Care Plan has been written, the case manager should revise the plan to incorporate those techniques, as feasible. Problem solving is important, whether applied as a reaction to an acute event or applied to the theme of prevention as age and disability combine, resulting in decreased function over time. As client needs change over time in ways that may not have been anticipated by the original life care planner, the case manager should update and revise the plan. Critical thinking is required to prioritize client needs in plan implementation and allocation of available resources. Life Care Plans should outline client needs dictated by the onset of disability; unfortunately, sufficient funding may not always exist to fully address all of the needs identified. The case manager must often not only find creative ways to supplement resource availability, but also work with the client to prioritize service needs identified in the Life Care Plan, carefully identifying relative risks associated with reduction or revision of specific services.

When implementing Life Care Plans, case managers coordinate and integrate services, available resources, communications, and expectations about the disability among the individual with a disability, family, treatment team, and payer source. The case manager's influence as an educator cannot be overstated. The education provided by case managers has a "snowball effect" of multiplying over time. For example, persons with disabilities and their families are given essential information, which assists in psychosocial adjustment to disability. The individual and the family members themselves then learn to be effective educators for others in their social environment, thereby increasing community awareness and sensitivity to the needs of people with disabilities. Each of those individuals impacted can, in turn, educate others. As a result, the case manager's influence as an educator extends far beyond the initial contact with persons with disabilities and their families. In many cases, the case manager may be the first healthcare professional to function effectively as an educator, cohesively bringing together the individual with a disability, her or his family, the treatment team, and payer source.

HISTORY AND DEVELOPMENT OF LIFE CARE PLANNING

Life care planning is an outgrowth of research begun in the late 1970s and was first addressed extensively in the publication *Damages in Tort Actions* (Deutsch & Raffa, 1982). The need for life care planning methodology was identified through the following:

- It was recognized that individuals with disabilities and their families (especially in pediatric cases) needed a concise summary of a plan that could be taken away from an evaluation and used as a guideline for future reference.
- It was important to have a means of communication among all parties involved in a litigated injury case regarding the precise needs dictated by the onset of a disability. The Life Care Plan became a tool to communicate this information in a clear, concise, and precise fashion.
- Catastrophic case management dictated the need for proactive planning, rather than simple reaction to circumstances dictating immediate needs.
- Life care planning was designed to break the effects of disability into the most basic components, allowing complex concerns to be more carefully assessed with a view toward prevention of problems rather than "management by chaos."

- Life care planning methodology was developed to take into consideration the injury or disability, the needs, goals, interests, and preferences of the individual, the needs of the family, and the realities of the geographical region in which the individual and family resided.

In 1987, the Rehabilitation Training Institute (RTI) was founded in Orlando, Florida as a national, post-graduate institute to encourage the development of life care planning and facilitate its use in case management of catastrophic disability and impairment. That program evolved into Intelicus, a public/private partnership training life care planners (as well as other health care specialists); the life care planning training component was later acquired by MediPro Seminars, LLC. Other training programs for the life care-planning specialty have also been developed, in online or in-person formats, sponsored by various universities or professional organizations.

The Commission on Disability Examiner Certification (CDEC) implemented a certification process in the area of life care planning; the name of that Commission later changed to the Commission on Health Care Certification (CHCC), but its Certified Life Care Planner (CLCP) certification process remains the same. The CHCC also posts a Code of Ethics for life care planners on its website. Standards of Practice for life care planners have been developed by the International Academy of Life Care Planners, and have been published in the *Journal of Life Care Planning* (Reavis, 2002).

APPLICATIONS OF LIFE CARE PLANNING

In its early stages, the foremost application of life care planning was through the consultation process. Consultation, primarily with insurance carriers and attorneys involved in injury litigation, developed into an important area of practice for rehabilitation professionals. The demands generated by participants in the litigation process significantly influenced life care planning and enhanced its credibility and acceptance, both within and outside the courtroom. Qualified life care planners are recognized in court as expert witnesses with knowledge and skills in rehabilitation and case management that are not generally available through traditional medical testimony. Their skills and expertise are utilized in an increasing number of applications outside the courtroom, as well.

Life care planning has become an integral part of the case management process for individuals with catastrophic injuries. Both service providers and funding sources are increasingly recognizing the importance of advanced planning, rather than attempts to manage disability through spur of the moment reactions to series of crises. Weed (1995) has discussed the importance of life care planning as a managed care tool; Reid, Deutsch, & Kitchen (2001), Weed

(1999, 2001), and Weed & Riddick (1992), have discussed its use as an effective case management tool.

REHABILITATION PROFESSIONAL'S ROLE AS EDUCATOR
After development of the Life Care Plan, the rehabilitation professional's first and foremost role is as a teacher who must be prepared to educate all parties concerned so that effective and well-informed decisions can be made regarding how to meet future needs. The Life Care Plan should serve as an educational tool to communicate complex issues in an understandable manner. Judges and juries need to be educated regarding the disability-related needs of an individual, to be able to make informed decisions. (A life care planner should not tell jury members how much money to award a plaintiff, but should instead educate the jury about the expected costs associated with that injury so that the jurors can make their own appropriate decisions.) Deutsch (1990) addresses ways to effectively communicate with judges and juries in *A guide to rehabilitation testimony: The expert's role as an educator*.

Catastrophically injured individuals and their families need to understand what services will be needed at what times throughout the lifespan, at what costs and from what resources, and what might be the consequences of not obtaining those services. In the absence of this understanding, there is a great risk of families spending most of the money from an insurance settlement without making provisions for increased service needs later in life.

LIFE CARE PLANNING METHODOLOGY

The most critical aspect of life care planning is the development of a consistent methodology for analyzing the needs dictated by the onset of a disability (Deutsch, 1995). This methodology takes into consideration individual, family, and geographic needs of the person. The goal is to meet an individual's rehabilitation and long-term disability-related needs, to prevent further injury, and to make feasible the best possible quality of life. Methodology details beyond the overview provided in this book are presented in Deutsch & Reid (2003) and Deutsch, Allison, & Reid (2003).

PRINCIPLE OF CONSISTENCY
The hallmark of effective life care planning is a consistent approach to gathering information, considering the implications of that information, and presenting it in an understandable format. Life care planners should not develop "luxury" plans including the most expensive options possible when hired by a plaintiff, yet search for ways to provide the barest minimum of services regardless of individual needs when hired by an insurance company. The most

respected life care planners follow a consistent approach to plan development with each and every case; their plans are based upon the demonstrated needs of each individual for whom a plan is created. To these planners, it does not matter whether they are hired by plaintiff or defendant in a litigated case, by an insurance company to assist with case management and reserve setting, or by any other party to develop a Life Care Plan—the plan developed will be tailored to the actual needs of the individual with a disability, which should not vary depending on the nature of the referral source.

BASIC TENETS OF LIFE CARE PLANNING

A distinction should be made between actual Life Care Plan development and the structuring of a plan constrained by specific financial limitations. Life Care Plans are based upon the actual needs of an individual, not the projected resources available. In some catastrophic injury cases, the actual needs may exceed the resources that become available to meet those needs. It is important, even in those cases, to identify the discrepancy between needs and resource availability and to educate the parties involved about potential implications of not meeting the identified needs. McCoy (1996) suggested that if life care planners are asked to generate a plan to best utilize a specific amount of funding, a different name be used for the plan, such as "Medical/Equipment Cost Projections Analysis."

Proactive, not reactive. Life Care Plans should be developed and implemented in a preventative manner that minimizes the occurrence of complications. The recommendations must be clearly related to evaluation data identifying specific individual needs, and must be expected to benefit the individual. If an individual is not expected to benefit from a given service or piece of equipment, that recommendation should not be made. On the other hand, if a recommendation is expected to benefit the individual, the expected benefit should be considered in developing the rest of the plan. For example, if an individual with paraplegia but no history of decubiti is provided appropriate wheelchair cushioning and training regarding pressure release, skin inspection, and other methods to prevent the development of decubiti, that individual's Life Care Plan should not include provisions for four surgeries per year to treat decubiti.

Benefits of maximizing potential. In addition to individual quality of life benefits, there can be financial benefits to maximizing rehabilitation outcomes through provision of timely and appropriate services. Consider the costs over a lifetime for two different 24-year-old individuals with a C5-6 spinal cord injury, for example. One can turn himself over at night or can tolerate six hours without being turned. The other cannot. The difference in expected costs over the lifetime for these two individuals is approximately two million dollars.

Multidimensionality. Each recommendation, driven by a specific deficit or dysfunction, will impact other recommendations both directly and indirectly. Some directly impacted items may force recommendation changes by limiting time available for other items. Multiple disabilities and multiple service providers might dictate multiple similar recommendations, resulting in service overlaps or duplications.

Consider the entire costs. Not only Life Care Plan developers, but also case managers implementing the plans, need to consider the entire cost of selecting a given service option or piece of equipment. For equipment, the overall costs take into account the costs of maintenance and frequency of need for replacement. Some issues related to the entire costs of hiring service providers are discussed by Thomas and Kitchen (1996), who compared the costs of hiring a personal care attendant through an agency or through private hire. When total costs of a private hire are considered, (including employer social security and Medicare matches, state unemployment taxes, fringe benefits, payroll expenses, background checks, appropriate supervision, et cetera), the appeal of hiring through an agency increases.

The entire costs provided do not include two important categories: potential complications and future technology. The costs associated with either of these cannot be accurately predicted. The degree to which complications will be experienced or future technology will be developed to meet a given individual's needs cannot be known. Those costs, therefore, are not included in Life Care Plans. It is important, however, for life care planners and case managers to inform decision-makers that there is potential for development of complications, as well as invention of future technology, which could have impact but have not been included in the Life Care Plan projections.

Psychological considerations. Psychological factors have a significant impact on the quality of life for individuals with catastrophic injuries. Not only medical and physical/functional needs, but psychological needs must be addressed in life care planning. Having choices and exercising control over one's environment are especially important for individuals with catastrophic injuries, which interfere with mobility and physical function. In some ways, for example, installation of an environmental control unit is a psychological intervention. If a tetraplegic individual has a personal care attendant available to turn the channels on a television set or to dial a telephone, a naive individual might question the need for a voice-activated system to operate those items. However, the psychological importance of restoring as much choice and independent control over one's environment as possible should not be underestimated. Choices can be made available in other ways, as well. Instead of just running through a standard physical therapy routine in a given order, a physical therapist could ask the client, "Would you rather work on your legs or your arms first today?"

Psychological interventions should take into consideration the current demonstrated needs of individuals and their families, as well as future adjustments anticipated over the lifespan. For an adult who is injured, adjustments are expected during life changes such as retirement. For children with disabilities, appropriate short-term psychological goals should be established for different developmental stages.

Disability interacts with aging. Not only psychological aspects, but physical aspects of function will normally vary with age. When disability interacts with the aging process, some body parts "wear out" faster than they would for an individual without a disability. An individual who uses a manual wheelchair during young adulthood may be expected to require a power wheelchair later in life. That person's shoulders, which were not designed to be weight-bearing joints, will lose function over time faster than they would for an individual who does not use a wheelchair.

PROCESS OF LCP DEVELOPMENT

Life care planning is a process that results in individualized plans tailored to the needs of a specific person. It is essential that the life care planner conduct an on-site interview of catastrophically injured individuals and, whenever possible, their families. Recommendations must be made within the context of individual, family, disability, and regional factors.

A comprehensive review of all available medical, psychological, and rehabilitation-related information is required. School records for children and work histories for adults should also be reviewed. The life care planner must be aware of all medical and rehabilitative aspects of the case, and determine what other evaluations may be needed to identify the individual's disability-related needs. Communication and consultation with the other members of the rehabilitation team are essential. Specific questions may be needed for each specialist, to ascertain and integrate the projected evaluations, treatment recommendations, and therapeutic modalities needed in each area.

Areas analyzed within the development of a Life Care Plan include projected health-related professional evaluations, projected therapeutic modalities, diagnostic testing and educational assessments, wheelchair needs, wheelchair accessories and maintenance, orthopedic equipment needs, orthotic or prosthetic requirements, disability-related home furnishings and accessories, aids for independent function, drug and medical supply needs, home care or facility-based care needs, projected routine future medical care, projected future surgical treatment or other aggressive medical care, transportation needs, required architectural renovations, leisure time or recreational equipment

235

requirements, and specific vocational rehabilitation needs. An example Life Care Plan with the accompanying narrative report and vocational summary are presented in Appendix A.

Recommendations in each of these areas are tailored to the expected short-term and long-term needs of the individual. Specific dates and frequencies of the needed services are detailed, as are the costs associated with those services. A section of the Life Care Plan addresses potential complications. This section is provided for informational purposes only; the frequency of complications and associated costs cannot be predicted. Well-developed and carefully implemented Life Care Plans should proactively minimize the occurrence of complications. If, despite appropriate care and services, a condition is expected to worsen or function is expected to decrease over time, the expected need for increased services and appropriate equipment should be addressed directly within the Life Care Plan. Such expected changes in need are not labeled as complications.

Computers and Life Care Planning
Given the need to keep track of multidimensional information and to present it in an easily understandable manner, most life care planners are attracted to a variety of computer applications. Databases are used to maintain updated information about resources; word processors and graphics programs are used to present the information in an accessible manner, et cetera. One integrated "case management system" software program for life care planning is LCPStat (Thomas, 1997). This program can be used to build databases of resources, summarize and organize medical records, track client information, and print Life Care Plan tables.

RESEARCH AND RESOURCE SUPPORT

Life care planners and case managers implementing Life Care Plans have a critical need to know and understand medical aspects of specific disabilities and the means by which programs can be set up to prevent the onset of further problems or complications. They need to understand the methodological steps for case management planning, and be able to maintain a current grasp of reference material and research literature critical to effective plan development and implementation.

Life care planning recommendations should be data based, rather than simple opinions. Planners should collect data from as many sources as possible, getting information not only about the individual client and about resources for service provision, but also about relevant research studies, which have been published, related to needs of similar individuals with disabilities. It is essential that life care planners utilize critical thinking skills to examine relevant literature and its appropriateness for a given case. If a given research article concludes that a particular set of services will be needed by individuals with bilateral above-the-knee amputations around the 10th year following amputation, can a life care planner assume that these services will be needed for her or his client with bilateral above-the-knee amputations? The answer to that question should be, "It depends . . ." How similar are the characteristics of the sample in the study to the characteristics of this client? Are study subjects the same sex, same age, with the same level of physical activity and similar interests? Do they have the same combination of disabilities, acquired in the same manner, as does the life care planner's client?

Life care planners need not only critical thinking skills, but also creativity and an ability to organize and maintain complex databases of information. Life Care Plans should be developed using cost estimates from suppliers who are located in the area where the catastrophically injured individual will be living. Locating providers of unusual services in remote locations sometimes requires considerable creativity and problem-solving ability. Once such resources are located or developed, it would be foolish for the planner to lose track of those resources. Development and maintenance of an updated set of resources in various local areas is important to life care planners, as well as the case managers who implement the developed plans.

Life Care Plans are projected to life expectancy and cannot depend on any one individual, service, or supplier to fulfill plan recommendations. More than one potential supplier should be identified to fulfill each recommendation. In situations where a family member plans to provide some of the services, the Life Care Plan should also reflect alternative options. It may happen that the family member becomes unable or unwilling, at some future point, to provide that service. Even if the family member chooses to provide the service, the value of that service, (what it would cost if another person were to be hired to provide it) should be included in the cost detailed in the Life Care Plan.

A variety of guides has been published to serve as "starting points" for factors to consider when developing Life Care Plans for individuals with specific disabilities. Examples include Deutsch and Sawyer's (2003) *A guide to rehabilitation*, which is updated annually and provides information about various disabilities. Life care planning with individuals who have had traumatic brain injuries has been addressed by Blackwell, Powers, and Weed (1994); Deutsch, Weed, Kitchen, and Sluis (1989); and Kitchen, Cody, and Deutsch (1989). Issues to consider in life care planning with people who have had spinal cord injuries have been discussed by Blackwell, Weed, and Powers (1994), and Kitchen, Cody, and Morgan (1990). Weed and Sluis (1990) have addressed life care planning with individuals who have had amputations.

KNOWLEDGE, SKILL, AND EXPERTISE REQUIRED

Life care planning has become a specialty area requiring not only global application of concepts of general case management, but also the development of skills specific to particular disabilities. Life care planners should be trained in the areas of medical aspects of disability, psychological and behavioral aspects of disability, facility placement (making effective referrals), preventative care techniques, rehabilitation engineering (equipment related to disability), and vocational aspects of disability.

The Commission on Health Care Certification (CHCC, 2003) describes the process of life care plan development as requiring data collection, resource development, and planning strategies in an interdisciplinary rehabilitation environment. The life care planner must be able to document the needs of catastrophically injured individuals and project the costs of needed services, treatment, and equipment over each individual's lifespan. Skills and expertise in the areas of research, development, coordination, integration, interpretation, and management of life care plans are required. For certification in this area, the CHCC requires a minimum of 120 hours of post-graduate or post-specialty degree training in life care planning, as well as an appropriate degree and certification/licensure within the planner's own professional area, and professional experience developing Life Care Plans.

It should be noted that, while the life care planner provides information about the current costs of services and equipment, it is usually an economist who is responsible for projecting those costs over the expected lifespan, taking into account differing growth trends for different categories of costs. The length of that expected lifespan is usually estimated by a physician, preferably a physiatrist with expertise and experience treating patients with the individual's specific disabilities.

Life Care Plans are generally completed by catastrophic case managers, rehabilitation counselors, rehabilitation psychologists, or rehabilitation nurses (although some other medical or allied health professionals also add to their professional training to develop relevant expertise). These professionals can effectively use their training as case managers and team leaders in an interdisciplinary approach to rehabilitation and long-term management of disability. In contrast, most physicians tend to be limited in responsibility to meeting the acute care needs of their patients, instead of bringing together medical, rehabilitation, educational, and family considerations into a unified and systematic approach to goal development (Deutsch and Kitchen, 1994).

Taylor (1996) reviewed the trial outcomes of several court cases in which Life Care Plans were presented. Taylor found that courts favored Life Care Plans "which (1) are prepared by qualified rehabilitation experts; (2) show the real need for the plaintiff to incur the expenses noted in the plan; and (3) demonstrate reasonable costs for future care" (p. 7). These criteria were more important than whether the life care planner was a physician or whether the planner was hired by plaintiff or defendant.

FUTURE APPLICATIONS OF LIFE CARE PLANNING

A well-developed Life Care Plan could be considered the ultimate facility discharge plan. Some hospitals and rehabilitation facilities providing excellent services have found themselves facing complaints from frustrated and disillusioned patients and their families several months after discharge. A carefully developed, understandable Life Care Plan, implemented by a qualified local case manager, could greatly facilitate successful transition from the facility to the home community or alternative living arrangements.

Life Care Plans can be used by case managers to continue educating their clients and clients' families about what to anticipate in terms of needs associated with disability, as well as to emphasize the importance of measures to prevent complications. The plans can also be used to educate others, such as insurance adjusters and supervisors, about disability-related needs and the cost-effectiveness of preventative measures.

Insurance carriers are increasingly being called upon to make more effective assessments of the impact of disability and the needs associated with that disability over time in order to more effectively accomplish financial reserve setting. Life care planning methodology can be a powerful tool to allow for accurate reserve setting.

Life care planning can also be an important tool for the development of structured settlements and special needs trusts. Structured settlements have become an increasingly integral part of the litigation and settlement process in catastrophic injury cases. The settlement should be structured in a manner that facilitates implementation of the Life Care Plan, so that funding for services needed at given points in time is available when specified. Requirements for establishing special needs trusts vary from state to state, but they can be a valuable resource establishing funding to pay for disability-associated costs while preserving financial eligibility for services.

SUMMARY

Life care planning (LCP) is an important tool to guide the provision of quality care and services throughout the lifespan of a catastrophically injured individual. Life Care Plans are utilized to organize the multidimensional information that must be considered for effective case management. A consistent methodology should be used to develop appropriate recommendations based upon the actual needs of the individual. Life Care Plans should not be used simply as litigation tools; they should serve as "roadmaps" for the case manager and educational tools for the individual with a disability, his or her family, and service providers. A systematic, coordinated approach to maximizing individual potential and preventing future complications can result not only in financial savings, but also in enhanced quality of life.

REFERENCES

Blackwell, T. L., Powers, A. S., & Weed, R. O. (1994). *Life Care Planning for traumatic brain injury: A resource manual for case managers.* Athens, GA: Elliott & Fitzpatrick.

Blackwell, T. L., Weed, R. O., & Powers, A. S. (1994). *Life Care Planning for spinal cord injury: A resource manual for case managers.* Athens, GA: Elliott & Fitzpatrick.

Commission on Health Care Certification (CHCC) (2003). *Standards and Examination Guidelines.* Midlothian, VA: CHCC.

Deutsch, P. M. (1990). *A guide to rehabilitation testimony: The expert's role as an educator.* Orlando, FL: Paul M. Deutsch Press.

Deutsch, P. M. (1995). Life Care Planning. In A. E. Dell Orto & R. P. Marinelli (Eds.), *Encyclopedia of disability and rehabilitation* (pp. 436-442). New York: Simon & Schuster Macmillan.

Deutsch, P. M., Allison, L., & Reid, C. (2003). An introduction to Life Care Planning: History, tenets, methodologies & Principles. In P. M. Deutsch & H. Sawyer (Eds.), *A guide to rehabilitation* (pp. 5.1–5.62). White Plains, NY: Ahab Press.

Deutsch, P. M. & Kitchen, J. A. (1994). Life Care Planning. *Seminars in Hearing, 15*(5), 207-223.

Deutsch, P. M. & Raffa, F. (1982). *Damages in tort actions* (vol 8-9). New York: Matthew Bender.

Deutsch, P. M. & Reid, C. (2003). Life care planning: A methodology for catastrophic disability analysis. In K. Anchor, J. Schmerling, & J. Anchor (Eds.), *The catastrophic injury handbook: Understanding vocational, economic, legal and clinical aspects of complex physical and mental trauma* (pp. 118–131). Dubuque, IA: Kendall/Hunt.

Deutsch, P. M. & Sawyer, H. (2003). *A guide to rehabilitation.* White Plains, NY: Ahab Press.

Deutsch, P. M., Weed, R. O., Kitchen, J. A., & Sluis, A. (1989). *Life Care Planning for the head injured: A step by step guide.* Orlando, FL: Paul M. Deutsch Press.

Kitchen, J. A., Cody, L. S., & Deutsch, P. M. (1989). *Life Care Plans for the brain damaged baby: A step by step guide.* Orlando, FL: Paul M. Deutsch Press.

Kitchen, J. A., Cody, L. S., & Morgan, N. G. (1990). *Life Care Plans for the ventilator dependent patient: A step by step guide.* Orlando, FL: Paul M. Deutsch Press.

McCoy, D. (1996). The purpose of a Life Care Plan. *Inside Life Care Planning, 1*(3), 1, 9.

Reavis, S. L. (2002). Standards of practice. *Journal of Life Care Planning, 1*(1), 49–58.

Reid, C., Deutsch, P. M., & Kitchen, J. (2001). Life Care Planning: An emerging rehabilitation intervention. In P. D. Rumrill, J. L. Bellini, & L. C. Koch (Eds.), *Emerging issues in Rehabilitation Counseling: Perspectives on the new millennium* (pp. 59–88). Springfield, IL: Charles C. Thomas.

Taylor, J. S. (1996). Neurolaw life: Life Care Plans in court. *Inside Life Care Planning, 1*(3), 7.

Thomas, R. (1997). *LCP STAT Life Care Planning Software* [Computer program, version 2.0]. Ridgeland, MS: TecSolutions.

Thomas, R. & Kitchen, J. A. (1996). Private hire: The real costs. *Inside Life Care Planning, 1*(3), 1, 3-4.

Weed, R. O. (1995, February). Life Care Plans as a managed care tool. *Medical Interface,* 111-118.

Weed, R. O. (Ed.) (1999). *Life care planning and case management handbook.* Boca Raton, FL: CRC Press.

Weed, R. O. (2001). Catastrophic case management and Life Care Plans. In R. O. Weed & T. F. Field, *Rehabilitation Consultant's Handbook (Revised)* (pp. 171–228). Athens, GA: Elliott & Fitzpatrick.

Weed, R. O. & Berens, D. E. (Eds.) (2001). *Life Care Planning Summit 2000 Proceedings.* Athens, GA: Elliott & Fitzpatrick.

Weed, R. O., & Sluis, A. (1990). *Life Care Plans for the amputee: a step by step guide.* Orlando, FL: Paul M. Deutsch Press.

Weed, R. O. & Riddick, S. N. (1992). Life Care Plans as a case management tool. *The Case Manager, 3*(1), 26-35

Appendix A
A SAMPLE CASE STUDY

NARRATIVE REPORT

Client: Joe Smith
Social Security No.: Unavailable
Date of Evaluations: August 13 & September 25, 1997
Date of Narrative Report: October 21, 1997

Joe Smith is a 7 year, 11-month-old Caucasian male referred for rehabilitation evaluation by his attorneys, xxxx and xxxx. The purpose of this evaluation is to assess the extent to which Joe has incurred handicapping conditions secondary to a birth onset of disability. The specific manner in which the resulting handicapping conditions impede his educational development and potential for vocational development, as well any supportive services he will require throughout life expectancy, have been considered in the conclusions and appendices attached to this report. In reaching these conclusions, consideration has been given to all of the medical, psychological, and rehabilitation data, along with appropriate test information.

Joe was seen for evaluation initially in the office of xxxx and Associates on August 13, 1997, by xxxx, CDMS, for the purpose of gathering initial background and demographic information. Subsequently, on September 25, 1997, he returned accompanied by his father, and a clinical history and child assessment were completed.

Joe presents as an active, seven-year-old Caucasian male, who is quite talkative and interacts easily and effectively with the evaluators. His father describes his vision as 20/200 bilaterally, which is considered legally blind.

Assistive devices currently employed by Joe include a slant board device on his desk at school to allow him to see the information more easily. His father (John) indicates that no other specific aids are employed; however, the school does use a white chalkboard for better visualization instead of the standard blackboard. Additional aids have been identified through his vision consultant, and these will be outlined within the Life Care Plan pages.

Joe's father gives a history of Joe being born prematurely at 23 weeks. He notes that Joe's birth weight was one pound, three ounces, and at one point Joe had dropped below the weight of one pound. Joe was the surviving member of a twin birth.

His father notes Joe, at first, came home on a heart monitor, and subsequently it was "a while before therapy could be initiated." He started a

242

program in xxxx, Florida; however, John is unsure of the specifics of the program. At age three, Joe participated in occupational and speech therapy two times per week for one hour each session. He was also involved in the Teaching Lab for about two years and was involved in a home schooling situation with his mother early on. John gained full custody of Joe in September 1996 by mutual agreement of both parents. Since September 1996, Joe had been in speech therapy fairly consistently with Ms. xxxx, CCC, until funding problems interfered with the continuation of services. He participates in physical therapy, which is provided through the school system. This therapy continued through the summer, during which he also participated in the xxxx Learning Institute two days per week. Joe is now in the first grade, which just began two weeks before our initial evaluation. His father noted that Joe is having difficulty paying attention and staying on task. He is not particularly hyperactive, but he does have difficulty staying focused. His father notes that the school system wanted to hold him back last year as he was not academically at age level; however, because of his age, he was moved on to the next level.

Chief complaints: During this portion of the evaluation, John is asked to outline for us Joe's primary problems. It is important to note that the demographic information and Chief Complaints, Physical Limitations, and Environmental Influences sections of this report are all as a result of client and family report, not based on any physical examination.

John begins by explaining that Joe is "frequently sick with colds and has an immune system deficiency. When he gets sick, it will stay with him for weeks. He has little immune system function to fight it at all. He has poor hand-eye coordination. His fine motor skills are bad—he cannot cut paper on the line; he is clumsy basically. He runs awkwardly, like something is out of rhythm. We took him to a podiatrist who said it was his hips, not his feet, which are causing the problems with the gait. When he runs, he waddles, and he falls down all of the time. The podiatrist says his pelvis rotates more than it should, and it throws his center of gravity off. His pediatrician just says he has multiple dysfunctions from prematurity. He has a high arched palate, thick tongue, and hence has speech problems as well as dental side effects, which the pediatrician says should be evaluated by a dentist. This has not been accomplished yet. His mother took him earlier, but she was told by the periodontist that later in life they could place a plate in his mouth to give his tongue something to hit. Ms. xxxx [Speech/Language Pathologist] feels that oral-motor exercises may also help. He has a weak voice; he cannot scream. His voice comes out in a breathy whisper. He has significant scarring and has had open-heart surgery due to heart valve malfunctioning and has had a hernia. Because he was so little, his skin kept separating from his legs and other areas when the sheets would come in contact with it. He had a tube taped to his mouth in the hospital, and at one point, when he had a problem, the tube and tape were jerked off and it just tore the skin right off with it."

Clearly, John has difficulty enumerating the many areas of deficits he sees in Joe. Joe does have problems in learning and retaining new information, as well as immediate and delayed memory problems. He is unable to follow serial instructions, and he has to be given one task at a time. Joe gets frustrated very easily if he cannot do something, and "he just shuts down." His father is convinced he has a "wandering eye," and this may be the cause of some of the headaches he gets about twice a week.

John notes Joe was in the hospital for four months. He came home on a heart monitor, and they had an in-house nurse during this time for the first month. Someone was needed to stay awake with Joe through the night to monitor him. The monitor was discontinued after about a month after he was home. Joe was fed through a tube through his mouth for three months. Upon discharge to home, he was initially fed through a preemie bottle.

John notes that, early on, Joe's mom found it difficult to deal with the reality of a special needs child. Dad has enrolled Joe in school and is trying to do everything he can to bring stability into Joe's life. The school system has suggested he be sent to a different school for visual impairments; however, his father has determined that there is only one "special" class that would be offered at this other school, as compared to what he is now receiving. He currently has enlarged print books and a special board overlay for him to be able to visualize the chalkboard. In trying to bring stability into Joe's life, Dad is reluctant to switch him to another school at this point in time. Additionally, his current school is very close to his home.

In continuing, Dad notes that Joe will chill easily, and his lips will turn blue. He cannot go to the beach on a hot day and enjoy the water, as he gets too cold. His father is trying to "put weight on him," but is not having much success. Joe does take vitamins but no food supplements. John notes that the pediatrician is not too concerned about Joe's weight.

In addition to the above, Joe's learning disabilities and behavioral problems, such as not listening and not paying attention, are also areas of concern. He is not in special education classes at this time.

John notes that this has been a tremendous strain on both parents. Joe's mother had been through three tubal pregnancies with artificial insemination and then in-vitro fertilization, which produced the twins, of which Joe is the surviving member.

John is unsure of any future surgery that Joe may need. He notes that there may be an eye surgery later in life. He also mentioned Joe's hips being "out," and he is unsure if bracing will help and be used or if surgical intervention will be required.

244

At this point in the evaluation, specific questions relating to developmental delay were asked. Joe has no seizures currently, with no history of seizures being present. He has had one heart surgery to open a valve in the past. His father is unsure of any other specific surgeries required in the future.

Joe currently attends school and is in an aftercare program for two hours each day. He also goes to XYZ Learning Institute during the summer to avoid a gap in his educational experience.

Joe's daily care needs include a highly structured learning and behavioral environment. This is particularly evident as some problems in his behavior have been seen in the aftercare program that are similar to the problems he has experienced during school, relating to his being rather rough with the other children.

When asked about self-stimulating behaviors, John indicates Joe used to stiffen up and make animal sounds and grunts, and now he still makes the sounds but does not stiffen up as much.

In the motor skills area, John was observed during a free play session. His grasp (left and right) is intact but not well coordinated. Vision is part of the issue but coordination is a separate issue. He is able to grasp with his thumb and forefinger and make voluntary, purposeful movements of the upper and lower extremities. He is able to ambulate but does have a gait disturbance that may be orthopedic in origin or it may be neurological. He does not regularly dress himself, although he is able to. He does have problems, such as when his underwear is inside out and "he has no clue as to how to turn it back." He does cooperate and assist with dressing. He does pick up his toys and clean up his closet with cueing and prompts. His father notes that when he does this, he insists on lining everything up in a straight line, such as all the shoes exactly placed in line. Regarding personal hygiene chores, he does require help and prompting. He does want to brush his teeth, but he is simply unable to coordinate that activity. Joe can ascend and descend stairs with caution and guidance, but he does fall frequently.

In the cognitive area, Joe is able to follow simple one or two-step commands. His father notes, "You have to be careful because he doesn't always avoid hazards." For example, if Joe is playing with a ball and it rolls out into the street, he will constantly run out into the road chasing his ball, without giving thought to the traffic. Joe's attention to task is very limited, with moderate hyperactivity shown during the evaluation and also near the end of the evaluation. Joe was observed punching his father and reaching out to squeeze his face and neck with both hands. Joe thinks he is playing, but he shows no sense of strength or if he is hurting someone during these activities.

Physical limitations: John is not aware of any loss of tactile sensation that Joe might experience. Joe does show a normal range of motion in the upper extremities. He can lift weights that are appropriate for his age and weight. Joe notes, at this point, that he can lift "five pounds for an hour." His prehensile action and grip strength are strong bilaterally. He has no physical restrictions with sitting, but he is constantly out of his seat due to his attention deficits. He has no physical restrictions on standing, however, again, is restricted only in terms of his attention span. Joe does have an altered gait and stumbles frequently when he tries to run. His podiatrist has indicated his hips do not rotate properly, and this needs to be evaluated by an orthopedist in the future. He has no physical restrictions with bending or twisting, stooping, squatting, or climbing. His balance is fair as he is uncoordinated and tends to "wobble." He does fatigue easily and displays no shortness of breath while at rest, but with an activity, he will tend to get out of breath. He does have headaches frequently, typically two times per week. He does not take medications for these. As noted earlier, Joe is considered legally visually impaired. His hearing is intact, as is his sense of humor. When asked if he is able to hear, he responded, "What?"

Joe does have bowel accidents on occasion, maybe once every couple of months, or maybe more. He notes that if he strains, he may have an accident. He is easily fatigued and his physical stamina and endurance are not at an age-appropriate level.

Additional data: Careful consideration has been given to a collection of data concerning activities of daily living, social activities, personal habits, socioeconomic status, and state or federal agency involvement in rehabilitation. Although not reported in its entirety within the context of this narrative report, the data remain available within the clinical notes and are utilized in developing rehabilitation conclusions and recommendations.

Current medical care: Currently, Joe is seeing xxxx, M.D., as his primary care physician. He is not currently treating with any other specialists.

Joe has been receiving speech therapy through Ms. xxxx, although those services have been temporarily interrupted due to funding issues; vision therapy through the school system; and additional speech therapy and occupational therapy as well through the school system. He has also been seen by xxxx, educational consultant, and xxxx, occupational therapist. Each of Joe's treating professionals was contacted with specific questions regarding his long-term care needs. Their recommendations will be outlined within the Life Care Plan.

At the current time, Joe is on no prescription medication.

Education and training: Currently, Joe attends first grade at xxxx Elementary School in xxxx, Florida. He is not in special education classes but does have the assistance of a vision teacher.

Behavioral observations: Joe is alert and oriented; his stream of thought is clear, however, it is not fully age appropriate. He is somewhat, but not severely, behind in his social maturation. His approach to the evaluation was positive, in line with his age level.

Test administration: Joe's school and medical records contain a range of standardized test results and it was not felt necessary at this time to repeat those items. I do feel consideration should be given to completing a neuropsychological workup, but I stress this is for establishing the right structured environment and enhancing educational development. I am not recommending this be done for trial purposes. I chose to administer the Slosson Intelligence Test as a means of gaining insight into his current fund of knowledge and his ability to function over time on a task.

Joe had to be constantly redirected to this task orientation, but with prompts and reinforcement, he was able to complete the effort. He developed a raw score of 61, a total standard score (IQ) of 103, and a mean age equivalency of 7.3. He falls in the 57% in this measure and shows his ability to learn and retain information if an effort is made to meet his individual needs.

Medical summary: Joe Smith is a seven-year-old, Caucasian male who was born on 11/26/89. Joe was delivered three weeks after his twin. The twin was delivered vaginally, and Joe was delivered by cesarean section. His twin died at birth.

On 8/14/90, Joe was seen at the xxxx Eye Clinic with a history of retinopathy of prematurity, status post cryo treatment. The impression was that Joe had an excellent result status post cryo treatment; however, he was significantly myopic. A prescription for glasses was made.

On 10/1/90, Joe was seen at Riverside Children's Hospital for a neurological consultation. Apparently, Joe was born with intraventricular bleeding, and since then he had been hyperactive. He had a short attention span. He had self-stimulating behavior, and he did not sleep well at night. His legs were stiff and he moved constantly. In relation to language, Joe did not make any sounds. He reached for objects mostly with his left hand, and he was unable to sit on his own. He scooted on the floor, but he was not able to maintain a crawling pattern. The diagnoses were (1) macrocephaly with cortical atrophy, probably secondary to prematurity; (2) extraocular movement imbalance with bilateral alternating internal strabismus; (3) spastic quadriparesis; (4) pseudobulbar palsy; (5) language disorder, receptive and expressive with practically no speech articulation; (6) rule out gastroesophageal reflux; and (7) behavior disorder, attention deficit disorder, hyperactivity, and irritability.

In a follow-up visit to the Neurology Clinic at xxxx Children's Hospital on 10/23/90, a CAT scan showed definite signs with moderate ventriculomegaly and sucal prominence indicating atrophic changes of the cortex and also of the central structures with central and cortical atrophy diffusely distributed. An EEG was within normal limits. He was seen by the speech pathologist, who recommended speech therapy. His speech development was below the three month level with no evidence of cooing and babbling. Continued physical therapy and occupational therapy were also recommended.

On 4/12/91, Joe was seen for a neurology re-evaluation at xxxx Children's Hospital. Upon examination, he appeared to be very hyperactive and had an attention deficit disorder. He also had self-stimulating behavior. He reached for objects fairly well. His gait was absent, and his sitting balance was very poor. His motor development was approximately six to seven months. At that time, medicine for hyperactivity was not necessary. Continued therapies were recommended.

In a follow-up visit to the xxxx Eye Clinic on 11/22/94, there was a slight increase in Joe's myopic correction.

On 10/28/96, he was seen for an oral motor evaluation at xxxx and Associates. The impression was dysarthria. Oral motor intervention one time per week with home carry-over was recommended.

In a letter dated 2/13/97 (xxxxl Vision Center), it was indicated that Joe met the definition of legal blindness.

On 4/4/97, Joe was seen for an evaluation by xxxx. It was believed that Joe would benefit from occupational therapy services to rehabilitate his visual motor skills. Joe had slightly hypotonic muscle tone and problems with bilateral integration, upper body control, graphomotor skills, and fine motor control. He had visual impairment and difficulty with initiation, completion, and planning out motor tasks. He functioned below his age level and capability due to these problems. It was felt that he would benefit from placement in a regular classroom with assistance from a vision teacher and an occupational therapist. A home program follow-through with therapeutic interventions was also recommended.

On 4/4/97, Joe was seen for a functional vision assessment. Overall, he utilized vision as his main learning modality. His performance was below average in two areas of assessment, which were ocular pursuits and acuity (distance and near). It was indicated that both areas could affect his performance, but with compensation strategies, they should not affect his ability to learn. It was believed that Joe would at least need large print with 18-point text for school. It was suggested that he would be able to succeed in a regular classroom with itinerant services from a teacher of the visually impaired (Ms. xxxx, M.A.).

Records reviewed:
xxxx: 4/4/97
xxxx MS, CCC-SLP: 10/28/96-4/14/97
xxxx, M.Ed., OTR/L: 4/4/97-6/17/97
xxxx Eye Clinic: 8/14/90-3/19/96
xxxx Pediatrics: 11/8/96; 6/90-10/93
xxxxl Vision Center: 2/13/97
Medical Bills: 9/96-4/97
xxxx Children's Hospital: 10/1/90-10/11/91
xxxx Primary Care: 9/24/97
Prescription Records: 1996
School Records (in file): 2/97-5/97

Conclusions: Careful consideration has been given to all of the medical, psychosocial, rehabilitation/mental health counseling, and test data contained within this file and my report. There is certainly no question that we are dealing with an individual who has incurred significant handicapping conditions that will affect his future educational and social development secondary to his premature birth and resulting sequela.

Joe will need a neuropsychological evaluation to help identify how he learns best; then all of his therapists, family members, and teachers must be trained accordingly. Based on the findings of the neuropsychological evaluation, it is suggested we follow through with a behavioral/developmental psychological evaluation and structure his home, behavioral, and educational environments using consistent cues, prompts, and reinforcers. Additionally, contact will be made with the Bureau of Vision Services to see if any services may be appropriate at this age and as he goes through each developmental stage.

The Life Care Plan (next section) outlines all of Joe's needs secondary to the sequela from his premature birth, which include psychological and educational supports as well as specific aids for independent function and medical follow-up.

The Vocational Worksheet indicates the impact this injury will have on his ability to be placed in the competitive labor market, when comparing his ability to compete for employment pre-onset as compared to his ability to compete post-onset. The Worksheet also outlines that through appropriate educational intervention and strong supportive intervention, with appropriate aids for independent function employed, he should be able to be channeled into a very productive work life scenario.

After you have had an opportunity to review this narrative report and the attached appendices, please do not hesitate to contact me should you have further questions.

Respectfully submitted,
xxxx, Ph.D., C.R.C., C.C.M.
Licensed Mental Health Counselor
XXXX & ASSOCIATES, P.A.

LIFE CARE PLAN
JOE SMITH

Item/Service	Age/Year	Frequency/ Replacement	Purpose	Cost	Comment

Projected Evaluations

Item/Service	Age/Year	Frequency/ Replacement	Purpose	Cost	Comment
Rehabilitation/ Long-Term Needs Assessment	Beginning 7 9/97 Ending 18 2007	2 X Only	Long Term Care Planning	→	1st eval. accomplished. Suggest second at age 13 upon entering middle school for phase changes (2nd eval. to cost $2500-$3000 plus expenses).
Psychological Evaluation	Beginning 8 11/97 Ending 18 2007	One time per three years	Routine assessment	Per Unit $450-$600	To help structure behavioral programming and develop protocols.
Vocational Evaluation	Beginning 16 2005 Ending 18 2007	2 X Only	Routine Assessment	→	Inital eval. at age 16 for exploratory purposes: $450-$650. Full eval. at age 18: $650-$750
Neuropsychological Evaluation	Beginning 8 11/97 Ending 18 2007	1 X /3-4 yrs. to	Assessment to determine best learning methods	→	Inital eval.: $450-$650. Full eval. at age 18: $650-$750
Nutrition Eval.	Beginning 8 11/97 Ending Life exp.	1 X /year to age 18; then 1 X/2-3	Routine Assessment	→	Initial eval. $110; Follow-up counseling $30/hr., $110/yr. To age 18, then $60-$90 every 2-3 years thereafter.

Joe Smith Plan (Continued)

Item/Service	Age/Year	Frequency/ Replacement	Purpose	Cost	Comment
Functional Vision Evaluation	Beginning 8 11/97 Ending Life exp.	1 X /1-2 years to age 18; then 1 X /3-4 years	Routine Assessment	Per Unit $150	Will assess appropriate equipment for maximum Independence
Speech/Language Evaluation	Beginning 8 11/97 Ending 18 2007	Yearly through developmental years	Routine assessment	Per Unit $100-$200 Per Year $200-$400	1 X /yr. thru public school program. Two additional annually are recommended for motoric functioning and semantics/articu-lation. Therefore, 2 evals. funded through age 18.
Occupational Therapy Eval.	Beginning 8 11/97 Ending 18 2007	Yearly through developmental Years	Routine assessment for visual/motor skills	Per Unit $300	
Physical Therapy Eval.	Beginning 8 11/97 Ending 18 2007	Yearly through developmental years	Routine assessment for functional delays	Per Unit $136-$272	

Projected Therapeutic Modalities

Item/Service	Age/Year	Frequency/ Replacement	Purpose	Cost	Comment
Psychological Counseling	Beginning 8 11/97 Ending Life exp.	26 sessions per ages 8, 11, 14, 17, and 20; then 4-6 X/yr. after	Routine intervention	Per Unit $100-$125	

Note: Anticipate 1 X/week for 6 months at specific ages for behavioral intervention [$2,600-$3,250]. After age 21, it is anticipated a yearly allowance be provided for supportive intervention--based on 4-6 times per year to life, or $450-$675/year.

Joe Smith Plan (Continued)

Item/Service	Age/Year	Frequency/ Replacement	Purpose	Cost	Comment
Family Counseling/ Education	Beginning 8 11/97 Ending 60 2049	See comment —>	Routine	Per Unit $100-$125	Anticipate family intervention counseling/education to be made available during specific phases in Joe's life. Est. 8-10 sessions at ages 8, 12, 15, and 18 for $900-$1125/specific age.
Career Guidance and Counseling	Beginning 18 2000 Ending 60 2049	2-3 X between age 18-60.	Assistance in career planning and implementation	Per Unit $75	See note below for costs.

Note: Allowance for two to three programs of Career Guidance and Counseling over his work life. More frequent job changes, etc. may result in the need for additional programs of counseling and guidance, but anticipate that sufficient skills will be learned throughout these programs to carry over. Career guidance to include (A) career exploration; (B) career decision making; (C) matching of interests, job satisfiers, motivators, and abilities to available alternatives vocationally or avocationally; (D) goal setting; (E) job seeking skills training; and (F) Counseling post placement to help ensure success. Total per each program: $900-$1,500 based on 12-20 hours.

Item/Service	Age/Year	Frequency/ Replacement	Purpose	Cost	Comment
Physical Therapy	Beginning 8 11/97 Ending 18 2007	1-2 X/Week (48 weeks per year)	Work on motoric functioning	Per Unit $136 Per Year $6528-$13056	School system will only provide therapies if they are determined to be educationally necessary It is important to privately fund PT services for this child.
Occupational Therapy	Beginning 8 11/97 Ending 18 2007	2 X/Week (48 weeks per year)	Rehabilitate Visual/Motor	Per Unit $100 Per Year $9600	School System will only provide therapies if they are educationally necessary. Additional OT services needed.

Joe Smith Plan (Continued)

Item/Service	Age/Year	Frequency/ Replacement	Purpose	Cost	Comment
Speech Therapy	Beginning 8 11/97 Ending 18 2007	1-2 X/Week (48 weeks per year)	Motor Skills and Semantics and Pragmatics	Per Unit $136 Per Year $6528- $13056	School System will only provide therapies if they Are determined to be educa- tionally necessary It is important to privately fund ST services for this child.

Education

Special Education Services	Beginning 7 10/97 Ending 18 2007	Throughout primary and secondary school	Special Ed. as Required	Per Unit $0	Costs covered under IDEA - Individuals with Disability Education Act

Note: Special education services secondary to the visual impairment and the attention deficit. (See provision of tutor made available, below.)

Tutoring	Beginning 8 11/97 Ending 18 2007	Throughout developmental years - see below	Assist in educational development	Per Unit $30-$47 Per Year $2880-$4512	

Note: 2 hours/week; 48weeks per year are recommended in order to provide the best possible future scenario in terms of education and work.

Vocational School or Two-Year College	Beginning 18 2007 Ending 21 2010	1 X Only	Assist in tuition for maximizing earnings	Per Unit $3367- $4200	Allow 3 years to complete a 2-year program

254

Joe Smith Plan (Continued)

Item/Service	Age/Year	Frequency/ Replacement	Purpose	Cost	Comment

Orthotics/Prosthetics

Item/Service	Age/Year	Frequency/ Replacement	Purpose	Cost	Comment
Orthodontist	Beginning undetermined Ending undetermined	1 X Only	Correction of Narrow Palate	→	Determined after evaluation by Orthodontist. Typical costs: $2475 - $3000

Aids for Independent Function

Item/Service	Age/Year	Frequency/ Replacement	Purpose	Cost	Comment
Computer	Beginning 8 11/97 Ending Life Exp.	1 X /3-4 Years	Visual training/ School work and Vocational Endeavors	Per Unit $1500- $1900	
Computer Service/ Upgrade	Beginning 9 1998 Ending Life Exp.	1 X/ Year	Maintain and up- grade Equipment	Per Unit $125- $190	Except in new purchase years
Enlarged Print Software for Computer	Beginning 8 11/97 Ending Life Exp.	1 X /2-3 Years	Visual training/ School work and Vocational Endeavors	Per Unit $50	
Symbol/Letter Tracking	Beginning 8 11/97 Ending 18 2007	4 X/Year	Visual training/ Schoolwork	Per Unit $10 Per Year $40	
Tape Player for Books on Tape	Beginning 8 11/97 Ending Life Exp.	As needed	Reading	Per Unit $0	No cost-funded through the Library of Congress

255

Joe Smith Plan (Continued)

Item/Service	Age/Year	Frequency Replacement/	Purpose	Cost	Comment
Miscellaneous Aids for People with are Visually Impaired	Beginning 8 11/97 Ending Life Exp.	Every 2-3 years Allowance	Independence in Activities of Daily Living	Per Unit $366-$400	

(Slant Board: $38; Large Display Alarm Clock: $49; Jumbo Playing Cards: $13; Big Button Phone: $80; Large Print Calendar: $8; Large Print Dictionary: $29; Low Vision Wall Clock: $$35; Low Vision Watch: $35-$48; Electric Time Switch to Control Household Devices: $79-85. Estimate: $366-$400/2-3 years.)

| *Alladin Rainbow Personal Reader* | Beginning 8   11/97 Ending Life Exp. | 1 X /3-4 Years | Independence in ADLs | Per Unit $3034 | Price includes shipping |

Note: This is a one-piece color personal reader that magnifies while producing high contrast images in either black and white or full color. This equipment has an unusually large depth of field which permits 3-dimensional objects such as prescription bottles and curved surfaces to be easily read.

| *Glasses* | Beginning 8   11/97 Ending Life Exp. | 1 X / Year | Visual Aid | Per Unit $175-$225 | |

Medications

| *Medications* | Beginning 8   11/97 Ending Life Exp. | See Note | Prescribed Pharmaceuticals | Per Unit Per Year | |

Note: Currently no prescription medications are utilized. There is the possibility that attention enhancing medications may be used in the future.

Joe Smith Plan (Continued)

Item/Service	Frequency Age/Year Replacement/	Purpose	Cost	Comment

Home Care/Facility Care

Item/Service	Frequency Age/Year Replacement/	Purpose	Cost	Comment
Case Management	Beginning 8 11/97 Ending Life Exp.	See Note	Routine Management of Rehabilitation Needs	Per Unit $77-$95	With the case mgt. available for resource intervention, I believe Joe has The ability to live independently.

Note: Anticipate 2-4 hours per month for first 6 months post initiation of the Life Care Plan ($1,032-$2,064); then reduced to 1-2 hours per month through age 22 to enable Joe to transition to independent community living ($1,032-$2,064/year through age 22). Thereafter, case management services should be made available 4-6 hours per year ($344-$516).

Future Medical Care Routine

Item/Service	Frequency Age/Year Replacement/	Purpose	Cost	Comment
Neurology	Beginning 8 11/97 Ending Life Exp.	1 X/Year	Routine Assessment	Per Unit Per Year $60-$95	
Ophthalmology	Beginning 8 11/97 Ending Life Exp.	2 X/Year to age 9; then 1 X/yr.	Routine Assessment due to Visual Impairment	Per Unit $80 Per Year	$160/Year to age 9; then $80/Year
Physical Medicine and Rehabilitation	Beginning 8 11/97 Ending Life Exp.	1 X/Year	Routine Assessment	Per Unit $75 Per Year $75	
Orthodontic Evaluation	Beginning 8 11/97 Ending Life Exp.	1 X/ Only	Assessment due to narrow Palate	Per Unit $275 Per Year $275	

Joe Smith Plan (Continued)

Item/Service	Age/Year	Frequency Replacement/	Purpose	Cost	Comment
Cardiology Evaluation	Beginning 8 11/97 Ending Life Exp.	1 X/Year	Assessment for Heart Problems	Per Unit $43-$125 Per Year $43-$125	
Orthopedic Evaluation	Beginning 8 11/97 Ending Life Exp.	1 X/Year	Assessment for hip rotation	Per Unit $85-$125 Per Year $85-$125	

Transportation

Transportation Allowance	Beginning 16 2005 Ending Life Exp.	See Note	Transportation	Per Unit Per Year $1800-$2400	

Note: This is to begin at the time a person typically begins to drive. It is difficult to quantify how much time would be spent in actual driving. Using the average of 1,000 miles driven in a month, at 35-45 miles per hour (40 MPH average), this is equal to 25 hours per month of typical driving time. If one hires privately a person to drive, at a rate of $6-8/hour, this would cost approximately $150-$200/month, or $1,800-$2,400/year. No consideration has been given to additional costs for taxes, insurance, advertising, replacement services, etc. Public transportation is another option; however, this is often unreliable and quite restrictive in terms of availability. The other option is to consider taxi services which are typically in the $2.00 mile range of costs.

Potential Complications
(For Information Purposes Only. No Prediction of
Frequency or Occurrence Available)

Complication	Cost of Complication	Comment
Falls/Fractures	Cost varies according to the extent of complication	Secondary to balance/gait problems and visual impairments

258

Joe Smith Plan (Continued)

Impaired Cognition	Cost of consequences varies	Greatest potential complications for this individual involve problems resulting from some reduced cognitive functioning and impaired decision making capabilities. A structured environment must be provided to maximize capabilities.
Respiratory Complications and other frequent illnesses	Cost varies according to the extent of complication	Impaired immune system
Surgical Intervention	Cost varies according to the extent of complication	Visual Needs; Orthopedic Surgery

*Growth Trend to be Determined by an Economist.

259

VOCATIONAL WORKSHEET

NAME: Joe Smith
AGE: 7 Years, 11 months
DOB: 11/26/89
DOA: 11/26/89

ANTICIPATED LENGTH OF REHABILITATION PROGRAM:
Joe will need to participate in a program of supportive intervention throughout the developmental years. Some additional services will be necessary through his life expectancy.

VOCATIONAL HANDICAPS

Restrictions/Limitations and/or Deficits include:
Physical Stamina and Endurance
Weakened Immune System Resulting in Numerous Illnesses
Altered Gait
Poor Balance
Poor Overall Coordination
Poor Eye-Hand Coordination
Poor Eye-Hand-Foot Coordination
Lack of Vocal Acuity
Attention Deficits
Visual Impairment (Legally Blind)

Emotional Sequela of Developmental Delay with Speech/Language Delays and Visual Impairment resulting in the following difficulties:
Decreased ability to relate to people and communicate ideas
Decreased ability to communicate ideas and influence others
Decreased ability to relate to people in a manner to win their confidence and establish rapport
Decreased ability to motivate people to work cooperatively
Decreased ability to relate to people in order to motivate and direct
Decreased ability to deal tactfully with people to put them at ease
Decreased ability to adjust to fluctuating circumstances
Decreased ability to flow with conversational agility
Lack of lucidity in expression
Lack of poise and composure
Lack of ability to work with people of different personalities

260

IMPACT ON PLACEMENT
Severe for obtaining and maintaining employment without intervention as noted in the Life Care Plan. With appropriate intervention and counseling techniques, as well as built-in supports for educational and vocational planning, the impact could be moderate.

IMPACT ON RANGE OF JOB ALTERNATIVES
Severe without intervention as noted in the Life Care Plan. With appropriate intervention and counseling techniques, as well as built-in supports for educational and vocational planning, and appropriate aids for independent functioning, the impact should be moderate. Those worker groups given consideration include: Administrative Detail, Business Administration, Communications, Customer Services, and Hospitality Services. I do believe work will prove to be an important therapeutic outlet for this child when he reaches adulthood.

REHABILITATION PLAN
See Life Care Plan.

VOCATIONAL DEVELOPMENT OPTIONS PRE-ONSET
• Direct placement in the labor market after graduation from high school.
• Direct placement in the labor market after graduation from high school, plus additional training received through a vocational/technical program, on-the-job training, or a two-year academic program.

VOCATIONAL DEVELOPMENT OPTIONS POST-ONSET
Post-injury, Joe continues to have the same developmental options available to him as indicated in his Pre-Injury status; however, given the severity of his visual impairment, along with the Speech/Language delay, it will be critical to afford him the intensive therapeutic, counseling, and educational interventions as outlined in the Life Care Plan. Additionally, tuition assistance is suggested in order to insure that this individual has the greatest possible opportunity to reach his maximum potential. The provision of tutoring in the developmental years is also suggested to help maximize his development.

PRE-ACCIDENT VOCATIONAL ALTERNATIVES
• Average earnings for a Caucasian Male, High School Graduate, ages 18-24 in the U.S. : $17,944*.
• Examples of jobs requiring on-the-job training or a vocational training:

Occupational Title	Mean Wage	Yearly Wage
Automotive Body Repairers	$11.29	$23,483.20
Data Processing Equipment Rprs.	$12.40	$25,792.00
Drywall Installers	$11.26	$23,420.80
Food Service and Lodging Mgrs.	$12.21	$25,396.80

Average of Mean Wage Based on 2080 Hours/Year: $24,523.20**

Source: *Money Income of Households, Families, and Persons in the United States: 1995. U.S.
Department of Commerce; Bureau of the Census.

Source: **1995 Florida Occupational Wage Survey Report. Florida Department of Labor and
Employment Security; Bureau of Labor Market Information.

POST-ACCIDENT VOCATIONAL ALTERNATIVES

If one assumes only the completion of high school and direct placement in the labor market, there is little question that both physical disability and psychological/cognitive limitations will severely restrict placement and earnings. I would have serious concerns about his ability to stabilize in consistent, full-time work. He would be eliminated from heavy and medium work classifications and likely find it difficult to obtain or maintain jobs involving constant public contact. Frankly, I would not anticipate him reaching more than 50% of his pre-injury earnings potential. Based on the wages above, this would place him earning approximately $8,972/Year*.

I believe the further developed his education, the more likely he will reduce wage loss. (He will not eliminate wage loss due to the visual impairment and limitations from his verbal/linguistic deficits, resulting in the reduction of opportunities for advancement and promotion.) First, the greater development would tend to indicate a more satisfactory result in psychological adjustment, and second it broadens the availability of employment settings and opportunities. For this reason, a great emphasis must be placed on combining psychological and educational development programs for maximum effectiveness in the training and interventions offered throughout the developmental years. It is difficult to quantify the amount of reduced earnings. He will be eliminated from the more physically oriented positions and those requiring close attention to detail, eye-hand coordination, and precision work. He will require special equipment to aid in his endeavors (such as are outlined within the Life Care Plan). Below is a list of examples of the occupations in which he can be expected to participate:

Occupational Title	Mean Wage	Yearly Wage
Bill and Account Collectors	$9.05	$18,824.00
Customer Service Representative	$9.53	$19,822.00
Insurance Claim Clerk	$9.04	$18,803.20
New Accounts Clerk	$8.38	$17,430.40

Average of Mean Wage Based on 2080 Hours/Year: $18,719.90**

Source: *Money Income of Households, Families, and Persons in the United States: 1995. U.S. Department of Commerce; Bureau of the Census.

Source: **1995 Florida Occupational Wage Survey Report. Florida Department of Labor and Employment Security; Bureau of Labor Market Information.

This page intentionally left blank.

Section 3

Case Management Practice Settings

In This Section

Section 3, *Case Management Practice Settings*, contains four chapters. In Chapter 10, Saunders discusses case management in the public rehabilitation setting, including the legislative history and evolution of the state-federal system, eligibility requirements for those served, the use of the status code system for case management and caseload management purposes, and contemporary issues and trends.

Degeneffe and Saunders, in Chapter 11, describe case management practices in the non-profit setting, including an overall description of nonprofit organizations, funding sources and issues, and case management services, issues and trends.

In Chapter 12, Chapin provides an overview of practice in the private sector of rehabilitation including an overview of the more important elements involved with vocational case management including insurance programs, vocational case management services, knowledge and skills required to perform vocational case management, and the application of such knowledge in practice.

Chapter 13 reviews how the field of disability management is responding to rapid changes and advances in the labor market. Rosenthal and colleagues discuss how, with parallel growth, the importance of case management practices within disability management has been acknowledged and demonstrated over past decades.

$$\approx$$

10

Case Management in Public Rehabilitation

Jodi L. Saunders

Chapter Highlights

- Evolution of the public rehabilitation system

- Structure of the federal-state system

- Process of case management in the public rehabilitation setting

- Principles and goals of case management

- Roles of the case manager

- Case management tasks

- Case management issues

- Automated case management systems

- Conclusion

Case management has been defined as a "creative and collaborative process, involving skills in assessment, consulting, teaching, modeling, and advocacy that aim to enhance the optimum functioning of the client served" (Woodside & McClam, 2003, p.4). Case management is becoming widely recognized as an effective method of service delivery to a wide variety of populations in the human services (Moxley, 1989). In addition to being an effective means of service delivery in rehabilitation (Cassell & Mulkey, 1985; Roessler & Rubin, 1982; Moxley, 1985), research has shown it is an important and frequently used knowledge and skill area by rehabilitation counselors (Leahy, Chan & Saunders, 2003). The goal of case managers is generally to help those who need assistance and to support them when expertise is needed or a crisis occurs.

EVOLUTION AND STRUCTURE OF THE
PUBLIC REHABILITATION SYSTEM

The public rehabilitation system, or state/federal vocational rehabilitation system, works with persons with physical, mental, and/or emotional disabilities in order to assist them in obtaining and maintaining employment. Many rehabilitation service delivery systems deal with specific aspects of an individual's rehabilitation (e.g. vocational evaluation, work adjustment training, job placement,) or a particular disability (e.g. residential facilities for persons with traumatic brain injury). The public rehabilitation setting is one of the few that deals with individuals who have one or more of hundreds of disabilities, and works with them from the intake interview through medical and psychological evaluations, career exploration, employment and life skills training, to obtaining and maintaining employment for a minimum of 60 days. As a result, the rehabilitation counselor/case manager who works in the public rehabilitation setting serves a population with one of the widest varieties of disabilities, and is also the provider of some of the broadest and most comprehensive services to these individuals. Rehabilitation counselors in public rehabilitation may have a caseload of persons with primarily the same type of disability (i.e., mental illness, traumatic brain injury) or they may work with people who have a variety of disabilities, which is often referred to as a "general caseload." In addition, rehabilitation counselors may have caseloads that are based on geographic areas such as a transition from school to work caseload work with clients from a specific school district, or they may be assigned clients from a specific rural or urban county. Considering the fact that many of the case management techniques necessary for dealing with specific types of disabilities are presented in other chapters, this chapter will focus on the unique case management strategies necessary for rehabilitation counselors operating within the public vocational rehabilitation (VR) sector.

EVOLUTION OF THE PUBLIC REHABILITATION PROGRAM

The legislative history of the public rehabilitation program is instrumental in understanding its' evolution. Federal rehabilitation legislation was rooted in Vocational Education as a result of the passage of the Smith-Hughes Act of 1917, which provided federal grants to states to support vocational education (Jenkins, Patterson & Szymanski, 1998). Shortly thereafter, civilian rehabilitation was initiated on a federal level as a result of the Smith-Fess Act of 1920 (Roessler & Rubin, 1980), with the early intent being to encourage state vocational rehabilitation programs by providing grants-in-aid to states. The Social Security Act of 1935 provided a permanent commitment to the public rehabilitation program and expanded financial support.

The funding base for the public rehabilitation program was increased substantially by the Vocational Rehabilitation Act Amendments of 1954 (P.L. 83-565) and special funding for a variety of areas including rehabilitation research and training programs was also included in this legislation. The passage of the Rehabilitation Act of 1973 provided for major gains in the public rehabilitation program including provisions for active participation by clients, establishing a priority of services for persons with severe disabilities, the authorization of independent living projects, provision of post-employment services, and client assistance programs (CAPs) to facilitate communication between clients and state rehabilitation agencies (Jenkins, Patterson & Szymanski, 1998).

Since 1973, several amendments to the Act have provided for increased service delivery, broadened the definition of eligible clients, and provided for several program additions. Amendments to the Rehabilitation Act of 1973 have included changing CAPs from being competitive grant projects to state grant programs (Amendments of 1984, P.L. 98-221), expanded the purpose of the legislation to include both vocational rehabilitation and independent living, authorized supported employment services (Amendments of 1986, P.L.99-506), and increased consumer choice and involvement (amendments of 1992). The Rehabilitation Act of 1973, and its amendments, continues to provide for the program and guide the programs' goals, areas of focus, and service delivery.

STRUCTURE OF THE FEDERAL-STATE SYSTEM

The Public Rehabilitation program is managed by the U.S. Department of Education's Rehabilitation Services Administration (RSA). "The U.S. Department of Education's Office of Special Education and Rehabilitative

Services (OSERS) administers the State-Federal VR programs through the RSA by providing funds, monitoring program operation, and interpreting legislative requirements for program implementation" (Brahbam, Mandeville & Koch, 1998, p.42).

According to RSA statistician Patricia Nash, (personal communication May 11, 2004) the State-Federal program currently has 80 agencies across the United States including all 50 states, Washington D.C., and 5 U.S. Territories. Twenty-four states have two agencies, one serving individuals with physical, mental, and emotional disabilities and another serving persons who are blind. The remaining 32 states and territories each have one agency that provides services to both individuals with blindness and all other persons with disabilities. In 2002, the state-federal program provided services to 1,044,062 individuals. The number of individuals whose cases were closed after achieving a successful employment outcome in 2002 was 221,031 (P. Nash, personal communication, May 11, 2004). Funding for state agencies is based on state population and per-capita income, with a federal-state matching formula involving federal participation of 78.7% (Brabham, Manderville & Koch, 1998).

Structure within the state public rehabilitation agencies. While there is individuality in regard to how state systems implement services, there are basic procedures that are consistent among all state agencies. Two processes, the *eligibility determination process* and the *Status code system* (i.e., the process of how cases move through the state system), are examples of processes that are utilized among all state agencies.

Eligibility determination. The eligibility determination process is the same in each state agency. When individuals apply for services within the public rehabilitation program, a determination is made about their eligibility to receive services. In order to be eligible for vocational rehabilitation services an individual must:

(1) " Be an 'individual with a disability', meaning a person who 1) has a physical or mental impairment which constitutes or results in a substantial impediment to employment for the individual; and 2) can benefit from VR services to achieve an employment outcome" (RSA Website, retrieved May 11, 2004).

(2) Require VR services to prepare for, secure, retain, or regain employment" (RSA website, retrieved May 11, 2004).

It is the responsibility of the rehabilitation counselor to make sure that the eligibility determination is made within 60 days of the date that the individual applied for services. If the determination cannot be made within that time frame—generally because adequate medical or psychological information has not been secured—then the rehabilitation counselor is responsible for filing

270

paperwork regarding the extension and sending a letter to the individual explaining the delay in eligibility determination.

Status codes. To facilitate the coordination and order of the rehabilitation process, RSA established a coding system for use by state VR agencies (Brabham, Manderville & Koch, 1998). Once learned, this system can greatly assist rehabilitation counselors in their work in the public rehabilitation setting. Each case is placed in a particular status code representing the point where the individual is in the rehabilitation process. Table I provides a visual flow chart of the various types of status codes used throughout the rehabilitation process.

Table I
CASE STATUS CODE SYSTEM

Referral Processing Statuses
00   Referral–agency obtains a referral and minimal information about a potential client.
02   Applicant–Agency secures a document signed by the client requesting services.
04   Accepted, but does not meet waiting list categories being served – some states who have gone to an order of selection are using a code for this purpose.
06   Trial Work/ extended assessment
Preservice Statuses
10   IPE (Individualized Plan for Employment) development
12   IPE completed
In-Service Statuses
14   Counseling and guidance only
16   Physical and mental restoration
18   Training
20   Ready for employment
22   In employment
32   Post employment services
Closure Statuses
08   Closed from referral (00), applicant (02), or extended evaluation (06)
26   Closed rehabilitated
28   Closed for other reasons after the IPE was initiated (not rehabilitated)
30   Closed for other reasons before the IPE was initiated (not rehabilitated from status 10 or 12)
34   Closed from post-employment services

Modified from Brabham, Manderville, & Koch, 1998

In 1993, the Council of State Administrators of Vocational Rehabilitation (CSAVR) recommended streamlining this process and the documentation that goes along with it by reducing the number of statuses in the status code system. Their recommendation was to have statuses that included eligibility, services, and outcomes. However, each state has been allowed the flexibility to develop their own simplification. Despite the individual agency simplification, the detailed status code system provides a detailed picture of the VR process (Brabham, Mandeville & Koch, 1998) and can prove to be an invaluable tool for the case manager in managing cases and the entire caseload.

Case statuses are often indicated on the outside of the file and there are numerous ways the counselor can "call up" the information from their caseload utilizing administrative support or through their computerized case management system, if one is available. For example, the rehabilitation counselor can request a list of everyone who is in application status (02) and the date of application to determine who is nearing the 60-day eligibility determination deadline or request a list of everyone in employment status (22) to do client and employer contacts.

Regardless of how individual states document the movement of cases through the system, specific information is collected by RSA from every state for each federal fiscal year. State VR agencies must report program performance data to RSA by December 1st. RSA has established minimum levels of performance. State agencies who fail to meet these performance levels must develop a program improvement plan outlining specific actions to be taken to improve program performance. Due to the nature of the populations served, performance levels are usually different for general/combined agencies and agencies serving only individuals who are blind (RSA Website).

PROCESS OF CASE MANAGEMENT IN THE PUBLIC REHABILITATION SETTING

While there are several different models of case management (Cassell & Mulkey, 1985; Frankel & Gelman, 1998; Moxley, 1997; Rubin & Roessler, 1982; Woodside & McClam, 2003), most of them include the same general processes of assessment, planning, implementation, monitoring, and evaluation. Given the broad array of services provided by rehabilitation counselors in the public rehabilitation setting, these processes are often repeated many times within the same case.

Assessment. In order for the rehabilitation counselor and client to identifying goals and services, they must begin by assessing the client's basic service and support needs. Assessment is critical because it is the primary means through which case management is individualized for each client

(Moxley, 1989). The intake interview is usually the first substantial point of contact between the rehabilitation counselor and client, and also where the assessment phase begins. Given that individuals who apply to receive services from the public rehabilitation system must have an eligibility determination within 60 days of application, the original assessment phase is often intensive.

Counselors in the public rehabilitation setting frequently make referrals to other professionals for various client assessments (e.g. psychological evaluations, medical evaluations). Making an effective referral is crucial to the quality of information received and involves developing clear and individualized areas for the professional providing the assessment to address. Though the process of assessment involves several skills, perhaps the most crucial at this point are the skills involved in gathering and assessing information.

Planning. The next phase of case management involves "determining future service delivery in an organized way" (Woodside & McClam, 2003, p. 16). When planning begins, it has usually been determined that the applicant has met the eligibility requirements of the public vocational rehabilitation system and has been accepted as a client. The planning phase involves identifying which services will be provided, when, by whom, and for how long. It is at this point that how those services will be provided, what outcomes are expected, and in what time frame, are determined. This plan, called the Individualized Plan for Employment or IPE is developed in conjunction with the client, documented in writing, and signed by both the client and counselor. Amendments to the IPE can be made as necessary.

A crucial component that overlaps both the assessment and planning phases in the public rehabilitation system is career exploration and decision-making. Beyond identifying functional limitations and how they will be addressed, the IPE's primary goal is employment within a particular job or profession. Assisting in the career exploration and decision-making process often involves utilizing information obtained in the assessment phase (i.e. computerized career assessments, medical and functional limitation information) and guiding the client through the exploration of various careers and ultimately in choosing a career. The processes of career decision making and planning often influence one another. For example, individuals may take into consideration the length of training required before making a career choice.

Implementation. Once the plan has been developed and services and service providers identified, implementation of the plan begins. This phase of case management begins when service provision begins and the rehabilitation counselor's tasks involve either providing services or coordinating service provision by other professionals and agencies. For the public rehabilitation professional, this phase also often involves contracting for services and authorization of funds for services not provided directly by the public rehabilitation professional.

Monitoring. The monitoring component of case management involves overseeing client services and supports as a way to maintain the momentum of service delivery (Moxley, 1989). In the public setting, the counselor reviews progress reports, tracks authorizations, schedules and attends staff meetings with service providers and the client, and maintains regular contact with the client. Roessler & Rubin (1982) refer to this phase as progress review and indicate that it involves the rehabilitation counselor determining whether goals have been attained and analyzing unmet goals to determine what should be done in the future. Utilization of supervisors, colleagues, administrative support staff, and case aides can assist in the monitoring of the numerous cases handled by the public rehabilitation counselor.

Evaluation. In an effort to evaluate the outcome, efficiency, and economy of services, the rehabilitation counselor also has the role of evaluator. By undertaking the evaluation function, the case manager can determine the beneficial aspects of services and revise service delivery as necessary.

Case review, report writing, documentation, and client participation are all part of each phase of the case management process. As new issues and needs arise, the case management processes of assessment, planning, implementation, monitoring, and evaluation are repeated.

PRINCIPLES AND GOALS OF CASE MANAGEMENT IN THE PUBLIC REHABILITATION SETTING

The guiding goals of case management have emerged through federal legislation and through both current practice and the work of the early pioneers in helping (Woodside & McClam, 2003). The primary case management goal in the public rehabilitation system is for the rehabilitation counselor to assist the client in developing and implementing a rehabilitation plan that enables the individual with a disability to successfully obtain and maintain employment. Woodside & McClam (2003) discuss additional goals of case management, which include integration of services, working with the whole person, and client empowerment.

Integration of services. The integration of services involves developing and implementing a rehabilitation plan that combines a variety of services to assist clients in reaching their rehabilitation goals. Services are designed in such a way that each service enhances and supports the efforts of the other services. Many people who are eligible for public rehabilitation services are frequently working with a variety of agencies and professionals. Coordination of professionals and services provided are an important part of providing integrated services. As a result, fragmentation and duplication of services can often be avoided.

Working with the whole person. Good case management involves recognition that the client is a whole person who has many dimensions to be considered in service delivery. Clients served by the public rehabilitation system often have multiple issues or needs (e.g., functional limitations, transportation, childcare, and training). Consideration of the individuals' medical, social, psychosocial, financial, and psychological needs, in addition to the vocational needs, must take place.

Client Empowerment. An important part of the case management process involves respecting clients as individuals, developing plans in conjunction with clients, and assisting them in moving toward self-sufficiency and success. Client empowerment also includes encouraging the client to manage the parts of their own case that are consistent with their skills and knowledge. For example, clients may participate in library, internet, or community research related to their occupational and/or employment goals; contact their physician to assist in medical records being forwarded; or contact friends and family for potential job leads.

ROLES OF THE CASE MANAGER IN THE PUBLIC REHABILITATION SETTING

Case management in the public rehabilitation setting often requires that the rehabilitation counselor perform more than one role. The rehabilitation counselor is often an advocate, broker, coordinator, collaborator, consultant, counselor, and evaluator (Frankel & Gelman, 1998; Woodside & McClam, 2003).

Advocate. As an advocate, the rehabilitation counselor often speaks on behalf of the client when either they are unable to do so, are not present, or when they speak and others dismiss them. As an advocate, the counselor can assist the client in gaining access to services, resources, or information. Rehabilitation counselors can assist clients in acquiring the skills to advocate for themselves.

Broker. Once the goals and client needs have been determined, the rehabilitation counselor assists in identifying and choosing service providers. In the role of a broker or facilitator, the counselor matches the client with necessary services.

Coordinator. As stated earlier, clients often have multiple issues and needs and, consequently, require more than one service to address them. As a coordinator, the rehabilitation counselor works with other agencies and professionals to coordinate necessary services. Monitoring the services provided and progress being made is an important component of coordination.

Collaborator. In order to be an effective rehabilitation counselor and case manager, it is important to be familiar with and knowledgeable about the community. The rehabilitation counselor must collaborate with other professionals in the community and establish and maintain good working relationships with them. Collaboration is also necessary during team or staff meetings.

Consultant. In the public rehabilitation setting, the rehabilitation counselor is often called upon to act as a consultant. These opportunities frequently arise as a result of current or future employer requests for information or assistance. Providing consultation in regard to dealing with employees with disabilities, assistive technology, ergonomics, and the Americans with Disabilities Act is common.

Counselor. The primary relationship most rehabilitation counselors maintain with clients is as their counselor. Discussions and assistance regarding goals, available services, client and rehabilitation concerns, and related issues are at the core of this "role."

Evaluator. The rehabilitation counselor also acts as an evaluator when reviewing and assessing client status and service provision. Evaluation is performed when the rehabilitation counselor is determining level of client functioning and progress, types and effectiveness of services provided, and outcomes of service provision.

Expediter. Woodside & McClam (2003) describe the role of expediter as one where the rehabilitation counselor assists the client through several potential problems such as duplicated services, seemingly closed doors, irrelevant services, or poor services. As an expediter, the rehabilitation counselors also functions in the role of advocate.

Planner. The planning role begins in the first stages of rehabilitation and involves determining how goals will be addressed, what outcomes are expected, and identifies the first stages of implementation. The primary purpose of planning is to prepare for the services the client is to receive (Woodside & McClam, 2003).

Record Keeper. A primary case management responsibility of the rehabilitation counselor is record keeping. There is often a large amount of paperwork required in the public rehabilitation system and developing, organizing, and updating the various forms and other case file requirements are an important part of the rehabilitation counselors' obligation.

Teacher. Occasionally the rehabilitation counselor is called upon to perform in the role of a teacher. While performing in other areas described, the rehabilitation counselor is often teaching clients skills that are necessary for decision making, becoming their own advocate, and increasing their capacity to become involved in their own rehabilitation program. Frankel and Gelman (1998) describe this role as "Moving from doing *for,* to doing *with,* to having clients do *for themselves.*" (p. 37).

CASE MANAGEMENT TASKS

Probably one of the most comprehensive listings of tasks required of, and performed by, case managers was developed by Bertsche and Horejsi in 1980 (Frankel & Gelman, 1998). The thirteen basic tasks developed by Bertsche and Horejsi provide a clear and concise description of case management responsibilities:

1. Complete the initial interview with the client and his or her family to assess the client's eligibility for services.
2. Gather relevant and useful data from the client, family, or other agencies, and so on to formulate a psychosocial assessment of the client and his or her family.
3. Assemble and guide group discussions and decision-making sessions among relevant professionals and program representatives, the client and his or her family, and significant others to formulate goals and design an integrated intervention plan.
4. Monitor adherence to the plan and manage the flow of accurate information within the action system to maintain a goal orientation and coordination momentum.
5. Provide "follow-along" to the client and his or her family to speed identification of unexpected problems in service delivery and to serve as a general trouble shooter on behalf of the client.
6. Provide counseling and information to help the client and his or her family in situations of crisis and conflict with service providers.
7. Provide ongoing emotional support to the client and his or her family so they can cope better with problems and utilize professionals and complex services.
8. Complete the necessary paperwork to maintain documentation of client progress and adherence to the plan by all concerned.
9. Act as a liaison between clients and their families and all relevant professionals, programs, and informal resources involved in the overall intervention plan to help the client make his or her preferences known and secure the services needed.
10. Act as a liaison between programs, providing services to the client to ensure the smooth flow of information and minimize the conflict between the subsystems.

11. Establish and maintain credibility and good public relations with significant formal and informal resource systems to mobilize resources for current and future clients.

12. Perform effectively and as a "good bureaucrat" within the organization to be in a position to develop and modify policies and procedures affecting clients and the effectiveness of the service delivery system.

13. Secure and maintain the respect and support of those in positions of authority so their influence can be enlisted on behalf of the client and used, when necessary, to encourage other individuals and agencies to participate in the coordination effort. (p. 96-97).

Specific case management skills that are used on a daily basis by rehabilitation counselors in the public rehabilitation system are those of case review and documentation. Case review is the periodic examination of the client's case file in order to monitor progress, add additional information (e.g. assessments, medical reports), or review case notes. Documentation is "the written record of the work with the client" (Woodside & McClam, 2003, p. 21) and involves making case notes regarding meetings and other contacts with the client or with other persons and professionals related to the case. Documentation also includes adding materials to the case file to document the receipt of services, a change in client status, client progress on certain goals, and other evidence about the client and their rehabilitation plan.

CASE MANAGEMENT ISSUES IN THE
PUBLIC REHABILITATION SETTING

There are several case management issues that arise in the public rehabilitation setting. Issues related to organizational structure, service delivery by teams, consumer involvement, persons with multiple needs, limited resources, and caseload size are all possible case management issues in this setting.

Working within the organizational structure. Case management takes place within the context of an agency, and client services often involve more than one agency (Woodside & McClam, 2003). In order to work within the public rehabilitation system, the rehabilitation counselors must be familiar with the agency's mission, organizational structure, policies and procedures, and resources. A challenge for the rehabilitation counselor in this setting is to not be constrained by the "bureaucracy," and instead, learn how to "work within the system."

Teamwork in service delivery. The team approach to rehabilitation generally can be productive and result in an effective and comprehensive rehabilitation plan for clients. Sometimes, however, problems can arise when clients are assisted by a team rather than an individual rehabilitation counselor in shaping the type, range, and extent of service delivery included in their rehabilitation plan. Team members may not agree with each other in regard to necessary service provision, or some team members may be more assertive than others may, and the client's view can occasionally be lost in the process. Several types of teams are used in the public rehabilitation setting including supported employment teams, transition from school to work teams, and teams from other social service agencies who are also serving public rehabilitation clients. Identifying a team leader or area leaders (e.g. the job developer in a supported employment team) can help in making sure the client is not lost in the process.

Increased consumer involvement. Legislation over the past few decades has increasingly included wording that places an emphasis on consumer choice and involvement. The Rehabilitation Act Amendments of 1992 specifically indicates that each State unit will enable each individual client to make informed choices and also requires that the state agency seek the comments and advice of clients (Brabham, Mandeville & Koch, 1998).

Plan development that is consumer driven is an important component in the public rehabilitation system, and prior to signing the IPE, clients check several boxes indicating their level of involvement in the plan. While the idea of consumer involvement is in no way problematic, in some cases the reality can be difficult. The fact that clients have a "right" to choose does not necessarily mean that they possess the skills to choose. Making decisions regarding systems or services they are unfamiliar with can be extremely difficult. Teaching the client decision making skills and providing as much information as possible can often be important and necessary components of facilitating increased consumer involvement.

Serving individuals with multiple needs. Due to medical advances and the variety of types of disabilities that individuals have who are eligible for services through the public rehabilitation program, the rehabilitation counselor is more than likely dealing with individuals who have a multitude of needs. Rehabilitation counselors are often called upon to prioritize these needs and organize services to address them. These cases can be very complex and often place the rehabilitation counselor in the position of dealing with a "chicken or egg" situation. For example, the client cannot get a job without a car and the client cannot get a car without a job, or the client cannot get a job until daycare arrangements for their children can be made, and the client cannot afford alternative daycare until having a job. Dealing with these situations often requires creativity and thinking outside the box for plausible alternatives.

Limited resources. In addition to assisting individual clients in achieving their rehabilitation goals, the rehabilitation counselor in the public rehabilitation system is also responsible for an annual budget to fund a large portion of the cost of client rehabilitation plans. Individual budgets are often reduced or services requiring funding from the rehabilitation counselor are limited at the end of the year, due to a dwindling budget. Client needs and available financial resources are occasionally in conflict with one another. The case manager must balance client needs with financial responsibility and often utilize creative approaches in regard to obtaining services or reaching certain rehabilitation goals.

Caseload size. One of the biggest complaints about the public rehabilitation system is the large caseload sizes and caseload management difficulties. It is not uncommon for counselors to carry a caseload of 100-200 cases each. Though caseloads these sizes are not ideal, learning how to deal with them is important. Finding ways to make practice more efficient is crucial, both for the purposes of meeting client needs and for maintaining the mental health of the rehabilitation counselor. Organization and efficiency are critical. Streamlining record keeping, developing a "tickler" system that meets the rehabilitation counselors' needs, developing collaborations, ensuring that clients are responsible for tasks/areas they are capable of handling, consultation with colleagues, and utilization of distance technology as opposed to travel for meetings and other responsibilities, are just a few of the many techniques that can be utilized.

AUTOMATED CASE MANAGEMENT SYSTEMS

Many state agencies have moved to automated case management systems for the purposes of improving case management, caseload management, services provided to individuals with disabilities, and to improve VR's ability to predict case service expenditures and improve the monitoring process. For example, many states are using AWARE (Automated Web-based Activity and Reporting Environment), a consultant group software used on a national basis that has some flexibility for customization by state. Other states have developed their own software for case management and caseload management purposes, such as Iowa, which has developed IRSS (Iowa Rehabilitation Services System).

The purposes of moving to an automated case management system include to reduce paper volume and flow; simplify the creation of authorizations; eliminate spreadsheets and databases maintained by staff; increase productivity; and improve relationships with clients and agency partners (Iowa DVR Website, retrieved May 10, 2004)—all tasks and responsibilities primarily of the rehabilitation counselor. Though initial training on automated case management systems can be cumbersome due to the need to maintain both computer records and paper records for a period of time until the transition is complete, many are finding the system be a critical tool for both case and caseload management.

CONCLUSION

"Systematic" should be a key word for case managers (Moxley, 1989). Viewing the client and the needs of the client within a holistic framework of interacting parts is critical. Given the nature of the work, rehabilitation counselors are often involved in a balancing act. Case management in the public rehabilitation system can be extremely complex and challenging. Large caseload sizes, variety of disabilities served, multiple needs of clients, the broad array of services provided, and working within a large bureaucracy can all pose challenges to even the best rehabilitation counselors. However, with an understanding of the variety of case management roles rehabilitation counselors assume and the processes involved in case management, in combination with acquisition of good case management skills (e.g. organizational, assessment, case recording, planning, coordination), rehabilitation counselors can expect to have an exciting, productive, and rewarding career working within the public rehabilitation system.

REFERENCES

Brabham, R., Mandeville, K. A., & Koch, L. (1998). The state-federal vocational rehabilitation program. In R. M. Parker & E. M. Szymanski (eds.). *Rehabilitation counseling: Basics and beyond* (pp. 41-70). Austin, TX: Pro-Ed.

Bertsche, A., & Horejsi, C. (1980). Coordination of client services. *Social Work, 25*(2), 94-98.

Cassell, J. L. & Mulkey, S. W. (1985). *Rehabilitation caseload management: Concepts and practice.* Austin, Texas: Pro-Ed.

Frankel, A. J. & Gelman, S. R. *Case management: An introduction to concepts and skills.* Chicago, IL: Lyceum Books, Inc.

Guransky, D., Harvey, J., & Kennedy, R. (2003). *Case management: Policy, practice and professional business.* New York, NY: Columbia University Press.

Iowa Rehabilitation Services System. *Division of Vocational Rehabilitation Services:Iowa rehabilitation service system.* Retrieved May 10, 2004, from the Iowa Rehabilitation Services System Web site: http://intranet.dvrs.state.ia.us/intranet/IRSS.html

Jenkins, W. M., Patterson, J. B. & Szymanski, E. M. (1998). Philosophical, historical and legislative aspects of the rehabilitation counseling profession. In R. M. Parker & E. M. Szymanski (Eds.). *Rehabilitation counseling: Basics and beyond* (pp. 1-40). Austin, TX: Pro-Ed.

Leahy, M. J., Chan, F. & Saunders, J. L. (2003). Job functions and knowledge requirements of Certified Rehabilitation Counselors in the 21st century. *Rehabilitation Counseling Bulletin, 46* (2), 66-81.

Moxley, D. P. (1989). *The practice of case management.* Newbury Park: Sage.

Moxley, D. P. (1997). *Case management by design: Reflections on principles and practice.* Chicago, IL: Nelson-Hall Publishers.

Rehabilitation Services Administration. *Frequently asked questions about RSA.* Retrieved May 11, 2004 from http://www.ed.gov/about/offices/list/osers/rsa/faq.html

Roessler, R. T. & Rubin, S. E. (1982). *Case management and rehabilitation counseling: Procedures and techniques.* Baltimore: University Park Press.

Woodside, M. & McClam, T. (2003). *Generalist Case Management: A method of human service delivery.* (2nd ed.). Pacific Grove, California: Brooks/Cole.

11

Case Management and Nonprofit Agencies

Charles Edmund Degeneffe
Jodi L. Saunders

Chapter Highlights

- Describing the nonprofit sector

- Future trends in the nonprofit sector

- Conclusion

Case management is a complex and multifaceted process that can support the vocational and independent living needs of persons with brain injury (Cunningham et al., 1999), psychiatric disabilities (Corrigan, Rao, & Calabresa, 1999), spinal cord injury (Crewe, 1999), HIV/AIDS (Reid, Kitchen, & Deutsch, 1999), substance addictions (Cardoso, Chan, Thomas, Peterson, Mpofu, & Leahy, 1999), chronic pain (Johnson, 1999), and aging related needs (Lamb, 1999). Shaw, Leahy, and Chan (1999) also noted that the practice of case management is quite diverse with examples of such duties as consulting with biotech firms, facilitating life care planning, giving nutrition training, and performing utilization review and bill auditing.

Given the diversity of client needs and practice activities, case management practice takes place in a variety of professional settings and environments. Case management, specifically in rehabilitation, has historically taken place in either the publicly funded and controlled State-Federal Vocational Rehabilitation System or the for-profit, worker's compensation funded, private rehabilitation system (Shaw et al, 1999).

Case management in the health, social welfare, and rehabilitation arenas is increasingly takes place in nonprofit agencies and organizations. Lewis (1989) suggested the propensity to meet human service related needs through the nonprofit sector is largely due to the frequent practice of public human service organizations subcontracting to nonprofit agencies, many of the tasks they are required by law to provide, such as developmental disabilities case management and case management services for persons with HIV/AIDS. The trend toward greater utilization of the nonprofit sector significantly took root during the Great Society expansion of social welfare programs of President Lyndon Johnson's administration in the 1960s (Gronbjerg & Salamon, 2002). Local, state, and federal public human service agencies in the United States now meet their service delivery needs more through the nonprofit sector than through their own entities (Salamon, 1995).

Testament to the size of the nonprofit sector is Salamon's (2002) data showing that in the United States there are approximately 1.2 million nonprofit agencies and organizations utilizing 11 million paid workers and another 18 million full-time volunteers. Within rehabilitation services, nonprofit agencies are commonly referred to as community-based rehabilitation providers (CRPs). Like the overall growth of the nonprofit sector, CRPs increasingly play a major role in providing a wide array of disability support services in such diverse areas as case management, residential support services, and work skills training. Menz, Botterbusch, Hagen-Foley, and Johnson (2003) noted there are over 8,100 CRPs in the United States serving over 9.1 million persons annually.

Menz et al. also pointed out the pervasive scope of CRPs. CRPs are located in cities and towns in every state and territory in the United States. Given the substantial role that nonprofits hold in meeting disability related needs, it behooves case management professionals to have an understanding of the distinctive characteristics and challenges faced by nonprofit agencies and organizations. In all likelihood, case management professionals will be employed in the administration of or create a CRP or other type of nonprofit agency at some point in their careers. To this end, this chapter will provide an overall description of a nonprofit organization and its funding. Since case managers will likely be employed by a CRP, specific attention is given to this component of the nonprofit sector regarding its services, issues, and trends.

DESCRIBING THE NONPROFIT SECTOR

The term "nonprofit" can share a variety of meanings and definitions. The essential underlying descriptor dictates what happens with any excess revenue that might be earned following the provision of a good or service. Instead of giving after-cost revenues to shareholders or owners (as occurs in the for-profit sector), nonprofit agencies reinvest any produced profits in the agency by buying equipment, increasing services, adding staff, et cetera (Crimmins & Keil, 1983). Working toward fulfilling a central mission and set of goals, rather than financial gain, is the primary motive behind the activities of a nonprofit agency (Rados, 1981).

TYPES OF NONPROFIT AGENCIES
Beyond these characteristics, nonprofit agencies and organizations are largely distinguished by the degree to which they provide direct services and programs to clients. Based on this organizing principle, Salamon (1995) identified four major types of nonprofit entities. The first type of nonprofit agency serves a funding or fund-raising purpose. These agencies usually do not provide any direct services, but rather channel funds to other nonprofits. Examples of nonprofits in this first group include United Way and Blue Cross / Blue Shield.

The second type of nonprofit agency has a member-serving function. Nonprofits in this second group only provide services and programs to its members, not to the community at large. Many times, member serving nonprofit agencies serve a professional or vocational organization such as attorney bar associations, labor unions, or trade associations.

A third type of nonprofit agency represents religious congregations that are working toward religiously or spiritually based purposes. Finally, the group most relevant for case managers is referred to as public-benefit organizations. CRPs are included in this category. These types of nonprofits serve society and the community at large and often work toward meeting humanitarian or social welfare goals. Membership in these types of nonprofits is not necessary to obtain their benefits. Lewis (1989, p. 4) explicated the motivating force behind the work these agencies do by stating, "...concern for quality and effectiveness is subordinate to a wider interest, that of rendering services that reflect the type of society they prefer and hope to achieve."

PROVIDING UNIQUE AND UNMET SERVICE NEEDS

Nonprofit agencies are sometimes viewed as creative and innovative resources tailored to meet existing human service gaps not being effectively met by public and for-profit entities. In suggesting this, Letts, Ryan, and Grossman (1999) argued:

> The nonprofit sector is filled with great ideas and thoughtful, caring people. In many ways, it represents our collective best inclinations: generosity, inclusivity, and determined optimism. The nonprofit sector attempts to bridge the many gaps in our society by bringing people together, proposing alternatives, advocating for change, and implementing remedies. In the course of proving extensive benefits to a diverse range of people and communities, it produces remarkably innovative programs. As one of the underpinnings of American society, the nonprofit sector has built an enduring legacy of community and service (p. 1).

Salamon (2002) added that because of this unique perspective, the nonprofit sector has been able to lead the way in creating significant social change in the United States through its advocacy with the disability rights, antislavery, women's suffrage, populist, progressive, civil rights, environmental, antiwar, gay rights, and conservative movements. Today, nonprofit agencies are actively involved in service provision and advocacy on a variety of controversial social issues through such nonprofits as the Sierra Club, National Audubon Society, National Association for the Advancement of Colored People, Christian Coalition, American Association of Retired Persons, and National Organization for Women (Boris & Krehely, 2002).

NONPROFIT SECTOR FUNDING

Case management professionals with academic backgrounds in such disciplines as rehabilitation counseling, social work, and nursing may find themselves ill prepared to work in the uncertain financial environment present by nonprofit agencies. To survive financially, nonprofit agencies need to draw economic resources from a variety of sources such as government bodies and service fees. Unlike for-profit and government run social welfare agencies (e.g., State-

Federal Vocational Rehabilitation System), CRPs and other nonprofit agencies also can receive economic support through a variety of sources of private giving such as United Way, individual donations, and corporate grants (Hodgkinson, Nelson, & Sivak, Jr., 2002; Lenkowsky, 2002; Letts et al., 1999). Hence, case managers, especially those in administration, may need to expand their repertoire of skills beyond providing direct services based upon their academic and training backgrounds (e.g., job placement, counseling, case management) to include assuming duties involved in marketing, grant writing, and fundraising.

GROWTH OF THE FOR-PROFIT SECTOR
Nonprofit agencies are increasingly concerned with budgetary issues. As noted earlier, one of the biggest areas of financial concern involves competition from the for-profit sector. Based on his analysis of relevant data, Salamon (2002) examined the percentage changes of nonprofit sector participation in various CRP and other social welfare enterprises compared to that provided by the for-profit sector. Many of these represent services requiring some type of case management skill. Table I illustrates percentage changes for 1997 as compared to 1982 to 1997.

Table I
PERCENTAGE CHANGES IN NONPROFIT SECTOR VERSUS
FOR-PROFIT PARTICIPATION

Service Entity	Percentage Change for 1997 compared to 1982-1986
Acute Care Hospitals	+2%
Home Health Agencies	-48%
Individual and Family Services	-3%
Job Training	-4%
Mental Health Clinics	-11%
Nursing Homes	+40%
Rehabilitation Hospitals	-50%

Salamon (2002) noted that although the growth of for-profit agencies has outpaced that of nonprofits (as demonstrated in Table I), the absolute number of CRPs and other nonprofit social welfare agencies continues to grow. In a variety of areas, there are more nonprofit than for-profit providers. For example, 70% of vocational rehabilitation facilities, 80% of individual and

287

family service agencies, 50% of hospitals, and 70% of foreign disaster assistance agencies are nonprofit.

GOVERNMENT FUNDING AND SERVICE FEES

In the face of this increased competition for their market share from the for-profit sector and consistent with their traditional source of financial support, CRPs and other nonprofit social welfare agencies continue to rely heavily on government funds, in spite of widespread budget problems faced by local, state, and federal governments. Salamon (2002) pointed out that from 1977 to 1997, the percentage of total revenue growth due to government support was 48% for health related, 21% for education related, and 51% for social service related nonprofit agencies. Within CRPs, government funds account for approximately 38.5% of their overall revenues (Menz as cited in Menz et al., 2002).

These increases are due, in part, to substantial growth among state and federal health and social welfare programs that may turn to the nonprofit sector to meet the needs of recipients of their programs. For example, the 1981 Medicaid Home and Community Services (HCBS) Waiver Program (Braddock, 1998) used federal and state Medicaid funds to pay for various types of CRP programs for persons with developmental disabilities. These federal dollars paid for case management, supported employment, habilitation training, respite care, supported living, and other types of supports. The federal reimbursements share of all HCBS funds was $1.2 million in 1982. It rose to $2.757 billion in 1996 (Braddock, Hemp, Parish, Westrich, & Park, 1998b).

Salamon (2002, p. 32) pointed out that nonprofit social welfare agencies increasingly receive revenues from client service fees rather than from government or philanthropic resources. This increased reliance on service fees reflects the unpredictable availability of government contracts and grants, as well as philanthropy, as a means to make budgetary plans. Salamon noted that the percentage of revenue growth from 1977 to 1997 due to fees was 47%. Comparatively, revenue growth from government sources was 37% and only 8% from philanthropy.

PHILANTHROPY

As noted earlier, reliance on philanthropy distinguishes the nonprofit sector from for-profit and government run human service agencies and organizations. Philanthropy derives from both institutional (Lenkowsky, 2002) and individual sources (Hodgkinson et al., 2002).

Institutional giving to nonprofit agencies is provided through various types of foundations, charity federations, and gift funds. Lenkowsky (2002) pointed out that the most common institutional giver to nonprofits is foundations. There are approximately 50,000 foundations in the United States. Lenkowsky noted that in 1999, foundations donated over $25 billion. There can be a variety of motives behind this type of giving to a nonprofit such as wanting to provide a living memorial, a way to improve a company's public image, a means to reduce taxes, among various other rationales. Administrators, staffs, and boards of directors in nonprofit agencies work toward trying to understand the motives of institutional givers when appealing for funds. An example of this strategy is provided by Letts et al. (1999, p. 141) in their description of how nonprofit boards of directors approach fundraising. They stated, "Perhaps most significantly, they can challenge the norms and attitudes of donors about the value of organizational support. For example, they can challenge the impulse that led philanthropist Ted Turner, upon making a one-billion dollar commitment to the United Nations causes, to vow that none of his funds would support overhead."

Individual giving to nonprofit agencies can be given directly to the nonprofit agency or indirectly through the different types of institutional giving modalities, such as the United Way or the Bill and Melinda Gates Foundation (Lenkowsky, 2002). In citing data from *Giving USA,* Hodgkison and associates (2002) noted that the bulk of individual giving—44% of all individual forms of charity—goes to religious institutions. Other outlets for individual contributions are human service agencies (8%), education (11%), and foundations (23%). The predominance of individual giving may partially explain why religious organizations play an ever-growing role among nonprofit social welfare providers. Testament to the trend, Catholic Charities USA is now the largest private provider of social welfare services in the United States (Catholic Charities, 1998).

Individual giving to nonprofit agencies is also expressed through volunteerism (Hodgkison et al., 2002). Nonprofit volunteers are motivated to donate their time for many different reasons, very much like financial giving. In reviewing reasons for nonprofit volunteerism for the period 1965 to 1991, Brudney (1994) listed such reasons as volunteers want to help people, do something useful, fulfill religious motivation, follow a sense of duty, enjoy volunteer work, a friend of relative received the service, the volunteer received the service, volunteering provides a learning experience, there is nothing else to do, the volunteer could not refuse the request to volunteer, to follow their interest in an activity or work, and the volunteer thought the work would keep taxes down. Nonprofit case management professionals may find themselves working alongside non-professional level volunteers in providing the agency's direct care services. Case managers might find this experience energizing, frustrating, or a combination of both, since a nonprofit volunteer might approach their work with zeal and enthusiasm, yet not possess the necessary training or proper motivation to do the work at a level consistent with the case manager.

COMMUNITY BASED REHABILITATION PROVIDER ORGANIZATIONS
Given its focus on supporting persons with disabilities, the CRP component of the nonprofit sector may be of primary interest to case managers since most will be employed in this type of nonprofit organization. The development and growth of CRPs is a result of a number of complimentary disability movements and legislative initiatives that have worked toward expanding the ability of persons with disabilities to maximize their participation in independent living and community-based vocational pursuits. A consequence of these developments has been the establishment of various types of CRP programs that can offer services on an extended, long-term basis and that are not typically provided by government entities such as the State-Federal Vocational Rehabilitation system. Public State-Federal Vocational Rehabilitation, mental health, developmental disabilities, workforce development, and welfare agencies often refer clients to CRPs to provide the services they do not offer.

HISTORICAL ANTECEDENTS AND PHILOSOPHICAL APPROACHES
The antecedents of CRPs reflect attempts of societies to meet the social welfare needs of persons with disabilities and other disadvantaged through private and voluntary means, rather than under publicly controlled and funded auspices. Prior to the 1500s, little is recorded regarding any society or community attempts to provide care, treatment, and rehabilitation services to persons with disabilities. In their literature review, Rubin and Roessler (1995) noted this was a period when mental illness began to be viewed as a sickness to be cured rather than the result of demonic possession.

Consistent with the contemporary practice of delivering social welfare services through both the government and the private sectors, early disability services included the establishment of both state-administered as well as charity supported special schools. For example, in 1760, Charles Michel established the publicly run Institution Nationale des Sourds-Muet in Paris for deaf children, while in 1791, Henry Dannett established the charity funded School of Instruction for the Indigent Blind in Liverpool, England (Wright, 1980).

Consistent with these European beginnings, early disability and social welfare services in the United States were provided from a number of public and private entities (Scheurell, 1987). Among the first of these was the Perkins Institute, opened in 1832 as the New England Asylum for the Blind (Holbrook as cited by Rubin & Roessler, 1995) and the state-run Kentucky Institution for the Education of Feeble-Minded Children and Idiots in 1860 (Wright, 1980).

As a precursor to the vast network of contemporary CRPs, the late 1800s to early 1900s was a period of significant growth of voluntary, private, and charity supported, social welfare agencies intended to serve persons with disabilities and other persons in need in the United States. One force underlying this growth was the influence of the Charity Organization Society (COS) movement. The COS movement used volunteers in the local communities of new immigrants to help in their care and adjustment. Since the COS movement was largely Protestant-based, Catholics also began to offer a network of immigrant settlement services for newly arrived Catholics (O'Grady, 1931). Examples of private, social welfare agencies and organizations supporting persons with disabilities founded in this period included Goodwill Industries in 1902 at the Morgan Memorial Institutional Church in South Boston and the National Association for the Study and Prevention of Tuberculosis in Philadelphia in 1904 (Wright, 1980).

One of the guiding forces behind the development of CRPs relates to the changes in services to persons with developmental disabilities. In the 1950s through the 1970s, disability advocates, professionals, and family members voiced views that institutional living for persons with developmental disabilities was inhumane and socially restrictive, based on such infamous examples as the Pennhurst institution in Pennsylvania and the Willowbrook institution in New York (Braddock, 1998). Persons with developmental disabilities subsequently moved out of institutions and into the community, requiring the establishment of CRPs to meet their vocational and residential support needs. Among these early CRPs were sheltered workshops. Scheurell (1987) noted that the State-Federal Vocational Rehabilitation System began its relationship with this type of CRP through passage of the 1965 Vocational Rehabilitation Act, which provided funding to sheltered workshops for persons with developmental disabilities.

In the 1980s and 1990s, focus shifted to creating CRP support services for persons with developmental disabilities that maximized community participation and inclusion (Bradley & Knoll, 1990). Degeneffe (2000) noted that subsequent community-based services emerged, such as supported employment, parent support services, family support programs, sexuality education, and supportive living programs. Among the factors contributing to current service approaches toward persons with developmental disabilities concerns are the Rehabilitation Act Amendments of 1986.

These amendments have played a large role in the establishment of CRPs that provide supported employment services. The 1986 Rehabilitation Act amendments classified supported employment as an acceptable Status 26 closure within the State-Federal Vocational Rehabilitation System (Hanley-Maxwell & Bordieri, 1989). Indicative of the growth of this CRP service, from

1987 to 1996, supported employment CRPs provided services to an additional 85,000 persons with developmental disabilities (Braddock, Hemp, Parish, & Westrich, 1998). From 1992 to 1996, supported employment CRP annual spending grew from $250 to $409 million (Braddock et al., 1998b).

Consistent with the client-focused philosophy inherent among social welfare based nonprofit agencies, CRPs have largely been guided by consistent and progressive themes regarding how to provide service to persons with disabilities. These include adhering to principles of consumer empowerment, self-determination, and quality of life. Proponents of such ideals often focus their discussions around the practice activities of CRP related activities. For example, Degeneffe (2000) pointed out that that the CRP delivery of supported employment services was founded on ideals of facilitating choice, empowerment, quality of life, and career development to persons with developmental disabilities. A variety of studies has examined how well supported employment actually meets such objectives.

Fabian (1992) examined the impact of supported employment services on quality of life for persons with severe mental illness. Fabian compared outcomes for 56 persons not placed in supported employment compared with 54 persons placed in supported employment positions. Fabian determined that overall gains in quality of life for persons in supported employment positions were found within such areas as global life satisfaction, job satisfaction, and satisfaction with finances.

Inge, Banks, Wehman, Hill, and Shafer (1988) also compared the quality of life effects for 20 persons with mental retardation placed in supported employment settings, compared to 20 persons in sheltered work. Sample members were compared on such factors as scores on an adaptive behavior rating scale, ratings of physical health (e.g., blood pressure), and parent/guardian ratings of sample member performance on various measures of independent living skills. On all measures of quality of life, superior results were found for those placed in supported employment versus sheltered work.

It is likely that the long-standing philosophical approaches of CRP related services have impacted the overall scope of case management and rehabilitation services. Themes underlying the development of CRPs are commonly voiced as needed directions for rehabilitation services, both within and outside of CRP related activities. For example, Kosciulek (2004) recently proposed a model for services in the State-Federal Vocational Rehabilitation System that goes beyond the traditional success benchmark of Status 26 closures to also examining organizational performance, informed consumer choice, consumer satisfaction, and contextually based employment outcomes (e.g., improved self-esteem, personal growth, increased opportunities for socialization).

292

Bishop and Feist-Price (2001) suggested that rehabilitation counselor education programs needed to train students that quality of life determination needs to be a desired outcome for any type of rehabilitation service. To do so, Bishop and Feist-Price outlined content areas that should be addressed in pre-service training, including the domains of subjective assessment of life satisfaction and objective measurement of disability related stressors, psychological/emotional functioning, social support/social functioning, environmental limitations, and choice-based vocational placement.

PRACTICE ACTIVITIES OF CRPs

Testament to the importance that CRPs hold in the provision of rehabilitation services, the Rehabilitation Services Administration currently funds a Rehabilitation Research and Training Center (RRTC) at the University of Wisconsin-Stout to examine best practice approaches and trends among CRPs across the United States. In a three-year research and development study conducted by the Wisconsin-Stout RRTC (Menz et al., 2003), 64 CRPs provided information on such areas as types of clients served, common practice activities, and service outcomes. CRPs in the study represented memberships and/or associations with such organizations as Goodwill Industries, Easter Seals, Commission on Accreditation of Rehabilitation Facilities accredited programs, NISH (formally the National Industries for the Severely Handicapped) affiliates, and Javits-Wagner O'Day participating organizations. The State-Federal Vocational System referred over half (51.67%) of the clients to the sample member CRPs with the remaining clients fairly equally referred from public mental health, developmental disability, Workforce Development, welfare, and other types of agencies.

Given the diversity presented by the presence of over 8,100 CRPs currently in existence across the United States, Menz and associates (2003) aimed to determine the types of clients commonly served by CRPs along with the types of practice activities undertaken by these nonprofit agencies. Reflecting the long-term service focus commonly found among CRPs, based on data from 828 clients from the CRP sample group, the two largest disability groups (in terms of a primary identified disability) were persons with mental retardation (32.04%) and psychiatric disabilities (17.90%). Other disability groups included persons with learning disabilities (11.26%), substance abuse (2.38%), brain injury (4.51%), co-existing primary disabilities (6.13%), other types of disabilities (15.77%), and no disability (9.51%). Table II ranks the 10 most common service components based on data from 692 clients from CRPs in the sample group.

Table II
CRP SERVICE COMPONENTS

Individualized and in-community supports
 1. Vocational planning and actions to achieve employment
 2. Training to acquire and keep job: Soft and hard job skills training
 3. Supports for community participation
 4. Direct supports to ensure job retention
 5. Job training and supports
 6. Job acquisition or job search and placement
 7. Case management and supports coordination
 8. Supports to remain in workforce
 9. Intake and orientation to services

Criser and Fowler (1981) pointed out the 1970s was the decade when graduates of rehabilitation counseling programs increasingly began to find employment in non-publicly based settings, such as CRPs. Given the continued reliance that the public rehabilitation sector places on CRP service delivery (as demonstrated in table II), participation of CRPs in case management and other disability support services will likely grow. Speaking to this reliance, Menz and associates (2003) pointed out that annually, CRPs assist 1 million persons in returning to supported and competitive employment.

ETHICAL CONSIDERATIONS
Case managers employed in nonprofit human service agencies are required to work in an ethical manner following standards set by applicable state licensing bodies (e.g., professional counselors, marriage and family therapists.), by relevant professional organizations like the Commission on Rehabilitation Counselor Certification and the National Association of Social Workers, and by their personal and professional value systems. The unique manner of board oversight and funding for CRPs and other nonprofit agencies presents a variety of ethical challenges for case managers employed in this sector of human service practice that are not present in other settings, such as the State-Federal Vocational Rehabilitation System. In short, the primary ethical challenges come from trying to compete with the for-profit sector as well as balancing the needs of clients versus the needs of those who control the activities of the agency (i.e., the board of directors) and the payers of the nonprofit agency's services (e.g., institutional and individual philanthropists). See Chapter 6 for a full discussion of ethical issues in case management.

CORE NONPROFIT ETHICAL VALUES

Jeavons (1994) suggested that those who work in nonprofit human service agencies should remind themselves that their core responsibility is to serve their clients, especially those who are poor and disadvantaged. In expressing this, Jeavons' (p. 198), noted, "The point being that service, service to people or service to a cause, is at the heart of the reason for being in all these organizations." He argued that nonprofits further express their ethical behavior through accountability, public scrutiny, and honesty in the ways they represent the work that they do.

For their survival, however, Lewis (1989) pointed out that nonprofit human service agencies sometimes tailor their services to fit the expectations presented by the payers of their services. This can result in a nonprofit agency limiting access to services based on criteria such as religious background, ethnicity, gender, age, geographic background, and financial criteria. Nonprofits sometimes take on an administrative position that is similar to for-profit agencies concerning what clients to accept and the range and types of services to provide, based on market competition with the for-profit sector.

Kissane's (2003) qualitative study of the experiences of 20 poor women (17 of whom were receiving Temporary Assistance for Needy Families funding living in the Kensington section of Philadelphia who received services from 50 nonprofit social service agencies explicated many of the financially related ethical problems inherent in nonprofit human services. Respondents perceived that many nonprofits restricted their range of services, or services were provided in an inconsistent manner, due to lack of financial resources. Moreover, respondents indicated that nonprofit agency staff appeared to more often provide services to what they deemed as "the most deserving poor (p. 145)," rather than to all eligible participants. Finally, because of funding source expectations, nonprofit agencies sometimes appeared to tailor and target their services to certain subgroups (e.g., the Latino population). Other barriers to participation included lack of information about available services, fear of using services when nonprofit agencies were located in dangerous locations, and not wanting to feel stigmatized by using the nonprofit agencies' services (e.g., waiting in line outside a soup kitchen).

THE CASE OF CATHOLIC CHARITIES USA

Boards of directors of CRPs and other nonprofits possess considerable control over many of the activities of a nonprofit entity such as setting the agency's mission, selecting an executive director, and monitoring the activities (e.g., financial) of agency administrators and staff (Anringa & Engstrom, 1998). Maddalena (1981, p. 32) went so far as to argue that, "The board is the ultimate decision-making body for the organization." Andringa and Engstrom (1998, p.

5) added that, "In most organizations, the board looks to the staff to implement its policy determinations. Board members expect the staff to act within policy limitations, and they simply want reports on how policy is being carried out."

Hence, nonprofit agency case managers, other staff, and administrators not only rely on their professional training and experience, they also provide services within practice parameters set by boards of directors, whose members may or may not have the appropriate professional training to set such parameters. One consequence of the nonprofit board to staff relationship is that services are not always provided in a manner consistent with standard codes of professional ethics, such as adhering to the principles of respecting clients' personal values, facilitating their right to make choices, and ensuring their access to services. Degeneffe (2003) explicates this issue through his historical and organizational analysis of Catholic Charities USA.

As a registered 501c(3) nonprofit organization, Catholic Charities USA is the largest private provider of social welfare services in the United States. It provides a variety of CRP related case management and services, including respite care, counseling/mental health, education, family support, health, refugee resettlement, pregnancy programs, residential care, permanent housing, adoption, and various other types of services. In 1996, Catholic Charities USA received approximately 1.4 billion dollars from local, state, and federal government entities to fund their programs. Federal funds came from the United States Departments of Agriculture, Housing and Urban Development, Education, Justice, Veterans Affairs, Defense, and Labor along with the Federal Emergency Management Agency, ACTION, and the United States Corporation for National and Community. In contrast, the Catholic Church funded only 5% of the organization's annual $2.15 billion dollar budget (Flynn & Benali, 1997).

Although the Catholic Church provides a small amount of funding, it possesses considerable influence over the practices of Catholic Charities USA through its organizational structure. In addition to an executive director and board of trustees, a bishop also oversees services provided by Catholic Charities USA within the diocese boundary (Reid & Stimpson, 1987). This system of oversight is designed to provide services consistent with the vision established by the national Catholic Charities USA office, which expresses a religiously based theme in their promotional materials. For example, Catholic Charities Vision 2000 statement asserts the following:

> Believing in the presence of God in our midst, we proclaim the sanctity of human life and the dignity of the person by sharing in the mission of Jesus given to the Church. To this end, Catholic Charities works with individuals, families, and communities to help them meet their needs, address their issues, eliminate oppression, and build a just and compassionate society (Orzechowski, 1997, p. 3).

Degeneffe (2003) suggested that sectarian nonprofit agencies, such as Catholic Charities USA, face ongoing ethical dilemmas when trying to balance meeting the requirements of the church body with that the needs of the agency's clients, many of whom may not adhere to the moral principles of the overseeing religious institution. In the case of Catholic Charities USA, Degeneffe asserted the organization might not be able to function from a separation of church and state framework in such areas as addressing abortion issues or advocating for rights of gay and lesbian clients. As the administration of President George W. Bush promotes a policy toward religiously based organizations providing more and more social services (Chaves, 2002), controversies regarding sectarian nonprofit agencies like Catholic Charities USA are sure to continue.

FUTURE TRENDS IN THE NONPROFIT SECTOR

The coming years will present sizable challenges to the viability of nonprofit human service agencies that provide case management and other supportive services. As mentioned earlier, nonprofits face competition for funding their agencies from other nonprofit agencies as well as from the rapidly growing for-profit service sector. Nonprofits also face ongoing service delivery problems such as addressing ethical concerns and providing a service that satisfies the needs of their clientele. Yet, from the same structural features that present the above noted challenges, nonprofit agencies possess the potential to offer targeted, cost effective, and community-building services at a level that is hard to match by the more financially driven for-profit sector or the more bureaucratically and rule controlled public sector.

Case managers who seek employment in a nonprofit human service agency are likely to find a work environment somewhat different from traditional practices in the for-profit sector. CRPs and other nonprofit agencies often try to strike a balance between borrowing management techniques from the business world with maintaining their traditional primary focus on meeting client needs.

FORMING ALLIANCES

One recommended idea from the business world involves nonprofit agencies engaging in mergers and partnerships. Andringa and Engstrom (1998) noted that alliances allow nonprofits to serve more clients and better fulfill their central missions. Alliances can be in the form of linkages with other nonprofit agencies with a similar focus, as well as with government bodies and agencies. Alliances can focus on such objectives as sharing resources, providing complementary services, or engaging in joint advocacy efforts (Herman, 1994).

Libby and Austin (2002, p. 82) provided a recent example of the benefits of nonprofit agency alliances. In 1995, 15 directors of nonprofit agencies met to discuss the following problems with human services in Napa County, California: (1) nonprofit human services were fragmented; (2) competition among nonprofit agencies; (3) reliance on the county health and human service agency for funding; (4) lack of collaboration among nonprofit agencies and the county: (5) no sense of shared vision, and (6) little understanding of the needs of their common client groups. By 1997, the group had grown to a coalition of 30 nonprofit agencies with an organizational title of Napa Valley Coalition of Non-Profit Agencies. This coalition has worked on collaborative goals such as creating adequate crisis services (e.g., establishing a crisis hotline), providing subsidized outpatient psychotherapy, and establishing a continuum of health care available for the uninsured and poor in Napa County.

ACCOUNTABILITY AND QUALITY CONTROL
Accountability is a second idea borrowed from business. Nonprofits are increasingly required to demonstrate such outcomes as financial efficiency and client satisfaction if they hope to maintain funding and client referrals. CRPs in particular own an extended history of quality control and measurement. It can be argued that CRPs have been more successful in measuring client outcomes from multiple objective and subjective perspectives, rather than from unitary measures such as successful Status 26 case closures, as used in the State-Federal Vocational Rehabilitation system (e.g., Szymanski & Danek, 1992). It is likely that the history of program evaluation in the CRP sector has influenced calls to examine client outcomes in the State-Federal Vocational Rehabilitation System from multiple perspectives as outlined by such authors as Walls (2001) and Kosciulek (2004).

An example of a CRP service where extensive outcome evaluation continually takes place is supported employment. Since its inception in the early 1980s, in addition to examining quality of life, outcomes studies on supported employment have examined a number of other areas such as consumer empowerment (e.g., West & Parent, 1992), client satisfaction (e.g., Melchiori & Church, 1997), and cost-effectiveness (e.g., Rusch, Heal, & Cimera, 1997). Multi-modal examinations of supported employment continue to be conducted. For example, Bond et al. (2001) examined converging findings on the effectiveness of supported employment based on their review of eight randomized controlled and three quasi-experimental studies of persons with psychiatric and other types of disabilities. The authors (pp. 319-320) noted the value of supported employment's extensive history of quality evaluation by stating, "No other vocational rehabilitation approach for persons with severe mental illness has attained the status of evidence-based practice despite a half century of program innovation and informal experimentation by many psychiatric rehabilitation programs. Proponents of other vocational approaches either have failed to empirically investigate their methods or have failed to find strong evidence."

Beyond individual researchers, there are a number of organizational resources in place to advance examinations of effectiveness and quality among CRP agencies. As noted, the Wisconsin-Stout RRTC focuses on the practice activities of CRPs across the United States. Their charter requires measurement of a variety of quality and effectiveness outcomes. The previously described study by Menz and associates (2003), for example, examined such consumer-based outcomes as client satisfaction, level of independence, employment status, economic self-sufficiency, and access to benefits.

CONCLUSION

The nonprofit sector presents numerous opportunities as well as challenges for case management professionals. Nonprofit agencies, such as CRPs, offer settings that value creativity and responsiveness to social problems. However, the nonprofit sector faces considerable competition for funding from other nonprofits as well as from the for-profit and government sectors. Working in the nonprofit sector can be attractive for many case managers, given this sector's commitment to the poor, to those with disabilities, and to those disadvantaged and devalued by society.

REFERENCES

Anringa, R. C., & Engstrom, T. W. (1998). *Nonprofit board answer book: Practical guidelines for board members and chief executives.* Washington, DC: National Center for Nonprofit Boards.

Bishop, M., & Feist-Price, S. (2001). Quality of life in rehabilitation counseling: Making the philosophical practical. *Rehabilitation Education, 15*(3), 201-212.

Bond, G. R., Becker, D. R., Drake, R. E., Rapp, C. A., Meisler, N., Lehman, A. F., Bell, M., & Blyler, C. R. (2001). Implementing supported employment as an Evidence-based practice. *Psychiatric Services, 52*(3), 313-322.

Boris, E. T., & Krehely, J. (2002). Civic participation and advocacy. In L. Salamon (Ed.), *The state of nonprofit America* (pp. 299-330). Washington DC: Brookings Institution Press.

Braddock, D. (1998). Mental retardation and developmental disabilities: Historical and contemporary perspectives. In D. Braddock, R. Hemp, S. Parish, & J. Westrich, J. (Eds.), *The state of the states in developmental disabilities* (5ᵗʰ ed. pp. 3-22). Washington, DC: American Association on Mental Retardation.

Braddock, D., Hemp, R., Parish, S., & Westrich,, J. (1998a). *The state of the states in developmental disabilities* (5ᵗʰ ed.). Washington, DC: American Association on Mental Retardation.

Braddock, D., Hemp, R., Parish, S., Westrich, J., & Park, H. (1998b). The state of the states in developmental disabilities: A summary of the studies. In D. Braddock, R. Hemp, S. Parish, & J.Westrich, J. (Eds.), *The state of the states in developmental disabilities* (5ᵗʰ ed. pp. 23-54). Washington, DC: American Association on Mental Retardation.

Bradley, V. J., & Knoll, J. (1990). *Shifting paradigms in services to people with developmental disabilities.* Cambridge, MA: Human Services Research Institute.

Brudney, J. L. (1994). Designing and managing volunteer programs. In R. D. Herman (Ed.), *The Jossey-Bass Handbook of nonprofit leadership and management* (pp. 279-302). San Francisco: Jossey-Bass Publishers.

Cardoso, E. S., Chan, F., Thomas, K. R., Peterson, D., Mpofu, E., & Leahy, M. (1999). In F. Chan & M. J. Leahy (Eds.), *Health care and disability case management* (pp. 663-704). Lake Zurich, IL: Vocational Consultants Press.

Catholic Charities (1998). *Fact sheet*-1998 [Brochure]. Alexandria, VA: Author.

Chaves, M. (2002). Religious congregations. In L. M. Salamon (Ed.), *The state of nonprofit America.* Washington, DC: Brookings Institution Press.

Corrigan, P. W., Rao, D., & Lam, C. (1999). Psychiatric rehabilitation. In F. Chan & M. J. Leahy (Eds.), *Health care and disability case management* (pp. 527-564). Lake Zurich, IL: Vocational Consultants Press.

Crewe, N. (1999). Spinal cord injury. In F. Chan & M. J. Leahy (Eds.), *Health care and disability case management* (pp. 565-588). Lake Zurich, IL: Vocational Consultants Press.

Crimmins, J. C., & Keil, M. (1983). *Enterprise in the nonprofit sector.* Washington, DC: Partners for Livable Places and the Rockefeller Brothers Fund.

Criser, J. R., & Fowler, N. L. (1981). Employment outcomes of graduates of a rehabilitation counselor training program: A comparison of graduate employment between 1965-1974 and 1975-1979. *Journal of Rehabilitation, 47*(3), 28-32.

Cunningham, J. M., Chan, F., Jones, J., Kramnetz, B., Stoll, J. & Calabresa, E. (1999). Brain injury rehabilitation: A primer for case managers. In F. Chan & M. J. Leahy (Eds.), *Health care and disability case management* (pp. 475-526). Lake Zurich, IL: Vocational Consultants Press.

Degeneffe, C. E. (2000). Supported employment services for persons with developmental disabilities: Unmet promises and future challenges for rehabilitation counselors. *Journal of Applied Rehabilitation Counseling, 31*(2), 41-47.

Degeneffe, C. E. (2003). What is catholic about Catholic Charities? *Social Work, 48*(3), 374-383.

Fabian, E. S. (1992). Supported employment and the quality of life: Does a job make a difference? *Rehabilitation Counseling Bulletin, 36*(2), 84-97.

Flynn, P., & Benali, O. (1997). *Catholic Charities USA 1996 annual survey.* Alexandria, VA: Catholic Charities USA.

Gronbjerg, K. A., & Salamon, L. M. (2002). Devolution, marketization, and the changing shape of government-nonprofit relations. In L. Salamon (Ed.), *The state of nonprofit America* (pp. 447-470). Washington DC: Brookings Institution Press.

Hanley-Maxwell, C., & Bordieri, J. E. (1989). Purchasing supported employment: Evaluating the service. *Journal of Applied Rehabilitation Counseling, 20*(3), 4-11.

Herman, R. D. (1994). Conclusion: Preparing for the future of nonprofit management. In R. D. Herman (Ed.), *The Jossey-Bass handbook of nonprofit leadership and Management* (pp. 616-626). San Francisco: Jossey-Bass Publishers.

Hodgkinson, V. A., Nelson, K. E., & Sivak, Jr. (2002). Individual giving and volunteering. In L. Salamon (Ed.), *The state of nonprofit America* (pp. 387-422). Washington DC: Brookings Institution Press.

Inge, K. J., Banks, P. D., Wehman, P., Hill, J. W., & Shafer, M. S. (1988). Quality of life for individuals who are labeled mentally retarded: Evaluating competitive employment versus sheltered workshop employment. *Education and Training in   Mental Retardation, 23,* 97-104.

Jeavons, T. H. (1994). Ethics in nonprofit management: Creating a culture of integrity. In R. D. Herman (Ed.), *The Jossey-Bass handbook of nonprofit leadership and management* (pp. 184-207). San Francisco: Jossey-Bass Publishers.

Johnson, K. L. (1999). Chronic disabling pain: A biosocial disability. In F. Chan & M. J. Leahy (Eds.), *Health care and disability case management* (pp. 623-638). Lake Zurich, IL: Vocational Consultants Press.

Kissane, R. J. (2003). What's need got to do with it? Barriers to use of nonprofit social services. *Journal of Sociology and Social Welfare, 30*(2), 127-148.

Kosciulek, J. F. (2004). Theory of informed consumer choice in vocational rehabilitation. *Rehabilitation Education, 18*(1), 3-12.

Lamb, G. S. (1999). Case management for older adults. In F. Chan & M. J. Leahy (Eds.), *Health care and disability case management* (pp. 639-662). Lake Zurich, IL: Vocational Consultants Press.

Lenkowsky, L. (2002). Foundations and corporate philanthropy. In L. Salamon (Ed.), *The state of nonprofit America* (pp. 355-386). Washington DC: Brookings Institution Press.

Letts, C. W., Ryan, W. P., & Grossman, A. (1999). *High performance nonprofit organizations: Managing upstream for greater impact*. New York: John Wiley & Sons, Inc.

Lewis, H. (1989). Ethics and the private non-profit human service organizations. *Administration in Social Work, 13*(2), 1-14.

Libby, M. K., & Austin, M. J. (2003). Building a coalition of non-profit agencies to Collaborate with a county health and human services agency: The Napa County Behavioral Health Committee of the Napa Coalition of Non-Profits. *Administration in Social Work, 26*(4), 81-99.

Maddalena, L. A. (1981). *A communications manual for nonprofit organizations*. New York: AMACOM.

Melchiori, L. G., & Church, T. (1997). Vocational needs and satisfaction of supported employees: The applicability of the theory of work adjustment. *Journal of Vocational Behavior, 50*, 401-417.

Menz, F., Botterbusch, C., HagenFoley, & Johnson, P. T. (2003). *Achieving quality outcomes through community-based rehabilitation programs: The results are in*. Presentation made at the NISH Annual Conference at Denver, CO, on April 7, 2004.

O'Grady, J. (1931). The Catholic settlement movement. *Catholic Charities Review, 15*(5), 134-144.

Orzechowski, E. (1997). Participation, participation, participation! In C. C. Anderson & A. Peeler (Eds.), *A vision for families and communities: 1996 annual report* (pp. 2-3). Alexandria, VA: Catholic Charities USA.

Rados, D. L. (1981). *Marketing for non-profit organizations*. Dover, MA: Auburn House Publishing Company.

Reid, C., Kitchen, J., & Deutsch, P. M. (1999). Case management with people who have AIDS or HIV infection. In F. Chan & M. J. Leahy (Eds.), *Health care and disability case management* (pp. 39-60). Lake Zurich, IL: Vocational Consultants Press.

Reid, W. J., & Stimpson, P. K. (1987). Sectarian agencies. In A. Minahan (Ed.-in-Chief), *Encyclopedia of social work* (18th Ed., Vol. 2, pp. 545-556). Silver Spring, MD: National Association of Social Workers.

Rubin, S. E., & Roessler, R. T. (1995). *Foundations of the vocational rehabilitation process* (4th edition). Austin: Pro-ed.

Rusch, F. R., Heal, L. W., & Cimera, R. E. (1997). Predicting the earnings of supported employees with mental retardation: A longitudinal study. *American Journal on Mental Retardation, 101*(6), 630-644.

Salamon, L. M. (1995). *Partners in public service: Government-nonprofit relations in the modern welfare state*. Baltimore: The John Hopkins University Press.

Salamon, L. M. (2002). The resilient sector: The state of nonprofit America. In L. Salamon (Ed.), *The state of nonprofit America* (pp. 3-64). Washington DC: Brookings Institution Press.

Scheurell, R. P. (1987). *Introduction to human service networks: History, organization, and professions*. Lanham, MD: University Press of America.

Shaw, L. R., Chan, F., & Leahy, M. (1999). Case management: Past, present, and future. In F. Chan & M. J. Leahy (Eds.), *Health care and disability case management*. Lake Zurich, IL: Vocational Consultants Press.

Szymanski, E. M., & Danek, M. M. (1992). The relationship of rehabilitation counselor education to rehabilitation client outcome: A replication and extension. *Journal of Rehabilitation, 58*(1), 49-56.

Wall, R. T. (2001). Measurement of client outcomes in rehabilitation. In B. Bolton (Ed.) (3rd ed) *Handbook of measurement and evaluation in rehabilitation* (pp. 311-338). Gaithersburg, MD: Aspen Publishers, Inc.

West, M. D., & Parent, W. S. (1992). Consumer choice and empowerment in supported employment services: Issues and strategies. *JASH, 17*(1), 47-52.

Wright, G. N. (1980). *Total rehabilitation*. Boston: Little, Brown, and Company.

12

Case Management in Private Sector Rehabilitation

Martha H. Chapin

Chapter Highlights

- Insurance Benefit Systems

- Case Management Process

- Forensic Rehabilitation

- Conclusion

$\mathbf{P}$rivate sector rehabilitation has been in existence since the early 1900s. It can be traced to the employment of rehabilitation nurses by the Travelers Insurance Company in 1908 (Kilbury, Benshoff, & Riggar, 1990) and by Liberty Mutual Insurance Company in the 1940's (Matkin & May, 1981). Private sector rehabilitation's growth was attributed to the passing of the 1970 Federal Occupational and Safety Health Act (OSHA) (PL 91-596). It recommended the development of a National Commission on State Workers' Compensation Laws, which supported the inclusion of vocational rehabilitation in workers' compensation. Before this time, vocational rehabilitation had been provided by publicly funded and private non-profit agencies (Jenkins, Patterson, & Szymanski, 1998). The commission suggested that workers' compensation was not doing enough to help injured workers return to work (National Commission on State Workmen's Compensation Laws, 1972). The commission recognized the historical problems inherent in attempting to serve the entire workers' compensation caseload through the state-federal system. This was reinforced by state-federal mandates that continued to require the provision of rehabilitation services to specific disability groups in addition to injured workers (Matkin, 1995). The commission recommended the creation of specific rehabilitation units with medical/rehabilitation divisions and employers were supposed to fund vocational rehabilitation programs for injured workers. As a result of these recommendations, many states enacted mandatory rehabilitation programs as part of workers' compensation policies (Jenkins, et al, 1998).

The Rehabilitation Act of 1973 and its subsequent amendments in 1978, 1984, and 1992 required that the state-federal rehabilitation program increase services to persons with severe disabilities. This decreased emphasis on services to injured workers (Matkin, 1995) resulted in the need for other rehabilitation providers to help industrially injured workers to return to work. International Rehabilitation Associates was founded in 1970 marking the beginning of private sector rehabilitation (Kilbury et al., 1990), an area where tremendous growth has occurred. With this extraordinary growth came an influx of professionals from many different employment settings–rehabilitation counseling, business and industry, nursing, and occupational therapy. These professionals have helped define medical and vocational case management strategies in private rehabilitation.

Role and function research over the years has documented the knowledge, skills, and abilities required to be an effective rehabilitation counselor and case manager (Chan, Leahy, McMahon, Mirch, & DeVinney, 1999; Emener & Rubin, 1980; Fraser & Clowers, 1978; Harrison & Lee, 1979; Jaques, 1959; Leahy, Shapson, & Wright, 1987a, 1987b; Leahy, Szymanski, & Linkowski, 1993; Matkin, 1983; Muthard & Salomone, 1969; Rubin et al.,

1984). Matkin (1995) addressed rehabilitation practitioners in the private sector's work activities and associated knowledge when he surveyed 3,500 Certified Insurance Rehabilitation Specialist (CIRS) (now known as Certified Disability Management Specialist [CDMS]) "applicants during the certification grandfathering period between 1985 and 1986, and again 5 years later at the end of the first certification maintenance phase" (Matkin, p. 389). The work roles of private sector rehabilitation practitioners included case management and human disabilities, job placement and vocational assessment, rehabilitation services and care, disability legislation, and forensic rehabilitation. He found similar findings in both years with the 1991 data offering clearer descriptions of the work roles. Between September 1992 and July 1995, 1,139 CIRS completed the *Certified Insurance Rehabilitation Specialist Commission–Standards Questionnaire (CIRCS-SQ)*, which included task items from Matkin's survey questionnaire and knowledge items obtained from a comprehensive literature review and through analysis of CIRS practitioner job descriptions (Leahy, Chan, Taylor, Wood, & Downey, 1997). The knowledge domains derived from the final factor analysis were vocational assessment and planning, case management and reporting, expert testimony, legislation and regulations, community resources, and psychosocial and functional aspects of disability (Leahy et al.). Although different methodologies were used in these two studies to obtain the knowledge requirements, the results reported by Leahy et al. are similar to those reported by Matkin. Rehabilitation counselors rated vocational assessment and planning, expert testimony, and job analysis and accommodation as more important than nurses did, while nurses rated community resources as more important than rehabilitation counselors did (Leahy et al.).

Case managers in private sector rehabilitation are often said to serve many "masters," which relates to the concept that case managers are hired by a payer to assist a person with a disability to return to work. They may be under increased pressure from the customer to perform activities that would compromise client welfare and the case manager's professional integrity (Matkin, 1995). The case manager will also work with a variety of other professionals and agencies to facilitate medical stability and return to work for the client. All of these professionals have their own priorities, which can cause potential conflicts of interest. The case manager must work hard to avoid compromising the client and his or her own professional integrity (Matkin & May, 1981).

Private sector rehabilitation nurses and counselors work in a variety of work settings. They may be self-employed, work for insurance companies or their subsidiary rehabilitation firms, at private sector rehabilitation companies, for self-insured employers, or at agencies overseeing workers' compensation.

306

As private sector rehabilitation expanded, the clientele they served also expanded to include recipients of other private disability compensation benefits. Services were provided to recipients of workers' compensation, automobile insurance claims, long-term disability benefits, Social Security, and for expert witness testimony. The purpose of this chapter is to provide an overview of private sector rehabilitation including (a) insurance benefit systems; (b) rehabilitation goals; (c) the case management process; (d) forensic rehabilitation; and (e) best practices and characteristics of effective case managers.

INSURANCE BENEFIT SYSTEMS

Private sector rehabilitation providers have a responsibility to understand and stay abreast of legislation and benefit systems that may impact their clients. Legislation may be federally regulated such as Social Security or legislated by states such as workers' compensation and automobile insurance claims. An employer may provide benefits such as short and long-term disability.

SOCIAL SECURITY
Social Security Disability Insurance (SSDI) and Supplemental Security Income (SSI) were enacted under the Social Security Act with the Social Security Administration (SSA) overseeing both programs. SSDI's purpose is to replace lost income when the wage earner is no longer able to work due to a physical or mental disability. Family members may also be eligible based on the work record of a spouse or parent. To qualify for SSDI, the wage earner must have worked long enough and recently enough. Generally, this means that the wage earner has earned 20 credits in the last 10 years ending with the year the disability prevented the person from working. A maximum of four credits can be earned per year. SSDI benefits include monthly cash benefits, Medicare to cover hospital bills, and supplementary medical insurance protection that begins 24 months after receipt of SSDI, work incentives and employment supports (SSA, 2003c).

SSI is a cash assistance program for individuals who have limited income and resources, who are 65 years of age or older, blind, or disabled and who are not covered by SSDI or who receive SSDI payments below certain minimum income levels. Medicaid is also a benefit, but the conditions for the receipt of this benefit may vary by state (SSA, 2003d).

Both SSDI and SSI define disability as "the inability to engage in any substantial gainful activity (SGA) because of a medically determinable physical or mental impairment(s): that can be expected to result in death, or that has lasted or, that we can expect to last for a continuous period of not less than 12 months" (SSA, 2003a, p. 15). Blindness is considered vision that cannot be corrected to better than 20/200 in your better eye, or if ones visual field is 20 degrees or less even with a corrective lens (SSA, 2003a).

The earnings limit considered for substantial gainful activity increases annually based on increases in the national average wage index. As of January 1, 2004, a person who had a disability other than blindness could earn a wage of $810 and still receive SSDI benefits. People who were blind could earn $1350 (SSA, 2004).

One of the reported knowledge domains previously indicated for CIRS/CDMS was forensic rehabilitation (Matkin, 1995) or expert testimony (Leahy et al., 1997). The SSA uses vocational experts to present an opinion regarding the employability of Social Security claimants. To become a vocational expert for the SSA requires an application process and, once approved, an annual renewal of one's contract (Weed & Field, 1990). For SSDI, a person's impairment must be the primary reason for the inability to engage in substantial gainful activity; however, age, education, and work experience are also taken into consideration. The person must also not be able to participate in work that exists in the national economy. It does not matter whether the work exists in their geographic area, whether a vacancy exists, or whether they would be hired. These are the issues that a vocational expert would review in preparation for testimony at a Social Security hearing. Social Security continues to use the *Dictionary of Occupational Titles* and the *Selected Characteristics of Occupations Defined in the Revised Dictionary of Occupational Titles* for information about the requirements of work (SSA, 2000). Expert witnesses should review a copy of the *Vocational Expert Handbook* (SSA, 1990) provided by the Office of Hearings and Appeals Social Security Administration prior to providing testimony.

The Ticket to Work and Work Incentives Improvement Act of 1999 (TWWIIA) has made some major changes in the SSDI and SSI programs. Its "Ticket to Work" program increases the demand for counseling services for persons receiving SSDI and SSI (American Counseling Association (ACA) Office of Public Policy & Information) and is voluntary (SSA, 2003b). Social Security beneficiaries are given a voucher or "ticket" to use for rehabilitation, job training, career, or support services from public or private providers who have joined the employment network (ACA Office of Public Policy & Information, 2000). Employment Networks can include, but are not limited to state vocational rehabilitation agencies; organizations administering vocational rehabilitation service projects for American Indians with disabilities; One-Stop delivery systems established under the Workforce Investment Act; alternate participants currently under SSA contracts; public or private schools providing appropriate services; employers offering job training, vocational rehabilitation or other job related services for persons with disabilities; and any public or private entity providing or arranging employment services for persons with disabilities (Ticket to Work, 2003). Maximus, Inc. administers the Ticket to Work program and approves Employment Networks. They can be contacted at http://www.yourtickettowork.com or at their toll free number 866-968-7842. TTDY users can call 866-833-2967 (SSA, 2003e).

Additionally, the TWWIIA removes the barriers that require recipients to choose between health care coverage and work by expanding "Medicaid and Medicare coverage to more people with disabilities who work" (SSA, 2003b, p.2). Medicaid may include coverage for people with disabilities who are working and may allow purchase of Medicaid if income guidelines are met. Medicaid provisions vary by state and they should be confirmed with the State Medicaid office. Medicare Part A coverage was also expanded to eight and a half years for most Social Security Disability beneficiaries who work. Disability benefits, Medicare, and Medicaid can also be more quickly reinstated should the SSDI or SSI recipients be unable to work due to their medical condition. A reinstatement request must be filed within 60 months of benefit termination (SSA, 2003b). If there is a dispute in a Social Security case, the Office of Hearing and Appeals supervises the hearings held, decisions made, and appealed cases, while Administrative Law Judges conduct the hearings.

WORKERS' COMPENSATION
Taking care of a person injured in the employ of another has been around since the beginning of master-servant relationships. The expectation was that the master was responsible for the servant's recovery from an injury that occurred during employment. Recovery insured the servant could continue serving the master (Obermann, 1965). This concept was incorporated into English common law (Matkin, 1995) and eventually workers' compensation laws.

The initiation of workers' compensation laws in the United States is attributed to the congressional enactment of the Federal Employers' Liability Act in 1908. This demonstrated a federal commitment to the principles of workers' compensation, because it covered federal employees. In 1911, 10 states enacted workers' compensation laws that survived later constitutional challenges (Matkin, 1995).

Accident prevention and compensation for an injury were the first two steps in the process to protect America's work force. The third step required that injured workers be treated for injuries and prepared for a return to work (Obermann, 1965; Wright, 1980), thus making vocational rehabilitation a part of the process.

Workers' compensation affords workers the right to benefits without consideration of who was at fault. The worker generally gives up the right to sue his or her employer for pain and suffering and loss of enjoyment of life following a work related injury, in return for secure access to benefits (E. M. Welch, 1994).

Employee benefits for wage loss, medical, and vocational rehabilitation services vary by state. When a wage loss system is used, benefits are usually two-thirds of the worker's pre injury wages (E. M. Welch, 1994). Wage loss benefits are designed to help the injured worker survive financially while recovering from the injury (Michigan Department of Labor, 1993).

Some states provide payments for lost wages using a rating guide and assessment of the disability's impact on work. This requires understanding the degree and nature of the disability or impairment. Physicians provide impairment percentages or ratings of an injury or illness once it is considered permanent, and the patient has reached maximum medical improvement (MMI). MMI means the impairment has stabilized and is unlikely to change substantially with or without medical treatment within the next year. Medical specialists develop the impairment percentages or ratings and these are found in *Guides to the Evaluation of Permanent Impairment* (2001). These ratings are consensus-driven estimates reflecting the severity of the medical condition and its impact on a person's ability to perform activities of daily living, excluding work. These ratings reflect functional limitations, not disability (Cocchiarella & Andersson, 2001).

There are four categories of disability on which wage loss benefits are based: temporary total; temporary partial; permanent partial; and permanent total (Rasch 1985; Weed & Field, 1994, 2002). Temporary total disability (TTD) benefits are paid to an injured worker who is "temporarily" unable to work due to a compensable injury and is receiving medical treatment (Rasch). These wage loss benefits are usually two-thirds of the injured workers' average weekly wage up to maximum allowable caps set by individual state statutes (Rasch; Novick & Rondinelli, 2000). The worker usually receives payment until MMI or return to modified work occurs (Rondinelli, 1996 as cited in Novick & Rondinelli). Should the injured worker return to work in a job that does not pay as well as his or her pre injury job or at a reduced physical functioning level, then the worker is classified as having a temporary partial disability (TPD) and receives a wage differential between his or her pre and post injury earnings (North Carolina Industrial Commission (NCIC), 1993; Rasch; Weed & Field). There may be a maximum time length this benefit can be received such as 300 weeks (NCIC, 1993).

Medical guidelines or state statues that classify the injury as either "scheduled" or "unscheduled" establish the "impairment rating" (Rasch, 1985; Weed & Field, 1994). Permanent partial disabilities (PPD) meet the criteria of a scheduled injury. This means that there is a permanent impairment to a part of the body such as an extremity, eyes (vision), or ears (hearing) (Novick & Rondinelli, 2000; Rasch; Weed & Field). In workers' compensation laws, scheduled injuries are listed alongside the corresponding compensable payment for the loss (NCIC, 2002). In North Carolina, for example, the loss of an arm is compensable at the current compensation rate times 240 weeks of workers' compensation. If only a partial loss occurs, workers' compensation is paid on a percentage basis (NCIC, 1993). Injured workers usually receive this PPD benefit whether or not they return to work. "Unscheduled" injuries are generally not found in the statutorily defined schedule. They include spinal cord injuries and double amputations, and they are called permanent total disability (PTD) (Novick & Rondinelli, 2000; Rasch; Weed & Field). Some states, such as North Carolina, use the term total and permanent disability (NCIC, 2002) instead of permanent total (Rasch; Weed & Field). Compensation is calculated differently for unscheduled injuries. At MMI and a release to return to work by the physician, the injured worker is compensated based on the difference between pre and post injury wages; the benefit is paid over the lifetime of the worker; and periodic adjustments can be made if the earning capacity of the worker changes (NCIC; Weed & Field). If an employee dies as a result of an occupational disease or accident, the family is paid survivor (death) benefits (NCIC, 1993).

Loss of earning capacity is an area where litigation occurs in workers' compensation. It includes how the injury or death impacts the individual's ability to earn money. Specific issues may include lost wages, projected earning power, reduced employment potential, and future earning power as a result of the injury (Weed & Field, 1990).

An employer generally pays for an injured worker's medical expenses (E. M. Welch, 1994). The medical benefits are designed to help cure or relieve the injured worker from the effects of the injury (Michigan Department of Labor, 1993). Vocational rehabilitation services are designed to assist persons with disabilities to receive appropriate services to help them cope with the effects of the injury and return to work (Obermann, 1965).

All states have agencies responsible for the administration of workers' compensation laws. Within the state agencies administering workers' compensation, some states have divisions that specifically oversee medical and vocational rehabilitation activities. The provision of rehabilitation services varies by state: some states provide direct rehabilitation services to injured workers; refer injured workers to state agencies, private providers, or monitor vocational rehabilitation cases; provide a combination of these services; or have no rehabilitation unit (E. M. Welch, 1994).

AUTOMOBILE INSURANCE

Besides workers' compensation, private sector rehabilitation companies work with clients receiving benefits from auto insurance carriers. Auto insurance policies and benefits vary by state. Some states have no-fault policies while others have liability policies where insurers pay what they are legally liable to cover. Rehabilitation related benefits might cover wage loss, medical benefits, and vocational rehabilitation. Benefits provided vary by policy and by the policyholder's selection of services. Medical benefits, for example, may be offset by the policyholder's health insurance or denied if the injury is work related. Wage loss is also often offset by workers' compensation benefits and SSDI benefits. Some companies offer replacement service coverage to pay for services the injured can no longer perform for their families or themselves. In this instance, a daily fee is received to help offset the expenses incurred in obtaining these services. This is a time-limited service and includes household chores and yard work (Office of Financial and Insurance Services, 2003).

LONG- AND SHORT-TERM DISABILITY

Long-term disability (LTD) is an income replacement benefit that generally covers the replacement of two-thirds of a person's salary when the insured cannot return to work. This is a tax-free benefit (Rasch, 1985). Group policies purchased from employers are relatively inexpensive, while an individual policy is quite expensive. There is often a waiting period of one-to-six months before benefits begin. Most policies have an "own occupation" (own occ) and an "any occupation" (any occ) clause (Rasch). The term own occupation means that people are unable to perform any and every duty pertaining to their regular occupation. This usually is applicable for two years from the date of the accident or illness. Any occupation means people are unable to perform the duties of any occupation for which they are reasonably qualified by education, training, and work experience. This can be a time-limited clause or a lifetime clause. In-group policies, wage replacement is usually offset or reduced by workers' compensation, SSDI, pension, and retirement benefits (Rasch). Individual policies usually do not coordinate benefits.

Short-term disability is a policy paid for by an employer that covers illnesses or injuries that last six months or less. It would cover maternity leave or a non work-related illness or injury. Clients receiving short-term disability generally are not referred for rehabilitation unless the medical situation is anticipated to be prolonged or likely worsen and eventually become a long-term disability case.

PRIVATE SECTOR REHABILITATION GOALS
The ultimate goal in private sector rehabilitation is to return the client to productivity. The standard process used within the industry is the return to work hierarchy:

1. Return to work—same job, same employer
2. Return to work—same job-modified, same employer
3. Return to work—different job (capitalizing on transferable skills), same employer
4. Return to work—same job, different employer
5. Return to work—same job-modified, different employer
6. Return to work—different job (capitalizing on transferable skills), different employer
7. Return to work—different job with re-training, same or different employer
8. Return to work—self-employment

(G. T. Welch, 1979; Matkin, 1981, 1995)

Returning to work with the same employer is emphasized because this usually expedites the return to work by focusing on the client's preexisting work relationships and skills thus reducing case cost through reestablishing a wage earning capacity for the client. It is likely to be the easiest, least expensive, and the most successful rehabilitation alternative. It increases the success rate of vocational rehabilitation and reduces the disruption to the client's pre injury lifestyle (Matkin, 1986). Clearly defining the steps of the rehabilitation process should help case managers maximize their success in rehabilitating clients.

CASE MANAGEMENT PROCESS

Case managers focus on the individuality of casework, as there is no standard way to treat each case. Each case has unique needs, which are considered in the creation of a strategy or plan for the case. The case manager selects from a menu of medical and vocational options (Mirch, 1997). The key to success in private sector rehabilitation, however, is the development of the client-case manager relationship (Chapin & Leahy, 1999; Mirch, 1997). Empathy, warmth, unconditional positive regard (Rogers, 1957; Lambert & Cattani-Thompson, 1996), and genuineness are essential (Rogers, 1957). Case managers must also establish trust and rapport, which can be challenging in this more adversarial environment that requires the case manager to be a client advocate and accountable to the customer or payer, medical personnel, and lawyers. Developing a strong client-case manager relationship is essential to help clients feel comfortable sharing medical and vocational information, expressing anger, and any fears they have about returning to work (Chapin & Leahy).

Casework is prioritized according to the client's rehabilitation needs, customer guidelines, and the policy of the private sector rehabilitation firm with which the case manager is employed. Time management is the key to prioritizing casework. Some case managers would say that there is a natural priority to casework, and that effectively servicing a client's case generates the casework activities that need to be done to resolve the case file (Mirch, 1997).

REFERRAL

Upon receipt of a referral, the rehabilitation process begins with an evaluation of the client's rehabilitation potential, which assists the case manager in predicting problems to achieving medical and vocational rehabilitation success. Evaluation occurs by thoroughly reviewing a case file. During this review, hypotheses are made regarding the client's rehabilitation potential. When developing hypotheses, the case manager looks at predictors of rehabilitation success such as the person's age, education, work experience, income, motivation, medical situation, and the local labor market. This phase is also used to clearly document a client's file if he or she is not an appropriate candidate for rehabilitation.

If an attorney represents a client, contact with the attorney may be required to obtain approval to meet with the client, following file review. Once this approval has been received, the client is contacted for the completion of a diagnostic interview to gather medical, psychological, vocational, and financial information useful in evaluating rehabilitation potential. During this interview, questions are asked to clarify your initial hypotheses about the client. In workers' compensation cases, the client's rights and responsibilities are reviewed.

Part of the referral process is to obtain a release of information from the client to contact medical and vocational resources or providers and to review with the client the Health Insurance Portability and Accountability Act of 1996 (HIPAA).

The Health Insurance Portability and Accountability Act of 1996. One of the newest regulations to impact private sector rehabilitation and the health care industry in general is the Health Insurance Portability and Accountability Act of 1996 (HIPAA), Public Law 104-191. This Act addresses the use and disclosure of a person's health information or "protected health information" by "covered entities" or organizations subject to the Privacy Rule. It addresses a person's privacy rights to understand and control how one's health information is used. The Office of Civil Rights implements and enforces the Privacy Rule.

314

Health plans, excluding workers' compensation, automobile, and property casualty insurance, are covered by the Privacy Rule, as are health care providers, health care clearinghouses, and business associates. "The Privacy Rule protects all 'individually identifiable health information' held or transmitted by a covered entity or its business associate, in any form or media, whether electronic, paper or oral" (United States Department of Health & Human Services (U.S. DHHS), 2003, p. 3). Protected health information must be disclosed to the individual or his or her personal representative and to the Department of Health and Human Services (DHHS) when it is undertaking a compliance investigation, review, or enforcement action. Written authorization from the individual is required for any use or disclosure of protected health information that is "not for treatment, payment or health care operations or otherwise permitted or required by the Privacy Rule" (p. 9). Public entities, however, can disclose protected health information for workers' compensation and other similar programs that are providing benefits for work-related injuries or illnesses (U. S. DHHS). Case managers can stay up to date on changes in HIPAA regulations by visiting the U. S. DHHS website at http://www.hhs.gov/ocr/hipaa. HIPAA regulations should be explained to clients and releases of information obtained before any medical information is requested or given to a third party.

MEDICAL MANAGEMENT
Depending upon state regulations for workers' compensation, medical case management may be handled by a nurse, allied health care professional, or a rehabilitation counselor. The case manager carefully reviews the medical information and, following the client meeting, requests any medical information that was not available at the time of the referral. This would include medical information from all treating physicians, occupational therapists, physical therapists, orthotists, prosthetists, psychologists or other medical or mental health professionals, and hospitals. (See Chapter 7 for further description of these resources.) This information will help the case manager understand the client's medical condition and will be used to assess the client's needs.

Case managers may meet clients in the hospital immediately after an accident or illness, in the rehabilitation unit, or at their home. If a client is hospitalized, working with the discharge planner or providing discharge planning may be necessary. Discharge planning can include transfer to a new facility, ordering durable medical equipment, home nursing or therapy care, pain management, transportation, and home modifications (See Chapter 7 for further description of these resources). Coordinating efforts with the primary Registered Nurse (RN), discharge planner, or social service administrator is essential to avoid duplication of services and to save cost (Mullahy, 1998). When a client is being transferred home, it may be necessary to assess safety factors in the home and arrange for safety aids and modifications (Mullahy, 1998). This may include grab bars in the showers, a shower chair, or modifying the bathroom to install a roll in shower. Architectural barriers may also need to be assessed (Mullahy). Can the client get into the home or is a ramp needed? Do doors within the home need to be widened or does the client need to move from a two-story home to a ranch style home? The case manager may coordinate authorization for these services, locate and compare costs among vendors, then facilitate the initiation of these services once payer approval is received.

The case manager will likely meet with the treating physician to discuss the client's diagnosis, prognosis, and treatment plan. The ability to contact a treating physician may vary by state. An insurance company may also refer a client for an independent medical examination. The purpose may be to determine the diagnosis, need for continued medical treatment, whether a disability is partial or total, the duration of disability, whether or not the client can return to work, and when treatment appears excessive, recovery is extended, or surgery is being recommended. Usually the insurance carrier sets up this exam and the case manager is not present for the examination, although the case manager could be asked to set up the exam and accompany the client to the examination (Mullahy, 1998).

A physician may also be contacted for a second medical opinion. This option may be used to determine a diagnosis, clarify a complex medical situation, to determine alternatives to current or proposed treatment, when surgery is being proposed, when treatment is questioned, or the current treatment is not producing the expected outcomes. A case manager may arrange and will probably attend this examination with the client (Mullahy, 1998).

When the client's medical condition is stabilized, a functional capacity report that outlines the client's specific work restrictions may be requested from the treating physician, or the client may be referred for a functional capacity assessment, which evaluates the client's physical capabilities for work. This information can be used to determine what type of job the client can pursue. If clients are unable to return to work based on their current functional capacity, work hardening may be pursued. Work hardening strengthens the client's physical capabilities for work. It is best used when the client has a job to return to upon completion of work hardening. Otherwise, the process may need to be repeated when a job opening develops, unless the client continues to remain active after work hardening.

EMPLOYER CONTACTS

As indicated with the return to work hierarchy, the case manager considers returning the client to work with the same employer in the same or a different job; returning the client to work with a new employer in the same or a different job (G. T. Welch, 1979); acquiring short term retraining to facilitate a return to work with the same or a new employer, and, in some workers' compensation arenas, self-employment is pursued (Matkin, 1981, 1995). Return to work with the same employer/same job and return to work new employer/same job may follow a similar process of contacting the employer, completing a job analysis, and obtaining physician support for the job.

The former employer may be contacted either in conjunction with the initial evaluation of the client or following clarification of the client's medical status. A visit to the work site is ideal, since the client and employer's perception of the client's job may be different from that of the case manager. Visiting the job site allows for the completion of a job analysis which is a thorough examination of the physical, mental, and environmental demands of the job, the tasks involved in the job, and the essential and nonessential job functions. Once the job analysis is completed, it should be reviewed with the employer to confirm its accuracy. It can then be reviewed with the physician to gain approval for the client to pursue this job. A written release to return to work from the physician may also be required by some benefit systems. If necessary, the case manager may want to discuss with the doctor the need for accommodations at the job site. Information on accommodations can be obtained from the Job Accommodation Network, 800-526-7234 (V/TTY) or http://janweb.icdi.wvu.edu/. This website provides free consultation on job accommodations, the Americans with Disabilities Act, and employment for people with disabilities. If necessary, an occupational therapist could be consulted for accommodations.

While case managers are at the job site, they can thoroughly assess creative job possibilities for clients in the event clients cannot return to their former jobs. While on this visit, case managers will have the opportunity to learn the culture of the job site. Employers may need to be contacted occasionally during a client's medical recovery to assess whether changes have occurred at the job site that might now allow the client to return to work. Clients can also contact their former employers to state their interest in returning to work. It is beneficial to keep the client in the employer's view via an on-the-job training program, participating in a work experience program, or engaging in job shadowing (Mirch, 1997).

Return to work with the same employer is the key to labor force participation by persons who obtain a work related disability. Once this tie has been broken, the injured employee may settle into the "income transfer system"

(Tate, Habeck, & Galvin, 1986, p. 6), which may make it difficult, if not impossible, for the injured employee to return to work. Many people interpret wage replacement benefits as a financial disincentive, because not working results in a cash incentive (Eaton, 1979; Headley, 1989; Tate et al.). Helping a client return to work with a new employer is more difficult than convincing an employer to return this person to work in their former position. This process makes sense based on the cost of disability at the workplace. These costs include the loss of productivity of the client and the cost of hiring and retraining a replacement employee (Tate et al.). These costs are even higher if the client must now be retrained in order to locate alternate employment. Other non-monetary costs to the employer but direct costs to the client include loss of self-esteem, emotional and psychological distress, feelings of worthlessness, and being unable to return to one's former occupational role (Tate et al.).

To facilitate clients' return to work, clients must continue to see themselves as valued employees (Shrey & Olsheski, 1992), or a relationship between the employee and employer must be present. The workplace should be used to its fullest advantage to help the client return to work. This means using the physical, psychological, social, and environmental components of the workplace (Shrey & Olsheski).

TRANSFERABLE SKILLS ANALYSIS, LABOR MARKET SURVEY, JOB SEEKING SKILLS TRAINING

Return to work with a new employer in a new job or training before job placement may follow a similar process consisting of contacting the treating physician, completing a labor market survey, teaching job seeking skills, and then contacting employers. A transferable skills analysis is completed more frequently when pursuing job placement, while a vocational assessment is more frequently used for training (see Figure 1).

Figure 1. Return to Work With a New Employer in a New Job or Retraining

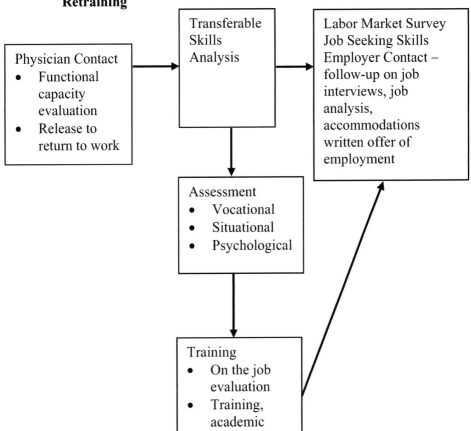

Return to work with a new employer can include using the client's same or similar skills. This may be required when the employer at the time of injury no longer has the previous job, is no longer in business, cannot accommodate the client's restrictions, or other issues prevent return to work. The procedures described in returning to work with the same employer could then be followed, which include contacting the employer, completing a job analysis, and gaining physician approval for the client's return to work.

Essential to assisting the client to return to work with a new employer in a new job is the development of a job goal. This may be accomplished by using a transferable skills analysis (TSA), which analyzes the skills a client has used in previous work to determine how the skills will transfer to a new position. Resources used to assist in this analysis include O*NET (http://online.onetcenter.org), the *O*NET Dictionary of Occupational Titles*

2001, Dictionary of Occupational Titles, and transferable skills analysis software and vendors that can be accessed online. (See Chapter 7 for further description of these resources.)

Confirmation of the viability of job goals is accomplished through a labor market survey (LMS). Direct contact is made with employers to determine the feasibility of the client's job or training goal, salary, physical or mental requirements of the job, employability, and placeability. Employability assesses whether the client has the education, skills, and work experience to perform the job. Placeability assesses whether job openings exist in that particular job market and whether the client would be hired (Rasch, 1985).

Clients may also need to be taught job search skills such as how to contact employers, complete employment applications, interview, and write a resume. It is important that clients be able to contact employers on their own behalf, so that they can always independently search for a new job. Clients who are actively involved in developing their own job goals and who have previously located and maintained employment prior to their injury or illness can actively seek placement on their own behalf, although some placement assistance may be needed. Clients with severe disabilities, such as a closed head injury, may need assistance in locating employment and with transition into the labor market. The use of a job coach may help with this transition (Mirch, 1997).

When a client interviews with an employer, the case manager follows up with the employer to learn the employer's impressions of the client. This information is then discussed with the client. If clients were not putting forth their best effort in the job interview, then the case manager would need to determine what is getting in the way of success. Once a position has been obtained, some insurance benefit systems require written documentation of a job offer and after placement may require copies of the client's pay stubs for calculation of wage differentials.

Research has shown placement and employer contacts are not given sufficient priority in rehabilitation practice (Gilbride, Stensrud, & Johnson, 1994). Gilbride and Stensrud (1993) said that success in placement of persons with disabilities would occur when we learn appropriate and cost-effective strategies to comply with the Americans with Disabilities Act. Case managers can help this process by educating employers. To do so, they need an accurate understanding of the personnel and disability management needs of employers. An understanding of job analysis, job modifications, accommodations, transferable skills analysis, accessibility evaluation, and job placement are also required skills for case managers. Employer concerns are recruiting potential employees with disabilities, building accessibility, interviewing employees with disabilities, disabilities impact on workers' compensation, affirmative action planning, and labor relations (Gilbride & Stensrud).

VOCATIONAL ASSESSMENTS

Interest and achievement tests may be administered when clients are unable to return to work with their former employer or when considering retraining. Testing may also be used when a client has no work history, no relevant work history, no transferable skills from prior employment, or when a new job is pursued. (See Chapter 7 for further description of these resources.) Vocational evaluations are used to identify a client's aptitudes, interests, and behavioral repertoire (Roessler & Baker, 1998). There are multiple reasons case managers would refer clients for vocational evaluations. These include behavioral problems, severe disabilities such as closed head injuries, troubled work histories, or difficulty interacting with others. Vocational evaluations can provide clients with a structured environment or it can be used to assess a client's stamina over a longer period of time than is available during the interaction with an administrator of a vocational test battery (Mirch, 1997).

Completing or referring a client for a vocational test battery allows the case manager to remain a neutral party when there is a conflict between the client's desire for training and the insurance carrier's desire to fund training. This method helps maintain the client-case manager relationship and the relationship with the customer. If the client does well, the payer can be approached about funding the training. If not, the client has suggestions of other vocational alternatives and does not feel "set up" for failure by the case manager or insurance carrier (Mirch, 1997).

RETRAINING

If a client cannot return to work with a former or new employer, retraining may be considered. (See Chapter 7 for further description of this resource.) Some workers' compensation programs limit the length and type of retraining available to clients. Vocational testing may be completed to help develop a retraining goal, and then a labor market survey may be completed to determine its feasibility. If retraining is pursued, the case manager will want to determine the location for training, the cost, and the length of the program. An individualized written rehabilitation plan may be developed to outline the training programs cost, length, and expectations.

SELF-EMPLOYMENT

Occasionally a client will choose to pursue self-employment. If this is the case, a referral to the Small Business Administration (SBA) office within the state is suggested for help in writing a business plan or applying for a loan. Information on the SBA can be obtained at their website http://sba.gov/. Another resource is the Service Corps of Retired Business Executives (SCORE), a group of retired businesspersons who provide free mentoring services. SCORE can be contacted at 800-634-0245 or http://www.score.org. Sometimes a self-employment plan is needed prior to the settlement of a workers' compensation claim or to aid in the negotiations.

FOLLOW-UP

Once a client has returned to work, to evaluate the success of the placement the case manager will follow-up with the client, and sometimes with the employer. Follow-up with the client should occur soon after the return to work to address any concerns the client may have regarding the return to work and the benefit system. These same issues may need to be addressed with the employer. Follow-up frequently will occur for 30–60 days after placement or self-employment. If no issues arise, the case will be closed.

FORENSIC REHABILITATION

Because of the nature of the fee-for-service relationship private sector rehabilitation case managers have with clients, they are required to testify more than public sector rehabilitation counselors (Matkin, 1995) and many other allied health professionals. Expert witness testimony may relate to workers' compensation disputes, legislation, and second injury certification. Private sector rehabilitation providers are also hired as expert witnesses to testify in medical malpractice, third party liability, wrongful discharge, personal injury, divorce, life care planning, and Social Security cases. Newer areas for vocational expert testimony include sexual harassment, injury claims from railroad workers, toxic torts, civil-criminal interface, and malpractice against mental health practitioners (Havranek, 1995, 1997). For medical malpractice and third party liability, the focus is often on loss of earning capacity. What would the person have earned had they not been injured based on their age, education, work experience, and family background? Either the vocational expert or an economist is used to project the loss of earning capacity over the lifetime of the client. Expert witnesses are used in divorce to help the attorney determine alimony payments. Does the spouse have the ability to earn a living, and what kind of wages can the spouse be expected to earn once the divorce is finalized? A life care plan (Deutsch & Sawyer, 1988) focuses on the whole person (See Chapter 9 for a sample Life Care Plan). What will be the client's future medical, psychological, educational, employment, and financial needs and what are the costs of these services? Social Security uses vocational experts to assess whether an individual's impairment prevents the person from performing past relevant work considering the person's residual functional capacity. The expert witness also assesses whether the impairment prevents the person from performing other work that exists in the national economy, in light of his or her residual functional capacity and the vocational factors of age, education, and work experience (SSA, 2000). Employability and placeability are often important areas to determine in expert witness testimony (Rasch, 1985).

Expert witnesses need knowledge and appropriate education, credentials, and work experience for the area in which they will be providing expertise. Attorneys generally make the initial contact with the case manager to determine whether they have the appropriate background to serve as an expert in the desired area and to clarify the goals of the case. If the case manager is selected the case is referred. The case manager may want to indicate the type of medical and vocational information he or she would like to review. Sometimes opinions are based only on the medical, psychological, and work records. If this is the case, the report should clearly indicate the information upon which the opinion was based (Weed & Field, 1990).

Medical and vocational records are received and a meeting with the client is held. The client must be informed of the nature of the relationship. Upon completion of the interview, the case manager decides what additional research is necessary to assist in formulating an opinion. It may include review of additional medical and/or occupational resources, completion of a transferable skills analysis, labor market survey, life care plan, wage earning capacity report, or administration of vocational testing. Upon formulation of an opinion, the expert witness discusses the opinion with the attorney who decides if the case manager will be used as a consultant with no written opinion or as an expert witness with a written report. Case managers are occasionally hired as consultants to provide insight into questioning an expert on the opposing side. Should the case go to trial, the expert witness may be required to complete a deposition or to testify in court (Weed & Field, 1990).

Expert witnesses can develop a reputation as a plaintiff or defense witness; however, providing testimony for both plaintiff and defense enhances the expert's credibility. The key to effective expert witness testimony is to provide an objective, unbiased opinion based on one's expertise in the field.

BEST PRACTICES

In Chapter 14, Chronister, da Silva Cardoso, Lee, Chan, and Leahy described the importance of evidence-based practice or using research to evaluate the effectiveness of a specific treatment approach in case management. They stated that providing evidence of effective and efficient rehabilitation services was crucial to the field's identity and survival in a managed care environment.

Studying the insights of exemplary rehabilitation counselors is one way to pursue evidence-based practice. Mullins, Roessler, Schriner, Brown, and

Bellini (1997) interviewed 11 exemplary rehabilitation counselors employed in public sector rehabilitation to gain an understanding of "What is Quality Rehabilitation Counseling (QRC), i.e., what do exemplary VR counselors do to help people with severe disabilities become employed?" (p. 21). This study discussed "best practices" as including a trusting client-counselor relationship, assessment of the client's assets and limitation, effective goal setting and planning, and intervention through educating the referral services regarding appropriate referrals and employer outreach. Rehabilitation counselors must give client's freedom of choice in their rehabilitation plan, while trying to minimize client failure. Clients also need a vision for success to help regain control of their lives. This includes information, support, and empowerment (Mullins et al.).

Chapin and Leahy (1999) defined best practices of exemplary private sector rehabilitation counselors after interviewing 20 rehabilitation counselors employed by private sector rehabilitation firms who were nominated as exemplary by peers, supervisors, and managers. They, too, defined best practice as including an effective client-counselor relationship, and providing client's with freedom of choice. The key in both studies was to provide clients with information. Chapin and Leahy discussed the importance of informing clients about their benefit system, medical status, and vocational rehabilitation. They also discussed the need for open communication among all parties involved in the client's rehabilitation to improve the case process and redefine success as focusing on impacting or touching a client's life no matter what the case outcome.

Mirch (1997) defined characteristics of effective private sector rehabilitation counselors, which would also apply to case managers. Some of these characteristics were previously described as important for best practices including a good client-case manager relationship and allowing the client to make his or her own decisions (Chapin & Leahy, 1999; Mullins et al., 1997). Other characteristics included being honest, compassionate, resilient, goal-oriented, knowledgeable, proactive, ethical, using good caseload management techniques, and having a continuous desire to learn, (Mirch).

CONCLUSION

This chapter provided a brief history of private sector rehabilitation. It reviewed the insurance systems from which private sector rehabilitation clients might receive benefits including Social Security, workers' compensation, automobile insurance, and long- and short-term disability. Additionally, it discussed the goals of private sector rehabilitation, the medical and vocational case management process, and forensic rehabilitation. Suggestions for best practices and characteristics of effective private sector case managers were provided.

REFERENCES

American Counseling Association Office of Public Policy & Information (2000, March). Briefing paper: Work Incentives Improvement Act signed into law (P.L. 106-170). Alexandria, VA: American Counseling Association.

Chan, F., Leahy, M. J., McMahon, B. T., Mirch, M., & DeVinney, D. (1999). Foundational knowledge and major practice domains of case management. *Journal of Care Management, 5*(1), 10, 14, 17-18, 26-28, 30.

Chapin, M. H., & Leahy, M. J. (1999). Factors contributing to rehabilitation counselor success in the private sector in Michigan. *Journal of Applied Rehabilitation Counseling, 30*(3), 19-28.

Chronister, J., da Silva Cardoso, E., Lee, G. K., Chan, F., & Leahy, M. J. (in press). Evidence-based practice in case management. In F. Chan, M. J. Leahy, & J. Saunders (Eds.), *Case Management for the rehabilitation professionals* . Osage Beach, MO: Aspen Professional Service.

Cocchiarella, L., & Andersson, G. B. J. (Eds.). (2001). *Guides to Evaluation of Permanent Impairment* (5th ed.). Chicago: American Medical Association.

Deutsch, P., & Sawyer, H. (1988). *Guide to Rehabilitation*. New York: Mathew Bender.

Eaton, M. W. (1979). Obstacles to the vocational rehabilitation of individuals receiving workers' compensation. *Journal of Rehabilitation, 45*(2), 59-63.

Emener, W. G., & Rubin, S. E. (1980). Rehabilitation counselor roles and functions and sources of role strain. *Journal of Applied Rehabilitation Counseling, 11*(2), 57-69.

Fraser, R. T., & Clower, M. R. (1978). Rehabilitation counselor functions: Perceptions of time spent and complexity. *Journal of Applied Rehabilitation Counseling, 11*, 31-35.

Gilbride, D. D., & Stensrud, R. (1993). Challenges and opportunities for case managers in the Americans with Disabilities Act era. *NARPPS Journal and News, 8*(2), 67-74.

Gilbride, D. D., Stensrud, R., & Johnson, M. (1994). Current models of job placement and employer development: Research, competencies and educational considerations. *Rehabilitation Education, 7*(4), 215-239.

Harrison, D. K., & Lee, C. C. (1979). Rehabilitation counseling competencies. *Journal of Applied Rehabilitation Counseling, 10*(3), 135-141.

Havranek, J. E. (1995). Historical perspectives on the rehabilitation counseling profession and disability management. In D. E. Shrey & M. Lacerte (Eds.), *Principles and practices of disability management in industry* (pp. 355-370). Winter Park, FL: GR Press.

Havranek, J. E. (1997). History of forensic rehabilitation services. In J. E. Havranek *Forensic Rehabilitation* (pp. 21–28). Athens, GA: Elliott & Fitzpatrick, Inc.

Headley, B. J. (1989). Delayed recovery: Taking another look. *Journal of Rehabilitation, 55*(3), 61-66.

Jaques, M. E. (1959). *Critical counseling behavior in rehabilitation settings.* Iowa City: State University of Iowa.

Jenkins, W. M., Patterson, J. B., & Szymanski, E. M. (1998). Philosophical, historical, and legislative aspects of the rehabilitation counseling profession. In R. M. Parker & E. M. Szymanski (Eds.), *Rehabilitation counseling basics and beyond* (3rd ed., pp. 1-40). Austin, TX: Pro-ed.

Kilbury, R., Benshoff, J., & Riggar, T. F (1990). The expansion of private sector rehabilitation: Will rehabilitation education respond? *Rehabilitation Education, 4,* 163-170.

Lambert, M. J., & Cattani-Thompson, K. (1996). Current findings regarding the effectiveness of counseling: Implications for practice. *Journal of Counseling and Development, 74*(6), 601-608.

Leahy, M., Chan, F., Taylor, D. Wood, C., & Downey, W. (1997). *Evolving knowledge and skill factors for practice in private sector rehabilitation* (Report No. 97-003). Rolling Meadows, IL: The Foundation for Rehabilitation Education and Research.

Leahy, M. J., Shapson, P. R., & Wright, G. N. (1987a). Professional rehabilitation competency research: Project methodology. *Rehabilitation Counseling Bulletin, 31*(2), 94-106.

Leahy, M. J., Shapson, P. R., & Wright, G. N. (1987b). Rehabilitation practitioner competencies by role and setting. *Rehabilitation Counseling Bulletin, 31*(2), 119-130.

Leahy, M. J., Szymanski, E. M., & Linkowski, D. C. (1993). Knowledge importance in rehabilitation counseling. *Journal of Applied Rehabilitation Counseling, 24*(4), 36-45.

Matkin, R. E. (1981). Program evaluation: Searching for accountability in private rehabilitation. *Journal of Rehabilitation, 47*(1) 65-68.

Matkin, R. E. (1983). The roles and functions of rehabilitation specialists in the private sector. *Journal of Applied Rehabilitation Counseling, 14*(1), 14-27.

Matkin, R. E. (1986). Insurance rehabilitation: Counseling the industrially injured worker. In T. F. Riggar, D. R. Maki, & A. W. Wolf (Eds.), *Applied Rehabilitation Counseling* (pp. 303-313). New York: Springer.

Matkin, R. E. (1995). Private sector rehabilitation. In S. E. Rubin & R. T. Roessler, *Foundations of the vocational rehabilitation process* (4th ed., pp. 375-398). Austin, TX: Pro-ed.

Matkin, R. E., & May, R. (1981). Potential conflicts of interest in private rehabilitation: Identification and resolution. *Journal of Applied Rehabilitation Counseling 12*(1), 15-18.

Michigan Department of Labor, Bureau of Workers' Disability Compensation (1993). *A summary of your rights and responsibilities under Workers' Disability Compensation* [Brochure]. Lansing, MI: Author.

Mirch, M. C. (1997). *A description and interpretation of the work of exemplary private rehabilitation counselors in Michigan.* Unpublished doctoral dissertation, Michigan State University, East Lansing.

Mullahy, C. M. (1998). *The case manager's handbook.* Gaithersburg, MD: Aspen Publishers, Inc.

Mullins, J., Roessler, R., Schriner, K., Brown, P., & Bellini, J. (1997). Improving employment through quality rehabilitation counseling [QRC]. *Journal of Rehabilitation, 63*(4), 21-31.

Muthard, J. E., & Salomone, P. (1969). The roles and functions of the rehabilitation counselor. *Rehabilitation Counseling Bulletin, 13*(1), 81-168.

National Commission on State Workmen's Compensation Laws. (1972). *The report of the national commission on state workmen's compensation laws.* Washington, DC: U.S. Government Printing Office.

N. C. Industrial Commission. (2002). *Rating guide.* Raleigh, NC: Author. Retrieved March 28, 2004 from http://www.comp.state.nc.us/ncic/pages/ratinggd.htm.

North Carolina Industrial Commission. (1993). *Information about the North Carolina Workers' Compensation Act.* [Bulletin]. Raleigh, NC: Author.

Novick, A. K., & Rondinelli, R. D. (2000). Impairment and disability under workers' compensation. In R. D. Rondinelli & R. T. Katz (Eds.), *Impairment Rating and Disability Evaluation* (pp. 141-156). Philadelphia: W. B. Saunders Company.

Obermann, C. E. (1965). *A history of vocational rehabilitation.* Minneapolis, MN: T. S. Denison & Company, Inc.

Office of Financial and Insurance Services. (2003, April). *Insurance Counselor: Insurance Consumer Information Sheet: Brief Explanation of Michigan No-Fault Insurance* (Publication #: 0202) [Brochure, Electronic version]. Lansing, MI: Author.

Rasch, J. D. (1985). *Rehabilitation of Workers' Compensation and Other Insurance Claimants.* Springfield, IL: Charles C. Thomas.

Roessler, R. T., & Baker, R. J. (1998). Vocational evaluation. In R. T. Roessler & S. E. Rubin, *Case management and rehabilitation counseling* (3rd ed., pp. 83-98). Austin, TX: Pro-ed.

Rogers, C. R. (1957). The necessary and sufficient conditions of therapeutic personality change. *Journal of Consulting Psychology, 21*, 95-103.

Rondinelli, R. D. (1996). Practical aspects of impairment rating and disability determination. In R. Braddom (Ed.), *Physical Medicine & Rehabilitation*. Philadelphia: W.B. Saunders Company.

Rubin, S. E., Matkin, R. E., Ashley, J., Beardsley, M. M., May, V. R., Onstott, K., & Puckett, F. D. (1984). Roles and functions of Certified Rehabilitation Counselors. *Rehabilitation Counseling Bulletin, 27*(4), 199-224.

Shrey, D. E., & Olsheski, J. A. (1992). Disability management and industry-based work return transition. *Physical Medicine and Rehabilitation, 6*(2), 303-314.

Social Security Administration. (1990, February). *Vocational Expert Handbook*. Baltimore: MD: Office of Hearings and Appeals Social Security Administration.

Social Security Administration. (2000, December 4). Policy Interpretation Ruling: SSR 00-4p: Titles II and XVI: Use of Vocational Expert and Vocational Specialist Evidence, and Other Reliable Occupational Information in Disability Decisions. Retrieved August 11, 2003 from http://www.ssa.gov/OP_Home/rulings/di/02/SSR2000-04-di-02.html

Social Security Administration. (2003a, January). *2003 Red Book: A summary guide to employment support for people with disabilities under the Social Security Disability Insurance and Supplemental Security Income programs* [Electronic version]. Retrieved August 8, 2003, from http://www.ssa.gov/work/ResourcesToolkit/redbook.html.

Social Security Administration. (2003b). *Fact Sheet: Ticket to Work and Work Incentives Improvement Act of 1999*. Retrieved August 11, 2003 from http://www.ssa.gov/work/ResourcesToolkit/legisregfact.html..

Social Security Administration. (2003c). *Social Security: Disability Benefits* (Publication #: 05-10029). [Brochure]. Author.

Social Security Administration. (2003d). *Social Security: Supplemental Security Income* (Publication #: 05-11000). [Brochure]. Author.

Social Security Administration. (2003e). *The Work Site: Ticket to Work*. Retrieved July 30, 2003 from www.ssa.gov/work/Ticket/ticket_info.html.

Social Security Administration (2004). The work site home > Resources Toolkit > Red Book. Retrieved April 3, 2004 from http://www.socialsecurity.gov/work/ResourcesToolkit/redbook_page.html.

Tate, D., Habeck, R., & Galvin, D. (1986). Disability management: Origins, concepts and principles for practice. *Journal of Applied Rehabilitation Counseling,* 17(2), 5-12.

Ticket to Work. (2003). *Employment Networks.* Retrieved June 26, 2003 from http://www.yourticketowork.com/whoen.

United States Department of Health & Human Services. (May, 2003). *OCR Privacy Brief: Summary of the HIPAA Privacy Rule.* Retrieved July 8, 2003 from www.hhs.gov/ocr/hipaa.

Weed, R. O., & Field, T. F. (1990). *Rehabilitation consultant's handbook.* Athens, GA: Elliott & Fitzpatrick, Inc.

Weed, R. O., & Field, T. F. (1994). *Rehabilitation consultant's handbook* (Revised edition 1994). Athens, GA: Elliott & Fitzpatrick, Inc.

Welch, E. M. (1994). *Employer's guide to workers' compensation.* Washington, DC: The Bureau of National Affairs, Inc.

Welch, G. T. (1979). The relationship of rehabilitation in industry. *Journal of Rehabilitation,* 45(3), 24-25.

Wright, G. N. (1980). *Total Rehabilitation.* Boston: Little, Brown and Company.

13

Workplace Disability Management: Case Management Implications

David A. Rosenthal
Norman C. Hursh
John Lui
Wolfgang Zimmermann
Steven R. Pruett

Chapter Highlights

- ☒ Historical evolution of DM

- ☒ Changing demographics and emerging practices in DM

- ☒ Evidence based disability management practice

- ☒ International trends in disability case management

- ☒ Conclusion

The growth of workplace disability management programs has resulted from recognition that employers and employees can collaborate to design and implement prevention and early return to work programs that result in reduced disability-related costs and enhanced productivity. Disability management (DM) is a remediation strategy, which is implemented in the workplace that utilizes directed prevention, as well as early intervention reflecting an employer's commitment to reduce the impact of injury and disability and to accommodate those employees who experience functional work limitations (Akabas, Gates, & Galvin, 1992; Shrey, 1995). With the growth of evidence-based practice, an increasing number of employers are reporting substantial financial savings and better vocational outcomes as the direct result of their DM programs and strategies (Habeck & Kirchener, 1999; Shutan, 2003; Watson Wyatt Worldwide, 2001).

The rising cost of health care and disability at the work place, in conjunction with a competitive business economy, provided the impetus for cost-containment strategies among large U.S. companies (Habeck, Kress, Scully, & Kirchner, 1994). Recent research indicates that the combined direct and indirect costs of disability and absence often exceed 20% of a company's payroll. This translates into more than $40 million in annual absence costs for a company employing 5,000 people at an average salary of $40,000 a year (Shutan, 2003). Claim rates and disability exposure within business and industry vary greatly, with workers' compensation claims rates showing tenfold differences and high claims firms reporting over twice the injury rates and over four times the claims rates of low claims firms (Habeck et al., 1994). Research has consistently demonstrated that the extreme variability in claim rates and disability exposure are often due to company policies and internal activities within the companies' control (Wyatt Worldwide, 2001).

The processes of preventing disability and of providing optimal strategies to maintain employee satisfaction and productivity in the occurrence of disability are highly interrelated (Hunt, Habeck, VanTol, & Scully, 1993). Proactive and coordinated integration of the prevention and post-injury/disability processes translates into significantly lower incidence of lost workday cases, reduced total lost workdays, and fewer workers' compensation claims (Hunt et al.). Within the context of disability management, the locus of all organizational directed and/or coordinated interventions is within the employee's workplace.

Disability management requires an organizational commitment—the active participation of the employer in prevention, early intervention, and return to work. These features of DM significantly contrast with third-party vendored rehabilitation services, which typically began long after the onset of disability.

Habeck (1996) referred to this traditional model of rehabilitation as the "reactive, provider-based, clinical model," describing the externally driven services approach as the "broken paradigm" for its failure to address the root causes of work disabilities that arise from internal organizational relationships, practices, and behaviors (Habeck, 1993).

A disability case manager who provides services to an injured worker within the context of the workplace must be proactive, must consider the needs or the worker and the employer, and function outside of the "clinical model." In the traditional model, case managers provided by an external, private, for-profit agency would be assigned to a case only if it had become problematic in terms of employer's expectations of the employee's return to work. Recent research indicates that case managers are "moving upstream," that is, providing prevention strategies as well as earlier interventions in the case of injury or illness. In this paradigm, medical management is moving from coordinating care to directing patient care toward resources that encourage and support return to work (Lui, 2000). Employers who provide case management to enhance both prevention and early intervention strategies within the workplace, avoid lost time, and reduce work-related disability claims.

This chapter reviews how the field of disability management is responding to rapid changes and advances in the labor market. With parallel growth, the importance of case management practices within disability management has been acknowledged and demonstrated over past decades (Crystal, 1987; Habeck et al., 1994; Hursh, 1997; 1990; Lui, 2000; Shrey & LaCerte 1995, Lipold, 2000).

THE HISTORICAL EVOLUTION OF DM

During the late 1970s and 1980s, rising disability costs became a major concern of employers; subsequently most states enacted workers' compensation reform. This reform movement targeted lowering disability-related costs, as many state legislatures sought to improve business climates. During this same period, disability insurers experienced significant and unexpected claim losses and were forced to re-examine their underwriting and contract provisions (Wood & Lui, 1999). Contemporaneously, employers began to realize that they needed to change the way they responded to workers with disabling conditions in order to reduce their workers' compensation losses. The first disability management programs appeared in late 1970s and early 1980s in companies such as Burlington Industries, AT&T, 3M Corporation, and Sears (Akabas et al., 1992). Adopting managed care strategies from the health insurance industry, large corporations began to implement managed care for work-related disabilities. These programs were developed to fulfill two goals: to demonstrate concern for employee welfare and to reduce direct and hidden costs associated with illness, injury, and disability (Habeck et al., 1994; Habeck & Hunt, 1999).

In the late 1980s and early 1990s, evidence began to accumulate that a growing number of employers were implementing disability management programs at the workplace (Breslin & Olsheski, 1996; Habeck, Leahy, Hunt, Chan, & Welch, 1991; Olsheski, 1996; Shrey, 1995; Shrey & Olsheski, 1992). As employers became better educated about the advantages of workplace DM programs, rehabilitation counselors, occupational health nurses, and other occupational health professionals discovered increasing opportunities to serve within these settings at both individual and organizational levels. Habeck (1996) found, however, that rehabilitation professionals who worked within companies placed more emphasis on services designed to affect organizational factors (e.g., return-to-work policies, job accommodations, communication among key stakeholders) than direct services to employees. Olsheski and Breslin described the role of the rehabilitation counselor in typical rehabilitation and disability management programs as one that requires a balanced focus on the functional capacities of the employee and the functional capacities of the work environment in responding to job accommodation and retention issues.

The evolving scope of practice for DM specialists has been researched extensively by the Certified Disability Management Specialist Commission (CDMSC) since 1991, when its original research on insurance rehabilitation roles and functions was first updated (Matkin, 1995). When the CDMSC surveyed practitioner roles and functions in 1991, the essential work role and function categories consisted of case management and human disabilities, job placement and vocational assessment, rehabilitation services and care, disability legislation, and forensic rehabilitation. Currier, Chan, Taylor, and Wood (1997) examined the roles and functions as well as the knowledge requirements for disability case managers, adopting Habeck's (1996) two-level concept of disability management. In their study, level I disability management is conceptualized as managerial or administrative in nature, with practitioners having limited direct contact with disabled or injured workers: intervention occurs at the organizational level and the theoretical basis of activity is "systems"-oriented. Level II disability management, on the other hand, is conceptualized as being more service-oriented, with practitioners having direct contact with the disabled or injured worker within the context of a disability management program: intervention occurs at the individual level and the theoretical basis is individual psychology. A continuum of practice complexity begins with level II disability management and ends with level I. In practice, one should expect to find disability management professionals practicing at numerous points along this continuum: while many nurses, counselors, and case managers would fall near level II, and many organizational consultants would fall near level I, some program managers responsible for managing service programs and coordinating service activities would fall somewhere in the middle. The organizational focus in level I practice makes it more business- or management-oriented, requiring analytic, design, evaluation, and organizational development knowledge and skills. The level I practitioner must possess expertise in benefit plan design, management information systems, and organizational behavior. The level II practitioner's human services orientation requires clinical rehabilitation skills and case management expertise, including job analysis and return-to-work (RTW) functions.

The distinction made by Habeck (1996) between direct service disability managers (level II) and organizational and policy development disability managers (level I), previously adopted and adapted by Currier et al. (1997), was later used by Currier, Chan, Berven, Habeck, and Taylor (2001) and Chan et al. (2001) as part of their theoretical frameworks for both the work behaviors studies and the knowledge and practice domains studies of disability managers. The Currier et al. study utilized a Delphi technique to generate a consensus among experts in the field of disability management with regard to the importance of knowledge and practice domains of the level I and level II disability managers. The Currier et al. report underscored that knowledge in the areas of disability management concepts, principles of insurance, benefit plans, medical case management, ergonomics, managed care concepts, and business practices and operations appear to be additional to the topics identified by Matkin (1992) and warrant attention in the training and credentialing of disability management specialists. The middle ground of the continuum between level I and level II involves program development, service coordination, education and training, and organizational development.

The Chan et al. (2001) study focused solely on level II disability managers to define further the knowledge and practice domains via factor analysis. According to the authors, the level II disability manager's major job functions are disability case management and the design and implementation of early return-to-work interventions. These disability managers may also perform limited vocational rehabilitation (i.e., counseling, assessment, and placement) and some middle management duties. They identified three knowledge domains as crucial for disability managers: case management techniques, psychosocial intervention skills, and vocational aspects of disability. Other knowledge domains deemed important include managed care, managed disability, and human resources. The study noted that the importance a disability manager attributed to a job function and knowledge domain was related to his or her professional background (i.e., those with a rehabilitation counseling background often ranked the vocational rehabilitation job functions higher than

334

nurses, who ranked medical case management higher). Yet the authors discovered a strong consensus that knowledge in both medical and vocational rehabilitation was highly important in the practice of level II disability management, which suggests the need for cross training.

Most recently, the CDMSC has undertaken another role and function study. Preliminary results of this research indicate that DM practice entails three primary knowledge domains: disability case management; disability prevention and workplace intervention; and program development, management and evaluation (CDMSC, 2003). To initiate this research, the CDMSC identified 12 experts in the field of DM and requested that they participate in a three-day exploratory fact-finding meeting to ascertain the current status of DM practice. The team, consisting of educators, employers, practitioners, and administrators, formulated a consensus-based model of current practice identifying the three primary domains. Table I depicts the three domains and the critical tasks identified for each.

The preliminary findings from the CDMSC study in progress indicate support for the contention that DM practice does exist on two primary levels. The first two domains seen in Table I essentially support the previous descriptions of the level II DM practice, while domain 3 supports the descriptions of level I DM practice. Subject matter experts involved in the CDMSC study emphasized that the domains are not discrete, mutually exclusive categories but rather exist on a continuum of service and work activity. The experts also maintained that the first two domains are foundational to the conduct of DM practice at the third (organizational) domain. The research also indicates that case managers involved in disability management programs are increasing their involvement in prevention as well as providing services at organizational levels.

Table I
CDMSC FINDINGS—THREE PRINCIPAL DISABILITY MANAGEMENT DOMAINS AND THEIR CRITICAL TASKS

Disability Case Management	Disability Prevention and Workplace Intervention	Program Development, Management and Evaluation
Perform comprehensive individual case analysis and benefits assessment using accepted practices in order to develop appropriate interventions.	Implement disability prevention practices (i.e., risk mitigation procedures such as job analysis, job accommodation, ergonomic evaluation, health and wellness initiatives, etc.) through training, education, and collaboration in order to change organizational behavior and integrate prevention as an essential component of organizational culture.	Analyze workplace practices (e.g., benefit design; policies and procedures; regulatory and compliance requirements; employee demographics; and labor relations) using a needs assessment to establish baselines and design effective interventions.

Review disability case management intervention protocol using standards of care in order to promote quality care, recovery, and cost effectiveness.	Develop a comprehensive transitional work program through consultation with all relevant stakeholders in order to facilitate optimal productivity and value in the workplace.	Present the business rationale for a comprehensive disability management program using baseline data, best practices, evidence-based research, and benchmarks and cultural and environmental factors to secure stakeholder investment and commitment
Promote collaboration among stakeholders using effective communication strategies to optimize functional recovery.	Develop an interactive process for job site modification, accommodation, or job task assignment, incorporating appropriate resources (e.g., ergonomics and assistive technologies) in order to facilitate optimal functioning in the workplace.	Collaboratively develop and manage the disability management program by specifying essential procedures and training components consistent with pertinent regulations and identifying appropriate services and metrics in order to offer effective services for stakeholders.

(table continues)

Table I (Continued)

Perform worksite/job analyses using observation, interview, and records review in order to determine the requirements of the job.	Support employment practices that align work abilities with essential job functions by serving as a resource for employees and management in order to prevent disabilities and optimize productivity.	Champion individual and organizational behavioral change by assigning responsibility to stakeholders at all levels of the organization in order to achieve strategic outcomes.
Develop individualized return-to-work plans consistent with standard practices and procedures by collaborating with relevant stakeholders in order to facilitate employment.	Recommend strategies to identify ergonomic, safety, and risk factors using available resources (e.g., data and assessment tools) in order to mitigate exposure and improve employee health.	Procure internal and external services using commonly accepted selection criteria to maximize consistency and desired program outcomes.
Implement interventions using appropriate counseling and behavior change techniques in order to optimize functioning and productivity.	Recommend strategies that integrate benefit plan designs and related services (e.g., employee assistance programs, community resources, and medical services) by evaluating and coordinating delivery in order to promote prevention, optimal productivity, quality care, and cost containment.	Manage service providers using stakeholder-defined performance standards in order to maximize the quality of services and the return on investments.

Coordinate benefits, services, and community resources (e.g., orthotics, prosthetics, FCE, IME, durable medical, home care, and vocational rehabilitation) through strategic planning in order to facilitate optimal functioning.	Recommend health and wellness interventions by targeting the specific needs of employees and the organization in order to increase organizational health and productivity while demonstrating measurable value.	Facilitate the exchange of data and metrics by integrating information systems for disability management programs in order to achieve and report desired program outcomes.
Monitor progress for achievement of targeted milestones through ongoing comparison with established best-practice guidelines in order to make recommendations, optimize functional recovery, and provide needed follow up.		Conduct ongoing formative and summative program evaluations using qualitative and quantitative methods to improve process and measure outcomes.
Manage caseload using ethical strategies in order to enhance effectiveness and efficiency.		Create disability management performance reports and other communication vehicles targeted to relevant stakeholders using a variety of media in order to promote stakeholder awareness and collaboration.
Prepare case notes and reports using applicable forms and systems in order to document case activities in compliance with standard practices and regulations.		

CORE COMPETENCIES: DM PRACTICE PREPARATION AND SKILL DEFICIENCIES

Akabas et al. (1992) described case management within DM as an essential element in dealing effectively with workplace disability. Case management services have repeatedly been identified as an integral component of DM in all DM role and function studies to date (CDMSC, 2003). Competence and experience in case management activities have evolved as central issues in the training of DM practitioners, largely in response to the knowledge and skill deficiencies among traditional rehabilitation professionals. In general, rehabilitation nurses and occupational health nurses possess adequate medical knowledge and skills but often lack understanding of the interaction between disability and work. On the other hand, rehabilitation counselors and rehabilitation psychologists often possess an adequate understanding of disability and work but have limited knowledge specific to medical problems (Rosenthal & Olsheski, 1999).

Research indicates that formal preparation for much of the disability case management skill set is lacking. Haw (1996), for instance, conducted a national survey of nursing programs regarding coursework in case management and found that very little formal preparation was available: only 4% of undergraduate programs had one course in case management. Chan, McMahon, Shaw, Taylor, and Wood (1997) used an adapted version of the same survey with masters-level rehabilitation counseling programs and found that only 20% of graduate programs had one or more courses in case management. The same research found that required clinical experience in case management was similarly limited. While the Council on Rehabilitation Education (CORE) provides for case management content in rehabilitation counselor education curricula, the authors assert that rehabilitation case management is related to, but not equivalent to, case management expertise in disability management.

In a study conducted by Habeck et al. (1994), some support was found for a natural fit between the background and skills of rehabilitation counselors and disability management work practice. Employers within such environments, however, noted that rehabilitation counselors had necessary but insufficient knowledge and skills to work effectively with disability management programs and employers. Rehabilitation counseling practitioners entering disability management also expressed frustration with inadequate levels of pre-service training to meet work demands.

Shrey (1992) noted that traditional rehabilitation counseling paradigms tend to overemphasize the characteristics of the individual injured worker while ignoring the significance of environmental factors. Traditional rehabilitation paradigms have focused upon reactive, provider-based clinical models. Rehabilitation counselors entering into disability management must have the skills to develop active partnerships with employers to enhance the employment status of injured workers while advocating for interventions that occur at the workplace. They must also be able to conduct ergonomics and disability prevention programs, including workplace safety programs and EAPs. Training in such components would focus upon comprehensive case management; emphasizing return to work, the importance of early intervention, and the concept of functional restoration.

Very few academic programs in the U.S. provide comprehensive DM curricula. Only a few CORE accredited master's degree programs provide an emphasis in disability management. CORE accredited master's degree programs have traditionally trained students to provide counseling and support to individuals with disabilities using private non-profit and public vocational rehabilitation systems as models. Concepts fundamental to disability management have not been emphasized within these models.

As new practice challenges emerge, expanded roles and responsibilities are being defined for DM professionals. This expanding scope of practice has been documented in research performed by the Certified Disability Management Specialist Commission (CDMSC) and incorporated into the work experience requirements and exam specifications for CDMS certification. Emphases on prevention have brought job analysis, reasonable accommodation, and ergonomics into the mainstream practice. Early intervention has focused attention on medical case management, necessitating knowledge of high quality medical care with an occupational health focus. As DM practice continues to evolve at organizational levels, increased attention to systems, work organization, and management structure have become increasingly important (Calkins, Lui, & Wood, 2000).

To summarize, formal preparation for clinical DM activity is quite limited (Calkins et al., 2000), and much of the knowledge and skill base is developed through on-the-job training. As DM becomes further defined and operationalized, it is expected that specialized academic curricula will follow. In addition, as disability case managers interact with more complex and varied injuries and disabilities, and employers seek justification for disability management program support, it is particularly important to move towards evidence-based DM education approaches that develop case management decision making skills to achieve optimal DM outcomes (Hursh, 2002).

CHANGING DEMOGRAPHICS AND
EMERGING PRACTICES IN DM

CHANGING DEMOGRAPHICS

Major demographic changes within the U. S., including an aging population, a lack of trained workers, and an increased number of citizens on private and public disability rolls, forecast a diminishing workforce. Current demographic data indicate that life expectancy is rapidly rising as birth rates decline, leading to fewer workers available to replace the growing number workers (Douglas, 2000). This increase results from a variety of factors including the maturation of the baby boomer population, the population living longer and relatively healthier, and the decreasing number of births since 1964. The growth rate of the labor force over the next 50 years is expected to be steady but slower than in the past 50 years. From 1950 to 2000, the labor force grew from 62 million to 141 million workers, an annual growth rate of 1.6 percent per year. By 2050, it is projected that the labor force will grow to 192 million, representing a growth rate of only 0.6 percent per year (Hursh, 2003).

Highlighting the dramatic demographic changes facing the U.S. workforce, Hursh (2003) provides the following projections:

- The number of older workers in the labor force will increase substantially over the next two decades. While there were 18.4 million workers over age 55 in 2000, older workers in the work force will number 31.9 million by 2015 (U.S. General Accounting Office, 2001).
- Older workers maintain the highest growth rate when compared to other segments of the labor force. In 2000, workers over 55 represented 13 percent of the labor force. The proportion of older workers is expected to increase to 20 percent of the total labor force by 2020 (Purcell, 2000). This has significant implications for the economy, as there are fewer younger workers entering the work force to replace positions left vacant by retiring workers.
- Not only are there increases in the number of older workers and in the proportion of older workers in the labor force, there is also an increase in the labor force participation rate by older workers. In 2000, 30 percent of the older population was in the labor force. It is projected that by 2015, the labor force participation rate of individuals over 55 will increase to 37 percent (Purcell, 2000). (Cited from Hursh, 2003, p.4)

Today, older workers in the U.S. are staying on the job longer (Rix, 2002), often needing health insurance coverage for themselves and their spouses as well as additional finances to support a desired lifestyle (possibly due to

342

unexpectedly poor returns on investments intended for retirement). To meet the needs of older workers, holistic approaches to both work and life planning must be taken into consideration. For such approaches to be effective, older workers should be viewed as a heterogeneous group with differing health, financial, and career needs. Although an older workforce may demonstrate the statistical realities of longer healing periods for illnesses or injuries, the focus should be on the planning for individuals, and not based on group data and statistics (Hursh, 2003; Hursh & Shrey, 1994). It is important to recognize that older workers contribute significantly to the work force. Many are loyal, skilled, careful workers who experience fewer work-related injuries than their younger counterparts. They have fewer family problems and often want to remain in the work force much longer than their predecessors who retired from age 60 to 65 (Douglas, 2000).

Another difficulty facing the American workforce is the increasingly unmet demand for high-tech workers. High-tech companies are often unable to hire an adequate number of skilled and well-trained employees and have been advocating for hiring more foreign workers. In reaction to critical employer needs, in the fall of 2000, the U.S. Congress passed a law allowing U.S. companies to request 195,000 H-1B visas for the 2001 fiscal year. The law specifically targeted allowing more highly trained high-tech workers from other countries into the US workforce. Even though 2001 saw an economic downturn, thousands of companies requested H-1B visa applications. Economic and hiring trends indicate that the high-tech industries will continue to have a great demand for highly skilled workers regardless of the general state of the economy (Lui, 2000).

Recent census data indicate that African Americans, Hispanic Americans, and Asian Americans presently comprise approximately 33% of the U. S. population, and the U.S. Census Bureau has announced that by the year 2010, European Americans seem certain to be a distinct numerical minority (U.S. Department of Labor, 2000). The workplace will likely become increasingly diverse, and cultural sensitivity within the workplace will become correspondingly important. Future research should investigate both how employees of non-European ethnicities are included in DM processes and services and whether such employees see outcomes comparable to their European American counterparts. Inequitable patterns of DM and rehabilitation services that fail to meet the needs of these employees would suggest that ethnically non-European employees were being limited in productivity and opportunity for advancement.

OUTCOME ORIENTATION

The competitive business economy coupled with rising costs associated with disability and illness in the workplace, have provided the impetus for companies to demonstrate accountability and improve the accuracy of their outcomes measurement. The benefits of disability and absence management are well known by most employers. Although practices such as facilitating early return-to-work, offering employee health and wellness programs, injury prevention and other programs to keep employees on the job and productive are known to be cost savers, most companies lack the tools to effectively measure and evaluate the impact of their disability and absence management programs and to benchmark their performance to other stakeholders. Employers, however, are finding new ways to demonstrate accountability and measure outcomes. A progressive example of increased efficiency and accuracy in outcomes measurement is the use of measures developed by "Employer Measures of Productivity, Absence, and Quality" (EMPAQ). The Washington Business Group on Health (WBGH), under the direction of its Council on Employee Health and Productivity (CEHP), is currently undertaking a multiyear effort to develop and deliver standardized "health related lost-time measures," branded as EMPAQ–Employer Measures of Productivity, Absence, and Quality. These industry-wide, consensus-based standardized measures will enhance an employer's ability to evaluate the performance of its disability and absence management programs and to purchase services more effectively. For providers of these services, particularly disability managers, these standardized measures will provide a better means to evaluate their efforts and to deliver services more effectively and assess their overall effectiveness (Stevens, 2003).

The multiyear EMPAQ project is expected to continue through 2005, with goals that include comparative and predictive analyses; specialized studies to include historical, impact, and outcome analyses; and ease of access to data for industry benchmarking through a WBGH's partnership with the Integrated Benefits Institute (IBI). This project will establish and implement a system of standardized measures. With industry-wide support for this project, a collaborative environment has been created. This will lead to a system of setting meaningful goals, establishing measurement criteria, and evaluating outcomes that will capture the overall benefits of disability management. EMPAQ standardized measures will provide professionals the means to benchmark their own practices and improve their competencies (Stevens, 2003).

PREVENTION

Once a case manager is involved in an injured or ill worker's individual case, the specific aspects of the role of case management functions in DM are very

344

similar to other applications (Akabas et al., 1992). The broader case management roles emerging in DM practice do not stay within traditional boundaries of individualized case management (Habeck & Kirchener, 1999). Case managers within DM are increasing their exposure to prevention strategies that were once only addressed by safety, risk management, or human resources personnel. The case managers within DM programs work closely with occupational health teams consisting of professionals from areas such as ergonomics, safety, risk management, and employee assistance. DM employs worksite-based prevention and wellness options for employees that address health and productivity issues. DM professionals communicate and cooperate with other occupational service professionals to serve employees and employers better in order to achieve the overall goal of reduced absences and enhanced productivity.

To optimize communication and cooperation across these disciplines (and sometimes across corporate silos), professionals must acknowledge that, while their approaches and areas of expertise may differ, they are all dedicated to helping employees return to work, remain at work, and work productively (Brunelle & Lui, 2003). There are, of course, clear distinctions in different fields of practice that must be understood and appreciated. For example, the focus of the disability manager lies on providing medical case management, job analysis, job accommodation, and other vocational and rehabilitative services to ill or injured employees; through job accommodation, an employee may be eased back into the workplace with modified duties or through transitional work as part of the company's early-return-to-work program. On the other hand, the primary focus for employee assistance professionals may be to identify and resolve physical or mental health, marital, family, addiction, or emotional issues that affect a worker's job performance (Brunelle & Lui).

Job analysis and concomitant job accommodation, job modification, and ergonomics are integral aspects of prevention. A return to the tried and true trait-factor roots of vocational rehabilitation can provide better employee-job matches. Job analyses are critical to this process. A job analysis should detail the essential and nonessential job tasks in accordance with the Americans with Disabilities Act (ADA) as well as provide insight into how an employee's medical restrictions may interact with the physical demands of a given job. When a physician indicates that an injured worker is able to return to work with modifications to selected job tasks, the vocational case manager may effectively serve as a consultant to attending physicians, employers, supervisors, employees and their families by clarifying essential tasks, identifying possible job modifications, and assuring compliance with ADA regulations. To ensure a successful return to work by the client, the vocational case manager should provide follow up services as needed.

One growing area of importance for enhancing worker productivity, helping workers remain at work, and assisting return-to-work efforts is in the use of assistive technology to supplement workers' abilities to perform certain functions. Assistive technology includes devices and software that enhance voice output, auditory capabilities, and vision. Ergonomic equipment that can optimize productivity and prevent or minimize workplace injuries is also considered assistive technology. This technology can be deployed to help workers who face age-related medical conditions, illnesses, or injuries, as well as those who become ill or injured and need accommodation. Employers must take care, however, to ensure that the technology actually assists the worker. Workers must be trained to use assistive technology in ways suited to their learning needs (as is true for any technology training). Otherwise, the assistive technology may become an obstacle to productivity or wellness. By working with a disability manager, companies can introduce the use of assistive technology as part of a comprehensive job-accommodation plan.

Lastly, Employee Assistance Programs (EAPs) are commonly used, employer-sponsored, programs available to employees that can address a wide variety of employee need and concerns. EAPs are typically free of charge to employees and confidential, and put employees directly in touch with trained counselors, social workers or other professionals. EAP programs also provide referrals to subject matter experts, such as attorneys or childcare or eldercare resources. One of the most commonly requested resource from EAPs is legal services for estate planning, family law, divorce, real estate, bankruptcy, or other non-workplace issues, accounting for some 60 to 70 percent of all referrals (Stevens, 2003). EAPs may also reach out to employees who are dealing with stress, anxiety, or depression due to these home/personal life concerns. The potential savings for employers goes beyond reaping more productivity from employees who are focused on their jobs and not distracted by other issues. Effective use of EAP or work/life programs can also reduce consumption of more costly medical benefits (Stevens, 2003).

RESPONSE

Timely and effective response to workplace injury or illness is critical to the provision of DM. Referral of a client for vocational case management services should occur as soon as possible after absence from work for an industrial injury. Too frequently, it does not occur until the claimant has recovered and is yet unable to return to work. With catastrophic injuries, referral must occur immediately. The referral should also be expedited in the event of an injury that clearly has the potential to limit the injured worker's return to his or her customary duties. The claims person or medical case manager monitors lost time and provision of medical services during the initial phase of the vocational case management process. The monitoring may occur within the employment setting (in-house), through the insurance carrier, or through a third-party administrator who handles claims for self-insured employers. Upon receipt of a referral, case managers respond in writing to the referral source to indicate receipt of the case and provide preliminary service recommendations. The case file is then reviewed to help the case manager understand the client's current medical and vocational status and to assess what additional information is needed to maximize medical improvement and a return to work.

TRANSITIONAL WORK RETURN PROGRAMS

Transitional work programs (TWPs) are an integral component of workplace disability management programs. Formal TWP programs have demonstrated impressive results in reducing the amount of time a worker is out of work due to injury, and in maintaining employment post-injury (Habeck & Hunt, 1999). By definition, transitional work involves any combination of purposeful and productive job duties, tasks, functions, and therapeutic activities that a worker with functional restrictions can perform safely and without the risk of injury to self or other workers (Shrey, 2000). Rather than receiving physical therapy at a clinic or occupational health center removed from the workplace, the worker is involved in meaningful work at the worksite that involves physical reconditioning, modified work, and accommodations or assistive technology. The worker is able to maintain his or her interactions with co-workers and supervisors, maintain his or her identity as a worker rather than as a worker out on disability, and is active in developing the program. The transitional program has a time-specific period where the worker is carefully monitored and work activities are progressively increased, resulting in a safe return to full time work.

The disability management coordinator is involved in developing and implementing the TWP and engages in several key activities:

- Initiates early contact with the injured worker to explain the program, discuss the type of work involved, review the benefits, answer any questions, and develop the preliminary program activity;
- Analyzes available job duties and physical demands consistent with the worker's residual abilities;
- Arranges for an objective worker functional evaluation, if needed;
- Reviews the TWP program with the medical staff or primary care physician and worker, including transitional work assignments, physical demands of work activities identified, any restrictions, on-site clinical supervision, time frames of the program, safety precautions, and expectations for full return to work;

347

- Collaborates with the treating physician in discussing with the worker how the TWP involves safe work activities and minimizes potential for reinjury;
- Discusses modified work duties with the work supervisor;
- Monitors the worker's progress with the on-site clinical supervisor during the structured period of transitional work and keeps medical staff informed of the worker's progress or any changes in work assignments;
- Arranges for realistic accommodations, assistive aids, or modified work if needed, to promote increased function and productivity;
- Communicates with all stakeholders about the worker's progress, any changes in the plan, and expected time frames.

The success of transitional work programs is largely dependent on effective communication and timely response on the part of the disability case coordinator to any questions or issues that develop. If communication is fragmented, or if response to a worker's or supervisor's concern is inconsistent, the credibility of the program can be diminished.

Post TWP Planning. Disability case management with the worker does not end after successful completion of a transitional work program and return to fulltime work. Attention to the worker's performance, productivity, and adjustment after return to work is essential if the goal of job retention and sustained employment is to be achieved. If the needs of the injured worker are not attended to after return to work, inadequate adjustment to the injury may result in poor productivity, employment instability, or job loss. Butler, Johnson, and Baldwin (1995) found that medical and disability management programs could be effective in returning workers to work after an injury, but that 60 percent of those who returned to work had one or more injury related absences, all too often resulting in eventual job loss.

FACILITATING ADJUSTMENT AND COPING

One CM area that remains applicable in the DM arena is attention to psychosocial issues at organizational and individual levels. Negative reactions to disability and job loss or work disruption have been identified as major cost drivers for employees and insurers (Habeck & Kirchener, 1999). Case managers in DM must assess and address (if necessary) individuals' adjustment to new circumstances (such as the onset of a disability or illness) and work within traditional roles of familial involvement, community resource and integration, and individualized psychosocial counseling. Psychosocial interventions applied to persons with illness, disabilities, or work-related injuries must seek to provide them and their families the necessary emotional,

348

cognitive, and behavioral support, as well as the adaptive coping skills to return to work and productivity as optimally as possible (Livneh & Antonak, 1999).

Olsheski, Rosenthal, & Hamilton (2002) emphasized the importance of attention to psychosocial factors to help employers control costs related to mental health disabilities and protect an individual's employability. The authors suggested that traditional DM paradigms can be broadened to include employees who have impaired mental capacities that compromise their abilities to meet the mental, psychological, or social demands of a given job, and that employers may find that, with some adaptations, the use of TWPs may be as effective in the accommodation and job retention of employees with psychiatric disabilities as it has been for those with physical impairments. They caution that, due to the stigma associated with mental illness, functions such as job coaching may have to be more discreet in order to protect the confidentiality of the employee. Effective integration of disability management and psychosocial rehabilitation requires policies and procedures that define the relationship between vocational case management functions and the mental health care functions that are often provided separately. Employment assistance program (EAP) and mental health providers have, traditionally, not been involved in RTW processes, and they may be unfamiliar with the vocational objectives, operations, and services of DM programs. Olsheski et al. concluded that by integrating mental health service delivery and DM programs at the policy level, employers can ensure that medical and vocational case managers and mental health service providers work together to coordinate appropriate job accommodations and a timely return to work for employees.

INTEGRATED DISABILITY MANAGEMENT

The successful application of DM principles and practices in the workers' compensation arena made it inevitable that managed care would also seek applications in the larger group health arena to help lower costs and to expand such techniques into the workers' compensation system (Daiker, 1995; Lui, 1993; Tabak, 1995). As a result, a growing number of large employers became interested not only in utilizing proven DM techniques but also in integrating all disability related benefit programs, including worker compensation, group health, and short- and long-term disability. Motivated by the pursuit of efficiency at all levels, these employers became concerned about duplications in benefit costs, administrative expenses, and cost shifting among these heretofore uncoordinated lines of insurance coverage. The natural result was the Integrated Disability Management (IDM) program, sometimes referred to as the *24-hour* model. This term indicates that regardless of the etiology or time of occurrence of the health problem (home or worksite, weekend or workday), health care and return-to-work services are provided in a consistent and coordinated manner.

IDM is regarded as a logical approach to dealing with disabilities without concern for their origin (occupational or non-occupational), and focusing on early and prompt intervention and appropriate medical and rehabilitation care. IDM has been defined as a single management system for occupational (workers' compensation) and non-occupational (short-term and long-term) disability (Douglas, 2000). Watson Wyatt Worldwide and WBGH (2000/2001), defined IDM as the coordination of occupational and non-occupational disability programs and other related programs such as group health plans, health promotion programs, and EAPs to reduce total costs and improve the overall health of the workforce. The report also emphasized that true integration encompasses illness and injury management and return-to-work (RTW) programs for all causes of disability.

Many employers and insurers claim to have fully integrated benefit systems and DM programs; however, the definitions, interpretations, and applications of IDM vary widely. For one employer, IDM may refer to improved convenience for payers, employers, or vendors of rehabilitation services, while for another employer the term may refer to centralized purchasing or administration of benefit plans. Upon closer scrutiny, one finds that many employers have some, but not all, of the components of a fully integrated benefits system.

While definitions are not universal, all address the wide range of benefit plans offered to employees. These benefits generally include group health, workers' compensation (WC), short-term disability (STD), long-term disability (LTD), employee assistance program (EAP), and other wage replacement programs. The focus of IDM is upon incorporating the full range of benefits, consolidating operation processes, or doing both. The key reasons for integration are clear: reduction of disability costs and improvement of productivity. From a service delivery standpoint, this translates to a philosophy that disability, regardless of causation (work-related or non-work-related; occupational or non-occupational) requires early management and appropriate intervention. The objective is to maximize quality of life for employees with serious health conditions while concurrently optimizing productivity for both employers and employees. According to the Fourth Annual Survey by Watson Wyatt Worldwide and WBGH (1999/2000), the IDM program elements consistently rated as the most effective means of controlling disability costs are:

- common case management;
- aggressive return-to-work policies or practices;
- responsible, internal, and active management of disability issues; and identifiable, simple, and coordinated points for intake and claims reporting.

INTEGRATED DISABILITY MANAGEMENT AND ABSENCE MANAGEMENT: NEW ROLES AND FUNCTIONS

Many employers have moved beyond integration-of-benefits issues, turning their focus to overall productivity and enhanced employee value. This has led management to pay attention to all forms of work interruptions and incidental absence programs such as sick pay, unauthorized time off, and absences allowed by the Family and Medical Leave (FMLA) (Chajewski, Parry, & Molmen, 1999). This new movement, referred to as *absence management*, is defined as the process of monitoring and controlling the use of unscheduled paid time off and of the Family and Medical Leave Act. Early identification of the reasons for absence from work enables appropriate and immediate intervention, which in turn reduces the risks of disability and other forms of work interruptions. "Disability prevention is the primary goal of absence management" (Douglas, 2000, p. 201).

The Benefits Institute (IBI) surveyed employers of various sizes regarding the structure and delivery of benefits programs. The effective response was small (7%), but still the respondent group included 11,854 employers. Results indicated a strong interest (45% of respondents) in improving the integration of workers' compensation, group health, non-occupational disability, and absence programs. The preferred approach involves integrating benefit programs with a centralized service, so that whenever an employee is absent, he or she calls one centralized area where his absenteeism is evaluated and an appropriate plan is made for his return to work (Chajewski, Parry, & Molmen, 1999). A global level of management analysis encompassing the whole phenomenon of absence facilitates even greater integration of all management strategies.

Even as employers are attending more to disability-related issues, these threats to productivity and reduction of lost time pale in comparison to that brought about by the aging workforce and the shortage of new labor market entrants (Watson Wyatt Worldwide and WBGH, 1999/2000). These issues are extremely concerning to employers because they have an immediate and absolute effect on the employers' competitive position in the marketplace. This is especially true in a global marketplace in which competitors may operate in countries with minimal regulation, lower management costs, and reduced labor expenses.

To maintain a competitive edge in the marketplace, the number of employers experimenting with some form of IDM, Absence Management program, or both, continues to expand. The two top reasons are the overall cost savings in benefits and the enhanced productivity that results (Chajewski et al., 1999). Employers experience much better control of their benefit costs, both medical and disability, within an integrated service model. Concurrently, their lost days are minimized, thereby controlling the indirect costs of lost time, which in turn translates to improved productivity. This leads to improved employee health and safety and, therefore, to improved morale. Administrative efficiency, lowered administrative costs and premiums, and reduced complexity are also realized. Integration also results in standardized data across all benefit systems, allowing for better tracking and comparison of key information to gauge performance. In the aggregate, these positive developments can improve profits, lead to a commanding position in the marketplace, and grow employer-based IDM and Absence Management programs. It is reasonable to expect that routine employer practices increasingly will include the 24-hour model in medical coverage along with team approaches in managing health-related problems, whether they are occupationally and non-occupationally induced.

ABSENCE MANAGEMENT IMPLEMENTATION

A primary impetus for the development of absence management programs is the correlation that exists between employee absence, turnover, and productivity (Cotter & Williams, 1997; Lipold, 2000; Ritter, 2000). Both Ritter and Lipold have defined absence management programs as the merging of IDM with non-occupational absence programs. This includes the management of workers' compensation, short-term disability (STD), long-term disability (LTD), group health insurance, Family and Medical Leave Act (FMLA) administration, employee vacation and sick time, military and educational leave, jury duty, and other reasons for work absence (Lewis, 2000; Lipold). Absence management is built on the conceptual framework of an integrated disability management model, yet has a broader range than merely integrating services and, thereby, a greater emphasis on productivity and information management on the corporate level (Lewis). In summary, the purpose of absence management is to attempt to prevent absences before they occur and manage them when the do occur (Ritter). Components of absence management programs include a RTW program, Medical Case Management, Disease Management, Health and Wellness programs, Safety and Accident prevention, and Employee Assistance Programs (EAPs) (Ritter).

Ritter (2000) suggested to employers implementing an absence management program that they take each of the following steps:

- Formulate a leave of absence policy delineating how long an employee will be absent by category (severe health condition, pregnancy, death in the family, adoption, military duty etc.).
- Create a same-job protection policy for work–related and non-work–related disabilities (including pregnancy).
- Generate specifications on how an employee's salary will be replaced while he or she is on leave.

- Ascertain how long an employee on leave will be treated as an active employee.
- Explain what happens if an employee discontinues health insurance or other benefits while on leave.
- Specify when COBRA health continuation coverage will be offered to employees on leave.
- Explain whether an employee's work will be reassigned while he or she is on leave.
- Adopt a leave policy, consistent with the workers' compensation law, which encourages employees to return to work.
- Make revisions to the employee handbook that include general information about employee rights and responsibilities under FMLA, workers' compensation and similar laws, and leave policies.

As employers gain awareness of the benefits of true integration, many have provided compelling testimony to the cost savings and effectiveness of IDM and Absence Management. The following are influential professionals' responses to IDM and Absence Management (Shutan, 2003).

PRESENTEEISM

Innovative and progressive companies are recognizing and addressing presenteeism, a new productivity equation that addresses the loss in productivity that occurs when workers are on the job, but not performing at their best or full capability. DM and Absence Management models have traditionally focused on work absences. In a presenteeism model, the focus shifts from the absence to the employee who is *present* but not performing at his/her best due to any number of outside factors including (but not limited to) chronic or episodic illness, distraction from family care needs, personal problems, or other concerns (Stevens, 2003).

Historically, the focus of DM programs have moved from primarily attending to long-term disability or catastrophic industry and worker's compensation cases to short-term disability and then the shorter absences of one- or two-days. Presenteeism is the next step on the continuum as companies continue to seek ways to reduce costs, improve productivity, and promote employee health and wellness. For employers striving to maximize their investment in human capital, addressing presenteeism and its impact on the workplace is the next frontier. Data indicates that presenteeism has a major impact on a company's bottom line, and is potentially more costly than incidents of absenteeism (Stevens, 2003).

Chronic health conditions such as diabetes, asthma, depression, pain disorders, and allergies can have a major presenteeism impact. To combat this

353

problem, several major companies have gathered and analyzed data from employees using health and productivity surveys. These survey tools include the *Health Productivity Questionnaire* (HPQ) developed by Harvard Medical School and the World Health Organization, and the *Work Limitation Questionnaire* (WLQ) developed by a team at the Health Institute, Division of Clinical Research at Tufts-New England Medical Center. Using the WLQ, researchers investigated employee health problems and health risks in relation to productivity. The findings were compelling: Of the 1,864 employees in large company who participated in the survey, 8.6 percent reported they experienced a pain disorder that impacted productivity. While this was below the national average of 13 percent, the pain disorders experienced by the employees cost an estimated $500,000 in lost productivity and an aggregate 1,600 in lost days per year. Obesity, at seven percent prevalence among the employees, cost an estimated $750,000. Allergies, with 38.5 percent prevalence at the time the survey was taken (April, 2003), resulted in an average of four days loss per year per employee and total productivity losses of $1,000,000 across the 1,864 workers (Stevens, 2003).

Employee issues ranging from taking care of aging parents and/or childcare, to financial troubles, addiction, or family problems can also impact the psychosocial well being of employees, thus, impacting employee productivity. Presenteeism issues may also arise due to negative perceptions in the work environment, including conflict with supervisors or colleagues or the perception of unfairness in the workplace. Many employers believe that helping employees to address these types of issues will pay off in productivity. Presenteeism requires a multi-faceted and integrated approach. If the identified problem is due to illness or injury, case managers or disability management specialists and occupational health professionals can work with the employee toward a solution. This may entail ergonomic analysis and workstation or job duty modification. In the case of chronic medical conditions, disease management techniques and employee wellness programs may be beneficial. If the problem is personal or emotional, workers can utilize employers' Employee Assistance Programs for referrals and/or counseling (Stevens, 2003).

LABOR RELATIONS
While not evident in the absence management literature, the role of organized labor must not be overlooked. As with the integration of disability benefits, any significant change in the handling of benefits should have the cooperation and support of the labor force (Bruyère & Shrey, 1991). The development of management of non-medical absences by the company most likely would be addressed in a collective bargaining agreement with a unionized labor force.

It is evident that aside from merely integrating benefits, a company must effectively communicate all these changes to all their employees and train supervisory and management personnel on the implementation of the program. While central to absence management, the duties and role of the case manager must be supported by all levels in the company.

EVIDENCE-BASED DISABILITY MANAGEMENT PRACTICE

Disability case managers are increasingly involved with more complex injuries, disabilities, and illnesses. Questions about interpreting medical and functional diagnostic information, identifying effective RTW interventions, estimating the prognosis for individual workers, or evaluating the effectiveness of a device or preventive intervention confront disability case managers daily. With increasing health care costs and shrinking profit margins, cost-conscious employers who are interested in the bottom line ask hard questions about expected outcomes of disability management strategies and demand objective evidence to justify their support of disability management services.

All too often in the past, disability management interventions have been developed based on team consensus, medical authority, or individual practitioner skill and experience. The assumption has been that traditional knowledge about diagnosis, occupational medicine practice, the consensus of stakeholders and experts, and common sense was sufficient to address RTW issues, to support new interventions, or to direct practice. However, the age of efficacy and accountability has resulted in the need both for disability management practice that is able to justify recommendations for interventions and for programs based on evidence with the confidence of valid research.

Evidence-based practice is an approach to health care that has been utilized in medicine for the past 50 years. In evidence-based medicine, information about interpreting diagnostic information, choosing appropriate treatment, or estimating prognosis is obtained through controlled research that follows the rigors of scientific study. The health care practitioner using the approach makes informed decisions about patient care based on the best evidence (Currier et al., 2001; Sackett, Straus, Richardson, Rosenberg, & Haynes, 2000). Evidence-based disability case management entails integrating individual disability management expertise with the best available observable evidence regarding a specific injury or disability (e.g., myofascial pain, carpal tunnel syndrome, or depression), obtained by systematic research. Using this approach, the case manager is able to understand the accuracy of vocational, functional capacity, and diagnostic evaluations made of injured workers and to base recommendations for prevention or intervention strategies on empirical information and reliable research findings.

Despite the increasing emphasis on accountability and demonstrated efficacy of disability management strategies, evidence-based practice has yet to become the norm in disability management. There is only a limited body of objective research related to illness, injury, and disability, and on how related factors influence prevention, productivity, and RTW outcomes. Case managers are challenged to overcome this limitation through several actions. First, they must understand and become skilled practitioners of evidence-based approaches to illness, injury, and disability as they relate to work and work productivity. The case manager must be familiar with available resources, databases, and web sites and must be able to apply critical review to evaluate information. In the best of worlds, disability management practice would be guided by information gained through randomly controlled research studies. The paucity of such information in the disability management field suggests that the best evidence may be the case manager's, or his or her colleagues, own experience. An accurate assessment of the limits of this information when making recommendations must be provided to all stakeholders. Second, the case manager must advocate for disability management research in order to increase the body of evidence in the field. This calls for case managers to truly understand research and encourage their employers, unions, and other interested stakeholders to become involved in collecting data, applying research standards, and utilizing data to make valid decisions, to influence performance and productivity, and to develop more efficacious cost-containment approaches.

INTERNATIONAL TRENDS IN
DISABILITY CASE MANAGEMENT

The global development of disability management practice and standards is a direct consequence of vastly differing societal approaches towards dealing with disability issues and the convergence of global economic markets, expanding technology and communication capability, international attention to human and civil rights, and increased interdependence of nations (Zimmermann, 2003). To understand the global dimensions of disability management, one should reflect on the fundamental principles that have dominated much of society's approach toward persons with disabilities. This approach is first characterized by providing benefits and second by providing opportunity to participate equitably in all aspects of society, including access to employment, education, transportation, recreation, and public facilities.

Access to and continued successful participation in the labor market has long been recognized as a critical element in both rehabilitating the injured and disabled worker and, more importantly, in maintaining his or her ability to achieve financial independence, ensure self-determination, and make an ongoing contribution to society. Within this context of access to and opportunity for employment, there are recognized distinctions between countries in their approaches to people with disabilities. These differences can be understood broadly as the distinction between *behavior-based* strategies that focus on societal outcomes and *attitude-based* approaches that are *process* oriented. Quota-based or grant-levy schemes, coupled with financial penalties or administrative charges, or both, provide fixed formulas that dictate employment participation rates for persons with disabilities. These schemes are associated with behavior-based strategies and have been in place for decades in many European jurisdictions, notably Germany and France. Durable success of these strategies has been dependent upon the type of application and level of enforcement, resulting in significantly increased employment participation for persons with severe disabilities, particularly in Germany. This public policy system is coupled with extensive rehabilitation and re-training efforts and offers a stable framework for vocational rehabilitation outside the pre-disability employer environment. The attitude-based, process-driven approach largely describes the Human Rights, Equal Opportunity, Employment Equity, and Anti-Discrimination legislation commonly found in the United States, Canada, the UK, Australia, and New Zealand. Operating without measurable targets, the aim of these approaches is to remove physical, attitudinal, and societal barriers to equal participation in all aspects of society. While these approaches have offered persons with disabilities occasional successful remedies in instances in which the disability was believed to be a discriminating factor, their net measurable contribution in raising overall employment levels of persons with disabilities has been extremely disappointing in all jurisdictions, particularly in Canada and the United States.

The introduction of DM strategies fundamentally shifts the direction of disability-addressing approaches from a public policy oriented, social security approach to a private sector responsibility model with defined and measurable financial targets and outcomes. Australia was one of the first countries to legislate workplace-based disability management within the context of COMCARE, its Federal Workers' Compensation legislation, effective in 1988. COMCARE legislation, grounded in best practice and evidence-based research gathered from around the world, successfully codified and advanced principles and experiences pioneered by large, progressive employers operating within self-insurance models. Their approach resulted in radically reduced overall disability costs, lowered claim duration, and reduced incidences of long-term disability. This provided unequivocal evidence that workplace-directed, consensus-based, and tightly administered disability management strategies, focused on the injured and disabled worker through an early intervention and safe RTW program, will consistently lower the socioeconomic costs of disability on employers, workers, and society.

In 1994, the New Zealand Accident Compensation Corporation (ACC), operating a 24-hour, no-fault occupational and non-occupational accident insurance system, introduced key elements of the COMCARE model within its "employer" program. It provided for increased workplace control and responsibility for disability initiatives in exchange for enhanced financial benefits. This approach has proven quite successful for the ACC and is operated with a range of variations to suit constantly evolving global socioeconomic and labor market conditions.

In response to these emerging experiences, the International Labour Organization (ILO), an agency of the United Nations, launched a major 8-country study in 1996 to articulate and define key issues facing disabled workers, including the impact of workplace-based disability management strategies on job retention and RTW strategies for disabled workers (Thornton & Lunt, 1997). In response to these developments and the release of the ILO study in 1998, a collaboration agreement was signed between the National Institute of Disability Management and Research (NIDMAR) in Canada and the ILO, leading to the first Code of Practice for Disability Management in Canada. This landmark agreement subsequently formed a key element of the ILO's Code of Practice on *Managing Disability in the Workplace* (ILO, 2002).

As disability case managers practice in businesses and industries having multi-national markets, knowledge of the different legislative structures, economic incentives and penalties, and workplace processes and standards will be essential to implement programs to maintain the injured/disabled worker with the pre-disability employer. At an operational level, understanding of these factors will determine steps the case manager must take to implement successfully programs such as transitional work. At an administrative level, the case manager must understand different regulatory structures that guide disability management program implementation, such as Duty to Accommodate in Canada.

Disability management as a global strategy is being advanced across a range of jurisdictions and organizations through a number of innovative measures including policy, legislation, economic incentives and penalties, standards, Codes of Practice, education, and certification programs. Within these contexts, the disability case manager finds common ground to promote return to work opportunities for workers with injuries and disabilities while reducing the socio-economic impact of the disability (Hursh & Shrey, 1999).

CONCLUSION

Case management will play an increasingly critical role in DM programs providing early interventions in hopes of preventing the occurrence of lost time. In the emerging models of integrated DM, case managers will have to demonstrate competency in all aspects of medical and disability management interventions. As more employers recognize cost savings demonstrated by DM programs, substantial growth in workplace-based programs will continue. DM is growing substantially for a number of reasons, including the continuing management of costs, the effort to maximize worker productivity, the management of employees as highly valued resources, the integration of workers with disabilities with an emphasis on "abilities," and the aging of the workforce, which will increase the number of employed workers with significant health conditions and impairments. All these factors will contribute to further growth in the DM field and implies the need for qualified personnel to administer or provide DM services.

DM is increasingly moving towards evidence-based practice by identifying best practices and developing appropriate outcome and performance measurements as well as guidelines and benchmarks. Demonstration of the efficacy of DM programs will become increasingly critical to DM stakeholders to ensure they share common reference points. As eloquently stated by and Wood and Lui (1999) "as we move forward in the parallel development of CM and DM, we begin to understand where we are going by examining where we have been. We have come a long way, but we need to keep learning to keep our competencies current. If we continue to evolve, we will serve both employees and employers through the best practices available. We believe that a focus on *competency* can drive the development of greater professionalism and innovation in our field." (p.45)

REFERENCES

Akabas, S. H., Gates, L. B., & Galvin, D. E. (1992). *Disability management: A complete system to reduce costs, increase productivity, meet employer needs, and insure legal compliance.* New York: AMACOM.

Bodenheimer, T. (2000). Disease management in the American market. *British Medical Journal, 320,* 563-566.

Breslin, R., & Olsheski, J. (1996). The impact of a transitional work return program on lost time: Preliminary data from the Minster Machine Company. *NARPPS Journal, 11*(2), 35-40.

Brunelle, A., & Lui, J. (2003). Disability management and employee assistance program: Building bridges on common ground. *Journal of Employee Assistance, 33*(2), 7-8.

Bruyère, S. M., & Shrey, D. E. (1991). Disability management in industry: A joint labor-management process. *Rehabilitation Counseling Bulletin, 34,* 227-242.

Butler, R., Johnson, W., & Baldwin, M. (1995). Managing work disability: Why first return to work is not a measure of success. *Industrial & Labor Relations Review, 48*(3), 452.

Calkins, J., Lui, J. W., & Wood, C. (2000). Recent developments in integrated disability management: Implications for professional and organizational development. *Journal of Vocational Rehabilitation, 15,* 31-37.

Chan, F., McMahon, B., Shaw, L., Taylor, D., & Wood C. (1997). Survey of rehabilitation counselor education programs regarding health care case management in the private sector. *Journal of Rehabilitation, 63*(3), 46-52.

Chan, F., Taylor, D., Currier, K., Chan, C. H., Wood, C., & Lui, J. (2001). A work behavior analysis of disability management specialists. *Journal of Vocational Rehabilitation. 5*(1), 47-56.

Chajewski, L., Parry T., & Molmen W. (1999, July). *Turning to benefit integration–Results from a survey of employers.* San Francisco, CA: Integrated Benefits Institute.

Cotter, D., & Williams, C. (1997). Managing health-related absences. *Compensation & Benefits Review, 29*(3), 58-64.

Crystal, R. M. (1987). Developing a business-industry emphasis in the curriculum. *Rehabilitation Education, 1,* 139-141.

Currier, F., Chan, F., Berven, N., Habeck, R., & Taylor, D. (2001). Job functions and knowledge domains for disability management practice: A Delphi study. *Rehabilitation Counseling Bulletin, 44,* 133-143.

Currier, K., Chan, F., Taylor, D., & Wood, C. (1997). *Disability management specialists: An investigation of major practice domains and associated knowledge areas.* Rolling Meadows, IL: Certification of Disability Management Specialists Commission.

Daiker, B. (1995). Managed care in workers' compensation. *AAOHN Journal,* 422-427.

Douglas, J. (2000). *Integrated disability management – An employer's guide.* Brookfield, WI: International Foundation of Employee Benefit Plans, Inc.

Goodwin, B. A., Taylor, D. W., Chan, F., & Currier, K. (2000). Perceived training needs of disability management specialists in five knowledge domains of disability management practice. *Rehabilitation Education, 14,* 229-242.

360

Greenhalgh, T., Herxheimer, A., Isaacs, A. J., Beaman, M., Morris, J., & Farrow, S. (2000). Commercial partnerships with chronic disease management: Proceeding with caution. *British Medical Journal, 320,* 566-568.

Habeck, R. (1993). Managing disability in industry. *NARPPS Journal, 6*(4), 141-146.

Habeck, R. (1996). Differentiating disability management and rehabilitation. *NARPPS Journal, 11*(2), 8-20.

Habeck, R. V., & Hunt, H. A. (1999). Disability management perspectives: Developing accommodating work environments through disability management. *American Rehabilitation, 25*(1), 18-25.

Habeck, R. V., & Kirchner, K. (1999). Case management issues within employer-based disability management. In F. Chan & M. J. Leahy (Eds.), *Health care and disability case management* (pp. 239-263). Lake Zurich, IL: Vocational Consultants Press.

Habeck, R. V., Kress, M., Scully, S. M., & Kirchner, K. (1994). Determining the significance of the disability management movement for rehabilitation counselor education. *Rehabilitation Education, 8,* 195-240.

Habeck, R. V., & Leahy, M. J. (1991). Employer factors related to worker's compensation claims and disability management. *Rehabilitation Counseling Bulletin, 34,* 210-226.

Habeck, R. V., Leahy, M. J., Hunt, H. A., Chan, F., & Welch, E. M. (1991). Employer factors related to workers' compensation claims and disability management. *Rehabilitation Counseling Bulletin, 34,* 210-226.

Haw, M. A. (1996). Case management education in universities: A national survey. *Journal of Case Management, 2*(6), 10-22.

Hunt, H. A., Habeck, R. V., VanTol, B., & Scully, S. M. (1993). *Disability prevention and management among Michigan employers* (Technical Report #93-004). Kalamazoo, MI: W. E. Upjohn Institute for Employment Research.

Hursh, N. (2003) *Pro-Work Strategies for Older Workers with Disabilities: A Disability Management Approach.* Presented at the 24th Switzer Seminar Series, Washington, DC, October 18, 2003.

Hursh, N. C. (2002). *Disability Management Education: Past, Present, & Future.* Presented at the International Forum on Disability Management, Vancouver, B.C. Canada. May 27.

Hursh, N. C. (1997). Making a difference in the workplace. In W. Zimmerman (Ed.), *Strategies for success.* Port Alberni, BC: National Institute of Disability Management and Research.

Hursh, N. C., & Shrey, D. E. (1999). Disability management - An international perspective. *Case Review, 1,* 35-41.

Hursh, N. C., & Shrey, D. E. (1994). Protecting the employability of the working elderly. In G. Felsenthal, S. Garrison, & F. Steinbert (Eds.), *Rehabilitation of the aging and elderly patient.* Baltimore: Williams & Wilkins.

International Labour Organization. (2002). *Managing disability in the workplace: ILO code of practice.* Geneva Switzerland: ILO. Retrieved March 28, 2004 from http://www.ilo.org/public/english/employment/skills/disability/download/code.pdf.

Kilbury, R. F., Benshoff, J. J., & Riggar, T. F. (1990). The expansion of private sector rehabilitation: Will rehabilitation education respond? *Rehabilitation Education, 4,* 163-170.

Leahy, M., Chan, F., Taylor, D., Wood, C., & Downey, W. (1998). Evolving knowledge and skill factors for practice in private sector rehabilitation. *NARPPS Journal, 6*(1), 34-43.

Lewis, R. A. (2000, March 13). Next gen trend: Total absence management. *National Underwriter Life & Health/Financial Edition,* pp. 16-17.

Lipold, A. G. (2000, November/December). Managing the guy who isn't there. *Business and Health, 18*(10), 25, 26, 29, 30.

Livneh H., & Antonak, R. F., (1999). Psychosocial aspects of chronic illness and disability, In F. Chan & M. J. Leahy (Eds.), *Health care and disability case management* (pp. 121-168). Lake Zurich, IL: Vocational Consultants Press.

Lui, J. (1993). Trends and innovations in private sector rehabilitation for the 21st century. In L. E. Perlman and C. E. Hansen (Eds.), *Private sector rehabilitation: Trends and issues for the 21st century.* (A report of the 17th Mary E. Switzer Memorial Seminar). Alexandria, VA: National Rehabilitation Association.

Lui, J. (2000, Summer). Disability management-An integrated view. *CDMS commission update.*

Marcus, A. D., (2003, June 17). Careful, your HMO is watching – Insurers monitor patients and nag them to get more tests. *The Wall Street Journal.* p. D1.

Matkin, R. E. (1985). *Insurance rehabilitation: Service applications in disability compensation systems.* Austin, TX: PRO-ED.

Matkin, R. E. (1987). Content areas and recommended training sites of insurance rehabilitation knowledge. *Journal of Applied Rehabilitation Counseling, 1*(4), 233-246.

Matkin, R. (1995). Private sector rehabilitation. In S. E. Rubin & R. T. Roessler (Eds.), *Foundations of the vocational rehabilitation process* (4th ed., pp. 375-398). Austin, TX: Pro-Ed.

Meaney, M. E. (2000). A deliberative model of corporate medical management. *Journal of Law, Medicine & Ethics, 28,* 125-136.

Norris, S. L., Glasgow, R.E., Engelgau, M.M., O'Connor, P.J., & McCulloch, D. (2003). Chronic disease management: A definition and systematic approach to component interventions. *Disease Management & Health Outcomes, 11,* 477-488.

Olsheski, J. A. (1993). Comments on Buys. *Journal of Rehabilitation Administration, 17*(1), 14.

Olsheski, J. A. (1996). Contemporary issues in disability management. *NARPPS Journal, 11*(2), 5-7.

Olsheski, J. A., & Breslin, R. (1996). The Americans with Disabilities Act: Implications for the use of ergonomics in rehabilitation. In A. Bhattacharya & J. McGlothlin (Eds.), *Occupational ergonomics: Theory and practice* (pp. 669-683). New York: Marcel Dekker, Inc.

Olsheski, J. A., Rosenthal, D. A., & Hamilton, M. (2002). Disability management and psychosocial rehabilitation: Considerations for integration. *Work: A Journal of Prevention, Assessment & Rehabilitation, 19,* 63-70.

Purcell, P. J. (2000). Older workers: Employment and retirement trends. *Monthly Labor Review, 23*(10), 19-30.

Quinn, J. (1999). *Retirement patterns and bridge jobs in the 1990s. EBRI Issue Brief, 206.* Washington, DC: Employee Benefit Research Institute.

Rix, S. E. (2002). The labor market for older workers. *Generations: Journal of the American Society on Aging, Summer,* 25-30.

Ritter, A. (2000, December). Total absence management: Practical solutions to prevent and minimize employee absence. *Employee Benefit Journal, 25*(4), 3-7.

Rosenthal, D. A. (1997). Disability management: Implications for rehabilitation counselor education. *Journal of Job Placement and Development, 13*(1), 10-13.

Rosenthal, D., & Olsheski, J. (1999). Disability management and rehabilitation counseling: Present status and future opportunities. *Journal of Rehabilitation, 65*(1), 31-38.

Sackett, D. L., Straus, S. E., Richardson, W. S., Rosenberg, W., & Haynes, R. B. (2000). *Evidence-based medicine* (2nd ed.). Edinburgh: Churchill Livingstone.

Shrey, D. E. (1992). Employer-based work return transition programs and the deinstitutionalization of America's injured workers. *Work Injury Management, 1*(4), 4-6.

Shrey, D. E. (1995). Worksite disability management and industrial rehabilitation: An overview. In D. E. Shrey & M. Lacerte (Eds.) *Principles and practices of disability management in industry* (pp. 3-54). Winter Park, FL: PMD Publishers Group, Inc.

Shrey, D. E., & Lacerte, M. (Eds.). (1995). *Principles and practices of disability management in industry.* Winter Park, FL: GR Press, Inc.

Shrey, D. E., & Olsheski, J. A. (1992). Disability management and industry-based work return transition programs. *Physical Medicine and Rehabilitation, 6,* 303-314.

Shutan, B. (2003). Mindful of who's missing. A Special Sponsored Report to the January 2003 Issue of *Employee Benefits News 17,*1. Retrieved March 28, 2004 from http://www. benefitsnews.com/disability/detail.cfm? id= 3914.

Stevens M. (2003). *Maximizing Human Capital: Presenteeism – The next Frontier for Health and Productivity Management.* Manuscript submitted for publication.

Tabak, M. H. (1995, February). Merging managed care and workers' compensation. *Risk Management,* 16-19.

Thornton, P., & Lunt, N. (1997). *International research project on job retention and return to work strategies for disabled workers: Key issues.* Geneva Switzerland: International Labour Organization.

U.S. Department of Labor, Bureau of Labor Statistics Web Site May 2001 http://www.dol.gov and http://stats.bls.gov

U.S. General Accounting Office. (2001). *Demographic trends pose challenges for employers and workers.* GAO-02-85. November. Washington, DC: US General Accounting Office.

Waldo, B. H. (2000). Disease management gains acceptance–and finds it legs– with automation. *Nursing Economic$, 18,* 208–210.

Watson Wyatt Worldwide (2001). *Staying @ Work: Integrated disability management around the world.* Washington DC: Author.

Watson Wyatt Worldwide & Washington Business Group on Health. (1999). Third Annual Survey Report – 1998/1999. *Staying @ Work. Increasing Shareholder Value Through Integrated Disability Management.* Washington DC: Author.

Watson Wyatt Worldwide & Washington Business Group on Health. (2000). *Fourth Annual Survey Report–1999/2000. Focusing On What Works – Integrated Disability Management. Staying @ Work.* Washington DC: Author.

Wood, C., & Lui, J. (1999). The evolution of disability care and case management: Identifying core competencies. *The Case Manager (TCM)*, *10*(4), 41-45.

Zimmermann, W. (2003, April). *International policy setter on disability.* Symposium conducted at the meeting of the 2003 International Association of Rehabilitation Professionals Conference, Baltimore, MD.

Zimmermann, W. (2004). Die globale dimension, In F. Merlhoff, (Ed.), *Disability management: strategien zur integration von behinderten menschen in das Arbeitsleben* (pp 21-31). Stuttgart, Germany, Gentner Verlag Publishing house.

This page intentionally left blank.

Section 4

Accountability

Chapter 14   Evidence-Based Practice
             in Case Management

In This Section

Section 4 is titled *Accountability*. In Chapter 14, Chronister and colleagues provide an overview of the general concept of evidenced-based practice. The authors identify available resources, and discuss issues related to evidence-based practice in rehabilitation case management.

14

Evidence-Based Practice in Case Management

Julie Chronister
Elizabeth da Silva Cardoso
Gloria K. Lee
Fong Chan
Michael J. Leahy

Chapter Highlights

- Evidence-Based Practice

- Resources

- Issues

- Summary

Since the passage of the Health Maintenance Organization (HMO) Act by the Congress in 1973, the American healthcare system has undergone a significant transformation underscored most notably by the implementation of managed care measures designed to control the rising costs of health care services (Mullen, 1995). Managed care, which can be defined as "the integration of both the financing and the delivery of health care within a system that seeks to manage accessibility, cost, and quality of that cost" (Mullen, 1995, p. 22) is, without a doubt, driven by economic correlates of capitation, integration and consolidation, treatment protocols, utilization reviews, and a move towards a consumer-driven, market-based system (DeJong, 1997). In a consumer-driven, market-based environment, consumer choice, consumer satisfaction, and health outcomes drive the success of health care organizations, while the monitoring of quality receives increased attention (DeJong, 1997).

This emerging model of health care has affected the rehabilitation healthcare system and forced researchers, practitioners, and other stakeholders to provide evidence to support the effectiveness of their services. Of particular relevance to the current managed care climate is the rehabilitation community's emphasis on consumerism, which has for many years, promoted consumer involvement, stressed program evaluation, and provided support for empirical research (Corthell & VanBoskirk, 1988; Emener, W. 1991; Houser, Hampton & Carriker, 2000; McAlees & Menz, 1992; Rubin & Roessler, 1995). While this tradition positions our field to adapt to a consumer-driven health care climate, providing evidence of effective and efficient rehabilitation services is crucial to the field's identity and survival in managed healthcare climate.

One way in which healthcare providers are responding to the demands of a managed care system is through *evidence-based practice*. Rosenburg and Donald (1996) defined evidence-based medicine as a process of turning clinical problems into questions and then systematically locating, appraising, and using contemporaneous research findings as the basis for clinical decisions. Sackett, Rosenberg, Gray, Haynes, and Richardson (1996) described evidence-based practice as the "conscientious, explicit and judicious use of current best evidence in making decisions about the care of individual patients" (p. 71). DePalma (2002) further refined the definition of evidence-based practice as a total process beginning with knowing what clinical questions to ask, how to find the best practice, and how to critically appraise the evidence for validity and applicability to the particular care situation. The best evidence then must be applied by a clinician with expertise in considering the patient's unique values and needs. The final aspect of the process is evaluation of the effectiveness of care and the continual improvement of the process.

Ottenbacher and Maas (1998) indicated that the 'best evidence' for evidence-based practice is derived from a series of research study results that form an empirical consensus regarding the effectiveness of a specific treatment approach. Within the field of medicine, with its positivist scientific methods tradition, the "gold standard" for scientific evidence is randomized clinical trials and the method of choice for determining the cumulative evidence of the effectiveness of a treatment is meta-analysis. The use of experimental research to validate the effectiveness of rehabilitation services is, unfortunately, uncommon due to the complex and holistic nature of the rehabilitation process (Johnston, Stineman, Velozo, 1997). Contemporary rehabilitation case management encompasses a broad scope of services, spans along the medical-vocational rehabilitation continuum from acute care to community based services, and is provided through an array of disciplines (e.g., nursing, social work, and rehabilitation counseling) for individuals with diverse and complex impairments and disabilities. The process typically involves a range of personal and environmental processes and the interactions thereof, making it difficult to determine what aspects of service delivery contribute to what outcomes (Johnston et al.).

While there is limited empirical support for rehabilitation case management interventions, the central focus of this service is to evaluate, manage, and coordinate services for people with chronic illnesses or disabilities. Medical case management, for example, has been defined as a collaborative process which assesses, plans, implements, coordinates, monitors, and evaluates options and services to meet an individual's health needs through communication and available resources to promote quality, cost-effective outcomes (Mullahy, 1995). Vocational case management refers to the movement of an individual client through the rehabilitation process, and includes the management and coordination of all services needed to achieve successfully the rehabilitation goal (Cox, Connolly, & Flynn, 1981). These roles and functions, which emphasize evaluation, outcomes, and quality-assurance, suggest that case managers are already working, in part, as evidence-based practitioners without explicitly acknowledging it.

Case management professionals have utilized standards of professional practice as an alternative quality assurance mechanism. The Case Management Society of America (CMSA), for example, has produced its Standards of Practice; the Individual Case Management Association (ICMA) has collaborated with Aetna Health Plans to develop the Case Management Practice Guidelines (Tarvydas & Peterson, 1999); and the Commission on Rehabilitation Counselor Certification (CRCC) has established its Code of Professional Ethics for Rehabilitation Counselors to guide the professional practice of rehabilitation counseling. The CRCC code describes exemplary rehabilitation counseling as a service that is client-centered, encourages a collaborative, multidisciplinary focus, is disability sensitive, is defined within the context of an established profession, and is vocationally inclusive (Tarvydas & Peterson).

While the roles, functions, and professional standards of rehabilitation case managers reflect an inherent focus on assuring and improving the quality and effectiveness of services, rehabilitation providers are part of a larger healthcare system that demands the effectiveness of services be proven based on the most credible scientific evidence, namely, evidence-based practice (Dubouloz, Egan, Vallerand, & von Zweck, 1999). Of equal importance is insuring that case managers' decision-making process is based more on a critical evaluation of scientific evidence and less on subjective experience. Rehabilitation researchers must conduct systematic research to demonstrate the effectiveness of case management interventions, and case managers must have the knowledge and skills required to gather this evidence. Case managers must be able to assist clients in selecting the most appropriate medical, psychological, educational, social, and vocational interventions for a client's particular situation and needs by critically appraising the evidence for interventions to determine the evidence's validity and applicability to the particular situation. To do this, they must be educated in research design and statistics and knowledgeable about how to access pertinent research from the library and the Internet so as to be able to determine the best evidence for a myriad of rehabilitation interventions considered in case management practice. The purpose of this chapter, therefore, is to provide an overview of the general concept of evidence-based practice, identify available resources, and discuss issues related to evidence-based practice in rehabilitation case management.

EVIDENCE-BASED PRACTICE

Defined as a process of turning clinical problems into questions and then systematically locating, appraising, and using contemporaneous research findings as the basis for clinical decisions, Rosenburg and Donald (1996) recommended the following steps to insure evidence-based practice of medicine:

1. Formulate a clear clinical question from a patient's problem.
2. Search the literature for relevant clinical articles.
3. Evaluate (critically appraise) the evidence for its validity and usefulness.
4. Implement useful findings in clinical practice.

While evidence-based practice originally emerged as an approach to be utilized by physicians, it has been extended to all health-related disciplines, with its fundamental assumption being the "conscientious, explicit and judicious use of current best evidence in making decisions about the care of individual patients" (Sackett et al., 1996, p. 71). Researchers applying this process to broader healthcare disciplines have identified an additional step, which involves evaluating the outcome of the intervention (e.g., Olsen, 1996). With respect to rehabilitation case management, for example, the application of evidence-based practice may assist professionals to answer the following types of questions:

- What processes/techniques make a specific rehabilitation intervention work?
- For whom is the intervention most effective?
- Are certain interventions/programs better for certain persons?
- Who should receive a specific intervention or program? When? And for how long?

To answer these types of questions using an evidence-based practice method, researchers have proposed using a hierarchical approach for categorizing evidence related to interventions (Holm, 2000; Nathan & Gorman, 1998). Moore et al. described a hierarchy of levels of evidence from which professionals can formulate an empirical consensus and determine "best evidence" regarding the effectiveness of a treatment approach. These include:

- Level 1 evidence is defined as strong evidence from at least one systematic review of multiple well-designed randomized controlled trials.
- Level 2 evidence is defined as strong evidence from at least one properly designed randomized controlled trials of appropriate size.
- Level 3 evidence is defined as evidence from well-designed trials without randomization, single group pre-post, cohort, time series, or matched case-controlled studies.
- Level 4 evidence is defined as evidence from well-designed nonexperimental studies from more than one center or research group.
- Level 5 evidence is defined as opinions of respected authorities, based on clinical evidence, descriptive studies, or reports of expert committees.

Evidence gathered from Level 1 and Level 2 is considered empirically validated treatments and reflects psychology's long tradition of using controlled experimental design to identify effective treatments. Chambless and Hollon

(1998) defined empirically validated interventions as psychological treatments that are clearly shown to be efficacious in controlled research studies with a delineated population. They further suggested that psychological treatments should be evaluated in terms of *efficacy* (statistical and clinical significance), *effectiveness* (clinical utility), and *efficiency* (cost-effectiveness). Level 1 and level 2 type studies, without question, are the most methodologically rigorous and statistically sound and follow the guidelines of the scientist-practitioner model of professional psychology initially set forth by the American Psychological Association's Division 12 (Clinical Psychology)– a division that has been active in reviewing the current empirical status of interventions/practices and in disseminating the findings since the early 1990s. The Division 12 Task Force on the Promotion and Dissemination of Psychological Procedures was originally patterned after the Food and Drug Administration (FDA) guidelines for approval of new drugs and established two criteria for establishing the empirical validity of a psychotherapeutic approach: (a) the approach is superior to a placebo or other treatment or (b) the approach is equal to an established treatment, in at least two studies established by different investigators. This approach is considered by many to be steadfastly aligned with the positivist approach of medicine and it continues to be revered–albeit not without controversy–as the gold standard for scientific evidence. Serious concerns have been raised regarding the methodological limitations of randomized clinical trials within the realm of behavioral sciences; the most common criticism being that controlled empirical research does not take into account the complexity of real world clinical populations and settings (e.g. Wampold, 1997).

Given the paucity of randomized clinical trials conducted in rehabilitation research, other valuable sources of evidence include levels 3, 4, and 5 type studies (Gray, 1997). Level 3 studies are considered quasi-experimental and derive their evidence from well-designed trials without randomization using cohort groups for treatment and control. Level 4 studies are descriptive studies that investigate relationships between variable but do not determine causality. Finally, Level 5 evidence represents the lowest level of the hierarchy of the evidence based on expert review and clinical opinion (Holm, 2000).

META-ANALYSIS

To determine the effectiveness of an intervention, a commonly used research method in education, psychology, medicine, and policy is meta-analysis (Hunt, 1997). Meta-analytic studies review the results of a collection of empirical studies in a specific research domain through statistical integration and analysis, and synthesize the results to determine the effectiveness of a given clinical treatment (Durlak, 1995). It is a mechanism by which professionals can understand the effectiveness of a practice/intervention domain in quantitative terms. The purpose of a meta-analysis is to identify significant relationships existing between study features (independent variables) and effect sizes (dependent variable). Similar to an individual experiment, a meta-analysis contains both independent and dependent variables, with the independent variables being such characteristics as participants, interventions, and outcome measures, and the dependent variable being the *effect size*, or the outcome of the results of each study selected for review, transformed into a common metric across studies.

In evidence-based practice, the focus of meta-analysis is on treatment effectiveness (e.g., is cognitive-behavioral therapy more effective than psychotherapy in treating depression?) The benefits of this statistical technique are its ability to (a) synthesize the results from many studies succinctly and intuitively to nonscientific communities; (b) illustrate the amount and relative impact of different programs on different criteria for policy decision-making purposes; and (c) identify the most effective programs and highlight gaps or limitations in the literature to suggest directions for future research (Durlak). A meta-analysis is conducted by following six major steps which include (a) formulating research questions; (b) identifying relevant studies through a comprehensive review of the literature (computer searches, manual searches, and examination of the reference lists of each identified study); (c) coding the studies (e.g., participants, research designs, therapist qualifications, control group, treatment type, presenting problem, number of sessions, and method of administration); (d) computing the index of effect; (e) conducting the statistical analysis of effects; and (f) offering conclusions and interpretations (Durlak, 1995).

A common index representing the size of the effect produced by each study is the effect size index g, which is the standardized difference between the sample mean of the treatment group and the sample mean of the control group (Wampold, 2001). A positive score indicates that the treatment group outperformed the control group, and a negative score has the reverse meaning. The effect size index g is a sample statistic and, therefore, it is a biased estimator of the true (i.e., population) effect size. Hedges and Olkin (1985) provided the effect size index d as a good approximation of the unbiased estimator and the index d_+ for aggregating the effect sizes across studies as an estimate of population effect size. The unbiased effect size indexes d and d_+ are commonly reported in meta-analytic studies. A typical way to interpret the size of an effect is to compare the d index with the standards set by Cohen (1988) as follows:

Table I
META-ANALYSIS EFFECT SIZE

Standardized Mean Difference	Effect Size
large effect:	$d = .80$
medium effect:	$d = .50$
small effect:	$d = .20$

Additional methods used to interpret an effect size include transforming the effect size index d to r^2 (the proportion of variability accounted for by the treatment), and examining the overlap of the control and treatment distributions by converting the effect size index to the value of the standard normal cumulative distribution (e.g., if $d = .85$ then $z = .85$ and compared to the normal distribution curve, a z-score of .85 would indicate that the average client receiving treatment will be better off than 80% of untreated clients).

There are many factors that can influence the effect size of a meta-analytic study including sample size, sensitivity of measurement instruments, design characteristics, and clinical significance. Of particular importance are the issues of homogeneity and power. In regards to homogeneity, it can be argued, for example, that studies included in a meta-analysis may have an array of different independent or dependent variables, and may not have a common population parameter. For this reason, researchers have developed a way to empirically test the heterogeneity and homogeneity of the studies. Hedges and Olkin (1985) developed a Q statistics for a large sample test of homogeneity and suggested that if the null hypothesis of homogeneity is rejected (i.e., Q statistic is significant), the studies should be partitioned based on meaningful categories. Specifically, a meta-analysis may include studies that differ in categorically predictable ways; for example, a 'better designed' study would produce a larger effect than a 'poorer designed' study, therefore, to control for this difference, the independent variable "quality of research design" can be used to partition studies into two groups (good design studies vs. poor design studies). The between group differences can then be tested using Q_B, a goodness-of-fit statistics, a statistic also developed by Hedges and Olkin. If a significant difference between groups (Q_B) is determined, and no difference within groups (Q), then d_+ can be computed to estimate the effect size for each group of studies. If there is significant difference within groups, then the groups should be further partitioned.

Having enough power to detect a significant difference between groups has been identified as a limitation in behavioral science research in general

(Ottenbacher & Maas, 1998) and rehabilitation research in particular. Meta-analytic studies that are comprised of studies with inadequate power may provide misleading or false information. As a demonstration of this phenomenon, Ottenbacher and Maas examined 30 occupational therapy intervention studies and found the median power values to detect small, medium, and large effect sizes in the 30 studies to be .09, .33, and .66, respectively, with the median power to be .37 (as compared to the traditional guideline of .80 for the adequacy of power) suggesting a high probability of Type II errors ($\beta = .63$) (A Type I error occurs when a researcher rejects a true null hypothesis and a Type II error occurs when an investigator retains a false null hypothesis.) While there may be many methodological factors and design features that contribute to insignificant results (e.g., small sample size, measurement error, and sample heterogeneity), inadequate power undoubtedly contributes to false conclusions (Type II errors) which strengthens the false impression that an intervention is not effective–particularly when replication studies are conducted. The presence of low-power studies with high rates of false negative findings prevents the development of a consensus and the establishment of guidelines for evidence-based practice and impedes the scientific progress of rehabilitation health professions.

In sum, evidence based practice begins with generating important questions and then using or facilitating research to answer these questions. To do this, practitioners must be able to know, understand, and critically evaluate an array of different types of research studies, such as those constituting the outlined hierarchy, and have a solid understanding of meta-analysis, effect size, and power. This knowledge base will position practitioners to think critically and evaluatively, and encourage the utilization of empirically supported research in the decision-making process.

RESOURCES FOR EVIDENCE-BASED PRACTICE

In response to the emerging needs of evidence-based practitioners, our healthcare system has set forth policies and initiatives to insure that healthcare professionals and other stakeholders have access to information regarding best treatment practices, performance and quality assurance measures, and evaluative feedback. Initially set into motion through policy, Title IX of the Public Health Services Act was amended to include the "Healthcare Research and Quality Act of 1999" and the Agency for Health Care Policy and Research (AHRQ, 2001) was reauthorized as the Agency for Healthcare Research and Quality (AHRQ). The agency's primary agenda is to research health outcomes, develop effective outcome measures, and to evaluate the overall quality of care. Important outcome research initiatives and quality assessment tools developed through AHRQ that rehabilitation professionals should be familiar with–particularly those professionals working in the medical or allied health field– include the following:

- Patient Outcomes Research Teams (PORTs)
- Clinical Practice Guidelines
- Clinical performance measures
- Report Cards

The AHRQ's PORTs are designed to determine the most effective treatment and pattern of care for a specified clinical area through exhaustive literature reviews and meta-analysis. PORTs typically involve a partnership with another agency (i.e. National Institute of Health). One AHRQ funded PORT was a collaboration with the University of Texas Health Sciences Center and was initiated in order to examine the effectiveness of alternative treatments for chronic disabling conditions such as Type II diabetes and mental health problems with emphasis on the Mexican American population (AHRQ, 2001). According to Johnston and Granger (1994), several PORTs are highly relevant to physical disability and rehabilitation, including secondary prevention of stroke, hip fracture repair and osteoarthritis, total knee replacement, and back pain treatment and assessment.

Another important contribution of AHRQ was the development and dissemination of *Clinical Practice Guidelines* (AHRQ, 2000). Often developed from PORT findings, Clinical Practice Guidelines offer healthcare providers well founded and reportedly cost-effective methods of treatment for certain clinical conditions. Findings from a PORT study on Stroke Rehabilitation, for example, developed into the Clinical Practice Guideline 'Post-stroke rehabilitation' (AHRQ, 2000). Development and use of Clinical Practice Guidelines has become so mainstream and well accepted that AHRQ no longer sponsors the development of these guidelines, as many public and private organizations are doing this independently (AHRQ, 2000). Clinical Practice Guidelines are easily accessible through the *National Guideline Clearinghouse*, an internet-based source of guidelines that is maintained through a partnership between the AHRQ, American Medical Association, and the American Association of Health Plans.

AHRQ has also taken the lead in sponsoring research in the area of *clinical performance measurement.* Clinical performance measures are used to assess the appropriateness and timeliness of, and access to services provided by a healthcare professional. Clinical performance measures "are detailed, often condition-specific, and focus on the relationship between the process of care and patient" (AHRQ, 2000) In short, clinical performance measures attempt to measure the *quality of care.* There currently are approximately 1,200 clinical performance measures grouped into 53 measure sets. This information has been organized into a classification scheme (CONQUEST) and database system (The Typology) for easy access, standardization, and comparing information on measures and evaluating their worth. These measures are developed by a wide range of organizations and they include such entities as:

- Joint Commission on Accreditation of Healthcare Organizations (JCAHO),
- Health Plan Employers Data and Information Set (HEDIS),
- Healthcare Cost and Utilization Project (HCUP),
- Outcome and Assessment Information Set (OASIS),
- University of Wisconsin Nursing Home quality indicators,
- VA External peer review program.

Clinical performance measures are also classified by conditions. There are currently 57 conditions included in the database that are considered common, severe, and known to consume significant healthcare resources (AHRQ, 2000). Clinical performance measures underlie many quality assessment tools and public information resources, and are undoubtedly a major tool that accreditation programs and internal and external quality assurance programs utilize to evaluate service delivery. Information obtained through these measures is also used for marketing and communication purposes to consumers and other purchasers through "Report Cards" (AHRQ, 2001). Report Cards are a response to the consumer-driven health care system and provide potential consumers with information on particular health care plans. Report cards provide information regarding the care recommended by clinical practice guidelines, outcomes expected for specific conditions, and the wide range of performance measures used to evaluate the quality of different aspects of care, offered in a user-friendly format. The CONQUEST 2.0 database and its User's Guide and Quick Start Summary can be downloaded directly from AHRQ's Web site at http://www.ahrq.gov/qual/conquest.htm. The set of disks (AHRQ Publication No. 99-DPO1) and printed copies of the User's Guide (AHRQ Publication No. 99-0011) and Quick Start Summary (AHRQ Publication No. 99-0015) are available from the AHRQ Clearinghouse.

Recently, the American Congress of Rehabilitation (ACRM) Medicine established an evidence-based practice section in their website containing valuable resources for evidence-based reviews in medical rehabilitation. The website can be accessed at:
http://www.acrm.org/Resources/Evidence-BasedResources.htm

ISSUES RELATED TO EVIDENCE-BASED PRACTICE
IN CASE MANAGEMENT

RESEARCH ISSUES

In comparison to medical, psychological, and educational research, the use of randomized clinical trials in rehabilitation research is not common–particularly with respect to rehabilitation case management. No randomized control trials have been conducted to examine the effect of rehabilitation case management interventions on specified outcomes. While studies have identified important rehabilitation case management functions (e.g., health care management and follow up, program management and evaluation, and disability case management) and knowledge domains (e.g., counseling relationship/process, health care management, community resources and support, psychosocial interventions, and disability case management) important in today's healthcare and disability services system (Chan et al., 2000), no empirical evidence supporting the effectiveness of these functions or knowledge domains on rehabilitation outcomes has emerged. Many would undoubtedly claim this to be a limitation, as research using strict experimental design is considered the "gold standard" for evidence-based research and a prominent tool for determining best practices.

While this is an area that demands empirical support, studies from allied disciplines (e.g., counseling and clinical psychology) can offer rehabilitation case managers evidence-based research regarding effective interventions/techniques that can be applied within a case management context. Meta-analytic studies or expert reviews within the broader field of counseling, as well as the growing body within the rehabilitation arena, can be accessed and applied within the rehabilitation case management context. Within the broader counseling psychology field, meta-analytic studies reviewing the effectiveness of specific therapeutic techniques can offer rehabilitation case managers insight into what counseling process variables affect outcomes. The working relationship between the client and counselor, for example, which is most often referred to in the literature as the "working alliance," has gained overwhelmingly strong empirical support as a primary influence on counseling outcomes. In a meta-analysis involving thousands of studies designed to investigate the efficacy of counseling interventions on client outcomes, Wampold (2001) determined that it was common factors such as allegiance, therapeutic alliance, empathic listening, and goal setting that underlie all psychotherapeutic approaches that affect outcomes, not techniques associated with specific theoretical orientations. He found that at least 70% of psychotherapeutic effects are due to common factors, 8% are due to specific factors (i.e. different theoretical orientations/techniques), and the remaining

22% was partially attributed to individual client differences. In this study, he defined allegiance as the degree to which the therapist is committed to the belief that the therapy is beneficial to the client. Therapeutic alliance was defined as (a) the client's affective relationship with the therapist; (b) the client's motivation and ability to accomplish work collaboratively with the therapist; (c) the therapist's empathic responding to and involvement with the client; and (d) client and therapist agreement about the goals and tasks of therapy.

While this research reviews a construct that is broad based and covers a wide array of counseling and psychotherapeutic arenas, it is, without a doubt, a factor that plays an important role in the working relationship of rehabilitation case managers and their clients, revealing the importance of teaching rehabilitation professionals to seek out evidence from related disciplines to assist them in identifying appropriate interventions and determining best practices. It is the goal of rehabilitation educators to develop a case management model that focuses on training case managers to be evidence-based practitioners who relying on the solid empirical research body within rehabilitation and allied fields to assist them in developing and utilizing these therapeutic techniques within the rehabilitation arena. Of equal importance is validating the effectiveness of broader counseling factors within a rehabilitation case management context and continuing to validate specific rehabilitation counseling variables using a true experimental research design–an important indicator of research quality.

Some examples of empirical research conducted within the rehabilitation arena include Bolton and Akridge's (1995) meta-analysis of 15 experimental evaluations of 10 skills training interventions (e.g., social skills, stress management, problem-solving skills, and career decision-making skills) that were measured on 61 outcome measures. Their review showed an estimated true effect size of +.93 indicating that skills training services substantially benefit the typical vocational rehabilitation client. Benton and Schroeder (1990) conducted a similar meta-analytic and found that behaviorally based skills training programs are effective tools for improving social and living skills of people with severe psychiatric disabilities. Specifically, they found that 69% (d = .50) of individuals with severe mental illness who received social skills training were better off than those who did not receive the training. Dilk and Bond (1996) further supported this finding in their meta-analysis involving 42 experimental studies investigating the effectiveness of skills training for people with severe mental illness, reporting a moderate effect size (d = .48). Finally, Bond et al. (2001) argued that providing supported employment services for people with severe mental illness is an evidence-based practice, identifying six randomized control trials comparing supported employment with a variety of traditional services. All six studies reported significant gains in employment outcomes (58% competitive employment rates vs. 21% for control groups).

PRACTICE ISSUES

Rehabilitation case managers must be aware of contemporary research in the rehabilitation profession as well as in allied fields so as to promote evidence-based practice and insure that persons with disabilities and chronic illness receive effective services (Bolton, 1979). In today's healthcare climate of accountability and cost control, rehabilitation professionals must be concerned with accurately assessing and documenting the contribution of rehabilitation interventions to rehabilitation related changes in clients (Rubin, Chan, & Thomas, 2003). While this is a desirable goal, providing effective training to instill an evidence-based approach toward service delivery is challenging and somewhat illusive. Within the rehabilitation counseling education curriculum, for example, there typically is only one course in research methods. It is, undoubtedly, the least popular course in most master level programs, which, unfortunately, is likely to translate into a negative attitude towards utilizing research in professional practice. Dysart and Tomlin (2002) surveyed 209 practicing occupational therapists regarding evidence-based practice and found that practitioners with 15 or more years of clinical experience did not believe that results from research studies could be translated into client treatment planning. Other barriers to research utilization, including lack of time on the job, the high cost of continuing education, and weak research analysis skills, were highlighted by Dsyart and Tomlin.

While many of these barriers to evidence-based practice are expected, especially in the area of research analysis and research utilization skills, efforts to remediate these barriers must occur in order for rehabilitation professionals to work effectively in our current healthcare climate. One way to begin addressing these barriers is for rehabilitation educators to reconsider course curriculums and teaching approaches used in research courses. A high priority must be placed on developing curriculums that are more creative and activities that will promote a working knowledge of manual and computer searches and a solid understanding of different research designs and issues related to power analysis, effect size, and meta-analysis. Another way to provide this training is through regular in-service trainings within rehabilitation work environments. These efforts will most assuredly contribute to bridging the ever-present gap between research and practice.

SUMMARY

Rehabilitation is one of many health-related disciplines facing the demands of a managed care system. Now, more than ever, professionals working in social and behavioral science arenas have to rely steadfastly on the most credible evidence available in order to maintain their identity in a healthcare climate driven by practice guidelines, performance measures, report cards, and outcomes. These external factors have spurred the debate regarding the split between science and practice within counseling and related fields, forcing professionals to begin looking at ways to bridge this gap. Chwalisz (2003) suggests that at the core of this debate is psychology's commitment to a positivist approach to science that reveres randomized clinical trials and devalues evidence from less rigorous research designs, preventing practitioners from seeking out or valuing additional sources of evidence. She suggests that in order to stay afloat in an evidence-based environment, the field needs to move away from upholding a strict positivist approach and open the door to other avenues of evidence. Wampold (2003) argues that relinquishing the positivist philosophy positions the field for evidence-based practice that does not discriminate strong evidence from weak. He further cautions that accepting evidence without appropriate methodological rigor will ultimately affect the field's viability in a managed care environment. Discerning what constitutes methodologically sound evidence appears to be the larger question. While randomized clinical trials are undoubtedly considered the 'gold standard' for empirical support, this type of research design does not automatically imply strong evidence, nor does qualitative research imply weak evidence. Contemporary research methods involving multivariate statistical methods and structural equation modeling are offering behavioral science researchers useful statistical tools to tease out what variables predict what outcomes in a field that involves complex and real-world variables. It is crucial to promote an understanding of a broad array of research and to understand what methodological factors discriminate strong from weak research.

Evidence-based practice and empirically validated interventions are in the forefront of our healthcare service delivery system and are, without a doubt, here to stay. The degree to which practitioners and researchers work together to respond effectively to these demands is crucial for professional viability. The American Psychology Association's (APA) Division 12 (clinical psychology) has, for example, taken steps to respond to the demands of managed care by publishing a list of 71 psychological treatments that are empirically validated (Chambless & Ollendick, 2001). In addition, the APA recently approved criteria for evaluating treatment guidelines organized around treatment efficacy and clinical utility. These criteria included real world factors such as complex clinical presentations, professionals' training/skill/experience, patient/treatment setting, culturally relevant research and expertise, and feasibility and acceptability to clients (Template Implementation Work Group, 2000). Parallel efforts need to occur among rehabilitation researchers and practitioners. Rehabilitation researchers need to conduct additional experimental studies to validate the effectiveness of specific case management interventions, as well as to determine the overall effectiveness of case management. This research will generate practice guidelines, outcomes measures, and quality assurance tools that are fundamental to providing services in today's healthcare climate. Rehabilitation educators need to focus on improving the quality and effectiveness of research methods courses so as to facilitate evidence-based practitioners. Students need to be able to understand a broad array of research designs and methodology, and be able to access and critically evaluate research from the rehabilitation literature as well as from allied resources such as medicine and psychology. Work settings need to provide pre-service and in-service trainings regarding evidence-based practice and incorporate this aspect of service delivery into job descriptions and responsibilities. Evidence-based practice has become a standard of practice in healthcare, and the degree to which rehabilitation case managers and researchers prepare for and accept this movement will dictate the degree to which the process can be performed correctly and adequately by the very professionals providing the service.

REFERENCES

Agency for Healthcare Research and Quality (n.d.). Retrieved March 7, 2001, from http://www.ahrq.gov/

Benton, M. K., & Schroeder, H. E. (1990). Social skills training with schizophrenia: A meta-analysis evaluation. *Journal of Consulting and Clinical Psychology, 58,* 741-747.

Bolton, B. (1979). *Rehabilitation counseling research.* Baltimore: University Park Press.

Bolton, B. & Akridge, R. L. (1995). A meta-analysis of skills training programs for rehabilitation clients. *Rehabilitation Counseling Bulletin, 38,* 262-273.

Bond. G., Becker, D. R., Drake, R. E., Rapp, C. A., Meister, N., Lehman, A. F., Bell, M. D., Blyer, C. R. (2001). Implementing supported employment as an evidence-based practice. *Psychiatric Services, 52,* 313-322.

Chambless, D. L. & Hollon, S. D. (1998). Defining empirically supported therapies. *Journal of Consulting & Clinical Psychology, 66,* 7-18.

Chambless, D. L., & Ollendick, T. H. (2001). Empirically supported psychological interventions: Controversies and evidence. *Annual Review of Psychology, 52*, 685-716.

Chan, F., Leahy, M. J., Downey, W., Lamb, G., Chapin, M., & Peterson, D. (2000). A work behavior analysis of certified case managers. *Care Management, 6*(4), 50-62.

Chwalisz, K. (2003). Evidence-based practice: A framework for the twenty-first century scientist-practitioner training. *The Counseling Psychologist, 31*, 497-528.

Corthell, D. & VanBoskirk, C. V. (1988). Client involvement: Partnership in the vocational rehabilitation process. Menomonie, WI: Stout Vocational Rehabilitation Institute, Research and Training Center.

Cohen, J. (1988). *Statistical power analysis for the behavioral sciences* (2nd ed.). Hillsdale, NJ: Lawrence Erlbaum Associates.

Cox, J. G., Connolly, S. G. & Flynn, W. J. (1981). Managing the delivery of rehabilitation services. In R. M. Parker, & C. E. Hansen (Eds.), *Rehabilitation counseling. Foundations-consumers-service delivery* (pp. 295-324). Boston: Allyn and Bacon.

DeJong, G. (1997, March). *The next revolution in American health care.* A presentation made to the 14th Annual Professional Development Symposium and National Leadership Summit, Tampa, Florida.

DePalma, J. A. (2002). Proposing an evidence-based policy process. *Nursing Administration Quarterly, 26*(4), 55-61.

Dilk, M. N. & Bond, G. R. (1996). Meta-analytic evaluation of skills training research for individuals with severe mental illness. *Journal of Consulting and Clinical Psychology, 64*, 1337-1346.

Dubouloz,m C. J., Egan, M, Vallerand, J., & von Zweck, C. (1999). Occupational therapists perceptions of evidence-based practice. *American Journal of Occupational Therapy, 53*, 445-453.

Durlak, J. A. (1995). Understanding meta-analysis. In L. G. Grimm & P. R. Yarnold (Eds.), *Reading and understanding multivariate statistics* (pp. 319-352). Washington, DC: American Psychological Association.

Dysart, A. M. & Tomlin, G. S. (2002). Factors related to evidence-based practice among U.S. occupational therapy clinicians. *American Journal of Occupational Therapy, 56*, 275-284.

Emener, W. G. (1991). Implementing the empowerment concept in rehabilitation: Contributions of social role theory. In W. G. Emerner & M. A. Darrow (Eds.), *Career explorations in human services* (pp. 295-306). Springfield, IL: Charles C. Thomas.

Gray, J. A. M. (1997). *Evidence-based healthcare: How to make health policy and management decisions.* New York: Churchill Livingston.

Hedges, I. V., & Olkin, I. (1985). *Statistical methods for meta-analysis.* San Diego, CA: Academic Press.

Holm, M. B. (2000). Our mandate for the new millennium: Evidence-based practice. *American Journal of Occupational Therapy, 54,* 575-585.

Houser, R., Hampton, N. Z., & Carriker. C. (2000). Implementing the empowerment concept in rehabilitation: Contributions of social role theory. *Journal of Applied Rehabilitation Counseling, 31*(2), 18-23.

Hunt, M. (1997). *How science takes stock: The story of meta-analysis.* New York: Russell Sage Foundation.

Johnston, M. V., & Granger, C. V. (1994). Outcomes research in medical rehabilitation: A primer and introduction to a series. *American Journal of Physical Medicine and Rehabilitation, 73,* 296-303.

Johnston, M. V., Stineman, M. & Velozo, C. A. (1997). Outcome research in medical rehabilitation. Foundations from the past and directions for the future. In M.J. Fuhrer (Ed.). *Assessing medical rehabilitation practices. The promise of outcomes research.* Baltimore: Paul H. Brookes.

Kosciulek, J. F., & Szymanski, E. M. (1993). Statistical power analysis of rehabilitation counseling research. Rehabilitation Counseling Bulletin, 36(4), 212-219.

McAlees, D. & Menz, F. (1992). Consumerism and vocational evaluation. *Rehabilitation Education, 6,* 213-220.

Mullahy, C. M. (1995). *The case manager's handbook.* Gaithersburg, MD: Aspen Publishers.

Mullen, J. K. (1995). *Introduction to managed care: Fundamentals of managed care coverage and providers.* New York: Life Office Management Association.

Nathan, P. E., & Gorman, J. M. (1988). *A guide to treatments that work.* New York: Oxford University Press.

Olsen, E. A. (1996). Evidence-based practice: A new approach to teaching the integration of research and practice in gerontology. *Educational Gerontology, 22,* 523-537.

Ottenbacher, K. J., & Maas, F. (1999). How to detect effects: Statistical power and evidence-based practice in occupational therapy research. *American Journal of Occupational Therapy, 40,* 181-188.

Rosenberg, W., & Donald, A. (1995). Evidence-based medicine: An approach to clinical problem-solving. *British Medical Journal, 310,* 1122-1125.

Rubin, S. E., Chan, F., Thomas, D. (2003). Assessing changes in life skills and quality of life resulting from rehabilitation services. *Journal of Rehabilitation, 69*(3), 4-9.

Rubin, S. E. & Roessler, R. (1995). *Foundations of the vocational rehabilitation process* (4th ed.). Austin, TX: Pro-Ed.

Sacker, D., Rosenberg, W. M., Gray, J., & Haynes, R. B., & Richardson, W. S. (1996). Evidence-based medicine: What is it and what it is not. *British Medical Journal, 312*, 71-72.

Tarvydas, V. & Peterson, D. (1999). Ethical issues in case management. In F. Chan, & M. Leahy, M. (Eds.), *Healthcare and disability case management*. Lake Zurich, IL: Vocational Consultants Press.

Wampold, B. E. (1997). Methodological problems in identifying efficacious psychotherapies. *Psychotherapy Research, 7, 21*-43.

Wampold, B. E. (2001). *The great psychotherapy debate: Models, methods, and findings*. Mahwah, NJ: Lawrence Erlbaum Associates.

Wampold, B. E. (2003). Bashing positivism and revering a medical model under the guise of evidence. *The Counseling Psychologist, 31,* 539-545.

Wilkerson, D. J., & Johnston, M. V. (1997). Clinical progress monitoring system: Current capability and future directions. In M. J. Fuhrer (Ed.), *Assessing medical rehabilitation practice: The promise of outcome research* (pp. 275-306). Baltimore: Brookes.

This page purposely left blank.

Index

A

B

C

D

E

F

G

H

I

J

L

M

N

National employment policy 90, 92
Nonprofit agencies 286-288

O

Occupational Outlook Handbook 191
Occupational therapy 182, 183
Outcome measurement 76, 377, 379, 383

P

Pain clinics 186
Partial permanent disability 313
POS plan 60
PPOs 56,60-62, 66
Principles of case management 31-33
Process of LCP Development 237-238
Program evaluation 36, 38, 372
Psychological evaluations 190
Public rehabilitation program 269-271

Q

Quality of life 76, 182, 144, 226, 252

R

Reasonable accommodation 97, 100, 102, 105, 106
Rehabilitation Act 6, 7, 9, 106, 108, 111, 117
Rehabilitation engineering 194, 202, 203
Rehabilitation technology 201, 203
Reimbursement patterns 21
RESNA 202, 203, 216
Role and function research 335, 353
Return-to-work hierarchy 315

S

Seating and positioning 212, 215, 216, 222
Second injury 324
Short-term disability 59, 71, 78
Situational assessments 190
Skills and knowledge requirements for case management
    34-41
Social Security Disability Insurance (SSDI) 89-93
State–federal system 272
Standards of Practice for Case Management 145, 151,
    153-155, 159, 160, 171
Strategies of disability prevention 71, 78, 79, 81, 337, 338,
    343, 353
Supplemental Security Income 107, 108, 309-311

T

TDD or TTY 226
Tech Act 200-202
Technology pyramid 208, 210
Telephonic case management 69, 70
Temporary Assistance for Needy Families 92
Temporary partial disability 186, 312

Temporary total disability 312
Ticket to Work Incentives Improvement Act 71, 107
Total permanent disability 312
Transferable work skills 315, 320-323
Transitional work return programs 339, 347, 349

Undue hardship 96, 100, 101, 106
Utilization review 55, 56, 62, 65, 68, 74

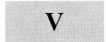

Vocational assessment 189
Vocational evaluation 189
Vocational resources 191

Work hardening 183, 184, 186
Work tolerance screening 184
Workforce Investmant Act (WIA) 91-95, 106
Workplace disability management 332, 349
Workers' compensation 9, 10, 19, 62, 68, 323, 324
Working Alliance 126-135